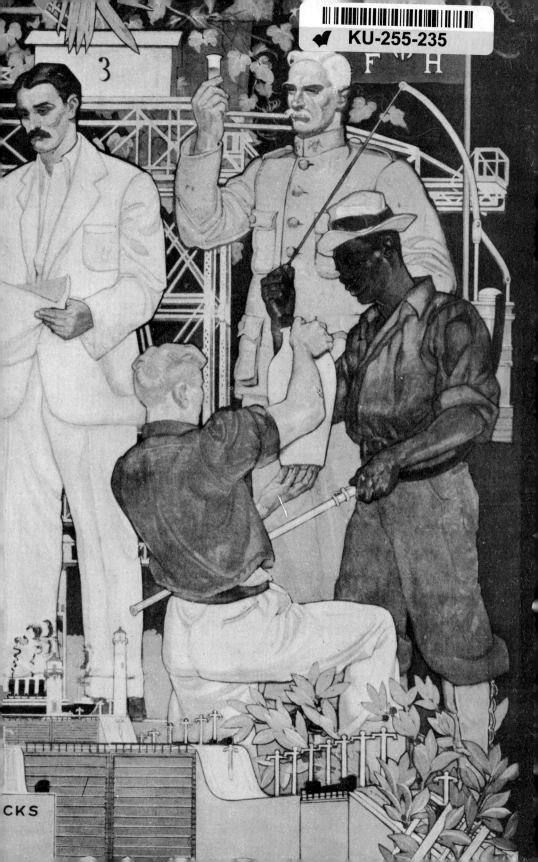

University of London

UNIVERSITY OF LONDON LIBRARY
Senate House, WC1

Heading

DuVAL (M.P.)

Title & Vol. No.

And the mountains will move.

Edition	Call Mark
Date of publication 1947	34 NUY Duv
Book number 87130	

The DuVal Panama Canal Series

And the Mountains Will Move

STANFORD BOOKS IN WORLD POLITICS

Graham Stuart, *Editor*

And the Mountains Will Move

The Story of the Building of the Panama Canal

By

Miles P. DuVal, Jr.

Captain, United States Navy

Stanford University, California

STANFORD UNIVERSITY PRESS

London

GEOFFREY CUMBERLEGE :: OXFORD UNIVERSITY PRESS

THE OPINIONS OR ASSERTIONS OF THE
WRITER CONTAINED HEREIN ARE STATED
AS A PRIVATE INDIVIDUAL AND ARE NOT
TO BE CONSTRUED AS OFFICIAL EXPRES-
SIONS OR AS REFLECTING THE VIEWS OF
THE NAVY DEPARTMENT OR THE NAVAL
SERVICE AT LARGE, OR OF THE
PANAMA CANAL

To

The Railroad Builders Who Pioneered—
The French Who Started—
The Americans Who Completed—
The Engineers Who Contributed—

THE PANAMA CANAL

AND TO

THE LATE WILLIAM FRANKLIN SANDS

PREFACE

The entire story of the Panama Canal has never been told. So stupendous is its history that it can never be fully told. The best that can be done is to present a few high lights along the four hundred years from the conception of the idea to the opening for traffic in 1914, to depict the main crises encountered on that way, to describe the parts played by some of its leaders in arriving at the great decisions, and to trace the development of its government and the evolution of the plan for the ultimate Canal.

The story comprises four epochs: first, the building of the Panama Railroad, 1849–1855; second, the great French effort, 1879–1889; third, the work of the United States, 1904–1914; and last, the era of modernization which is now in progress. These four parts are essential to an integrated story of the building of the Panama Canal which will show how the idea grew through the years.

This work was written on the Isthmus while the author was on duty with the Panama Canal as Captain of the Port of the Pacific Terminal during the period of 1941 to 1944. Thus it was possible to obtain directly much first-hand knowledge, to examine numerous original records, to talk with many Canal builders, some of whom had worked for the French, and to learn about the Isthmus—its geography, climate, and people.

The great work of the French at Panamá has never received proper recognition in the United States for its true worth. The French contributions in exploration, engineering, and organization were notable achievements that became the heritage of the United States and served as a foundation for the success of the later effort. It was the distinguished French engineer, Adolphe Godin de Lépinay, who gave to the world the fundamental plan for the construction of the Panama Canal.

In preparing this work it has been possible to examine the

Archives of the Panama Canal at Balboa Heights, the papers of John Barrett, Theodore Roosevelt, and William Howard Taft in the Manuscript Division of the Library of Congress, and the files of the *Panama Star and Herald*.

I express my appreciation to all on the Isthmus who have been more than generous in their contributions and suggestions. There are too many to permit listing of all, but among those to whom I am indebted are:

Major General Glen E. Edgerton, Governor of the Panama Canal, and Brigadier General J. C. Mehaffey, Engineer of Maintenance of the Panama Canal, for their co-operation and encouragement.

Mr. John F. Stevens, Jr., Mr. C. A. McIlvaine, former Executive Secretary of the Panama Canal, Captain L. C. McNemar, U.S.N.R., Legal Officer of the 15th Naval District, Mr. E. Sydney Randolph, Consulting Engineer of the Panama Canal, Mr. H. H. Evans, Acting Superintendent of the Mechanical Division of the Panama Canal, Mr. Donald P. Bean, Director of the Stanford University Press, and Dr. Graham Stuart, professor of political science, Stanford University, for their reading of the manuscript and helpful suggestions.

Mr. George M. Wells, who, as a young engineer, served on the Canal under its three chief engineers from 1904 to 1914, for his reading of the manuscript and the suggestions which his vast knowledge of the Canal enabled him to make.

Mr. Arthur Raggi, a French engineer in the employ of the New Panama Canal Company from 1894 to 1904, who read the chapters dealing with the French effort.

Mr. A. V. McGeachy, editor of the *Panama Star and Herald*, and Major Ford Lewis Battles, Air Corps, U.S. Army, formerly of West Virginia University.

Special appreciation is expressed to the personnel of the Panama Canal Library and of the Executive Secretary's Office, who through many months were so gracious and kind.

It was Mr. Frank H. Wang, Executive Secretary of the Pan-

ama Canal, canal builder, lawyer, scholar, and authority on
Isthmian history, who in 1939 first suggested undertaking this
work and co-operated so fully during its preparation.

My sincere appreciation is expressed to Brigadier General
James G. Steese, soldier, canal builder, engineer, scholar, and
statesman, for his critical reading of the manuscript and for his
careful explanations of Canal history.

MILES P. DuVAL, JR.

BALBOA HEIGHTS, CANAL ZONE
June 1, 1944

The endsheet of this volume is from a mural painting by William
Andrew Mackay in the Roosevelt Memorial Hall, American Museum of
Natural History, New York. Courtesy of John F. Stevens, Jr. Theodore
Roosevelt and John F. Stevens are there shown discussing plans for the
Panama Canal. At the extreme left stands General George W. Goethals,
and at the right General W. C. Gorgas.

TABLE OF CONTENTS

LIST OF ILLUSTRATIONS

ISTHMIAN HEROES

Hail to those men who dreamt of mountains moved
That oceans might by water-steps be bound;
Conceived across the land a passage grooved
Through treacherous shifting rock and swampy ground.

Hail to those men whose steadfast hand and head
Directed shovel, dredge, and track, to rear
A peaceful lake from Chagres' troubled bed;
To pierce Culebra's ramparts, wild and sheer.

Hail to those men who wage unending war
Upon the ravening jungle's thousand jaws;
O'er slides and floods and plagues prevail, to bar
Relentless Nature's triumph of her laws.

Hail to those men on ship and shore whose skill
In tireless sequence plots unerringly,
Through tortuous ways, by island and by hill,
The silent path of ships from sea to sea.

Hail to those men who know each struggling hour
Of building; clearly see the present task;
Above confusing murmur, say with power,
"Not ended; let us ever build, not bask."

—FORD LEWIS BATTLES
May 20, 1943

PROLOGUE

The American Isthmus was the great barrier that interrupted the westward voyage of the early Spanish from Cadiz to Cathay. It became the scene of intensive explorations to discover a water passage between the seas. None was found, but the Spanish did discover the regions where the land was narrow, where the mountains were low, and where rivers traversed part of the distance—regions prepared by nature for the earliest travel routes across the Isthmus.

One of these regions was the Isthmus of Panamá—a land of distinct contrasts. On the Atlantic side the land is low and flat. On the Pacific there are mountains, with the continental divide running parallel to the coast line ten miles away. In the highlands, irregular peaks, ridges, and valleys predominate; in the north, large swamps.

The low mountains of the Isthmus form a natural path for moisture-bearing winds that give this zone one of the heaviest rainfalls in the world and a most prolific vegetation.

In the low flat regions there are large mangrove swamps; in the higher parts, the jungle. The swamps and jungle form luxuriant homes for insects, birds, reptiles, and larger animals and make the Isthmus a path of egress for many forms of life in their movements from the Caribbean to the Pacific.

The Chagres River valley penetrates from the north and meanders in a southeasterly direction nearly two-thirds of the way across the Isthmus to the highlands; there it divides, the Chagres valley swinging to the northeast toward its headwaters while the valley of its branch, the Obispo, continues to the southeast toward the summit of the continental divide. From the Pacific the tortuous Rio Grande valley extends northeastward until its headwaters approach those of the Obispo—a configuration that has made the development of trade routes there almost inevitable.

1

When Hernando de la Serna explored the Chagres and the Rio Grande in 1527, he opened a new transit route across the Isthmus. Although first used as early as 1530, it was destined to survive all other routes in Panamá as the gateway of Spain to the South Sea. Vessels of light draft ascended the Chagres to Cruces and connected there with pack trains to Panamá City, thus forming the most convenient means of Isthmian transit, later known as the river route.

For over two hundred years this highway was the treasure trail of Old Spain, as pack trains transported the gold and silver of Peru, the wealth of the colonies, to the mother country. The route became an index of empire. It witnessed the rise of an expanding Spain, served at the height of her power, and was the scene of incidents presaging her decay. With the disintegration of the Spanish Empire it ceased to exist as a highway of world trade, but not until the idea of making a waterway across the Isthmus had become firmly ingrained in the Spanish mind and literature—an idea that was passed on to other European nations, notably France.

Coincident with the decay and collapse of Spain in the New World was the rise of the United States of America. Although at first only a group of weak and struggling states along the East Coast, these developed an aggressive expansion toward the West. Under the impetus of that westward movement came the purchase of the Louisiana Territory and its exploration by Lewis and Clarke, the settlement and occupation of Oregon, the Mexican War, and the acquisition of the Far West—events which gave the country two coast lines and made the United States a Pacific power.

With the East and the Far West separated by great distances, by trackless wastes of desert, and by high ranges of the Rockies, the difficulties of crossing the continent were so great that travelers were forced to seek less perilous routes. Some migrated around the Horn. Many sought a shorter route to the Pacific Coast by way of the Isthmus of Panamá.

Chapter I

TWO STREAKS OF RUST IN THE JUNGLE

The railroad across the Isthmus of Panama will speedily lead to the construction of a ship canal between the two oceans, for a railroad can not do the business which commerce will require for it; and by showing to the world how immense this business is, men will come from the four quarters to urge with purse and tongue the construction of a ship canal.—MATTHEW FONTAINE MAURY, Superintendent, United States Naval Observatory, 1849.[1]

PROMOTING THE RAILROAD

When the westward expansion of the United States in the late forties of the last century required another avenue to the Pacific, the historical significance of uniting the two oceans and the commercial opportunities to be found in the settlement of the Pacific basin were recognized by three men of vision—John Lloyd Stephens, most distinguished travel writer of his day, diplomat, and explorer; William Henry Aspinwall, financier and founder of the Pacific Mail Steamship Company; and Henry Chauncey, financier—the three who in 1847 organized the Panama Railroad Company in New York.

Among the organizers it was Stephens who had widest vision. With a background of law in New York, of extended travels in Europe and the East, of diplomacy, and of exploration among the remains of early civilizations in Central America, it was natural that his active imagination should be fired with the importance of linking the two oceans by rail through a land he knew and loved so well. To this end he dedicated his life and became the founding genius of the Panama Railroad.

In 1848 the United States Congress, desiring to link the two coast lines of the newly expanded republic, authorized contracts with two steamship lines to provide services to the Isthmus, where their traffic would be connected by the river transit route.

[1] *Senate Report No. 1* (57th Cong., 1st sess.), p. 504 (Hearings No. 17) (U.S.).

The contract for the line from New York and New Orleans to Chagres was taken by George Law and was generally considered a profitable business venture. The other, from Panamá to California and Oregon, was taken by Aspinwall[2] in a move which made people wonder why a man of his standing should have engaged in a venture with so precarious a future. But Aspinwall knew. He did not expect much from the steamship line alone. In his mind was the concept of a grand transportation plan—a plan by which a railroad across the Isthmus would connect the two mail lines and make possible the commercial development of the entire Pacific basin, including China, Australia, and the East Indies, as well as California and Oregon.

At that time vessels customarily stopped at Chagres, almost within the shadow of the decaying ruins of old Fort San Lorenzo located high upon the mouth of the river. Here passengers were transferred to small dugouts, often when the sea was rough. With carpet bags in hand they had to jump into the small boats that rose and fell alongside their ship in swells, wind, spray, and rain and then had to land at Chagres in a dangerous surf.

Boats loaded with passengers were poled slowly up the Chagres, with overnight stops at small villages. In the dry season they ascended as far as Gorgona; in the wet season, to Las Cruces. At these points passengers were transferred to mule-pack trains for Panamá City—the entire journey across the Isthmus being always a harrowing experience of four to eight days. The slow speed of the hand-propelled bungos, the lack of food, the sleeping on skin mats cushioned with grass in insect-infested huts, the long ride on muleback, the exposure to sun and rain, and the frequent personal dangers, all combined to take away, particularly in the wet season, whatever joy there might have been in seeing the incomparably rare beauty of the Panamá jungle, even for the most appreciative.

Following their plans, the promoters of the railroad went to the Isthmus in the winter of 1847–48 on a preliminary explora-

[2] F. N. Otis, *Isthmus of Panama*, pp. 16–17.

tion to get exact knowledge of Isthmian conditions for transit. Stephens, accompanied by Aspinwall, Chauncey, and James L. Baldwin, explored the proposed route, following the valleys of the Chagres and Obispo rivers to the continental divide, where they discovered a 300-foot pass, and thence down the valley of the Rio Grande to Panamá.

Deciding that the plan was practicable, the promoters then sought and obtained an exclusive concession from New Granada (later Colombia), signed in Washington December 28, 1848, which embodied many of the terms in a previous grant obtained by Mateo Klein for a French "Panama Company" but which was later forfeited on June 8, 1848. The scheme of the American company was based on the business proposition of eliminating the long journey to the West around the Horn and opening a shorter way to Asia, Australia, and the Indies.[3] It left the company free to decide whether the traffic way should be all rail, a combination of rail and steamer, or a macadamized road for horse power.

Armed with this concession, the company on April 7, 1849, obtained a charter from the New York State Legislature to construct and maintain the Panama Railroad. As the "body corporate" it listed James Brown, Cornelius Van Wyck Lawrence, Gouverneur Kemble, Thomas W. Ludlow, David Thompson, Joseph B. Varnum, Samuel S. Howland, Prosper M. Wetmore, Edwin Bartlett, Horatio Allen, and the three promoters. The capital stock was set at only $1,000,000, with the privilege granted of raising it to $5,000,000,[4] a figure amended on April 12, 1855, to $7,000,000.

Early in 1849 a large party of United States engineers under Colonel George W. Hughes went to the Isthmus to make location surveys. Accompanied by Baldwin they ran lines, the first stake of which was driven by Captain John Jay Williams.[5] The work

[3] *Ibid.*, p. 18.

[4] Panama Railroad Company Charter, 1849.

[5] Tracy Robinson, *Panama: A Personal Record of Forty-six Years, 1861–1907,* p. 7.

of such earlier engineers as John Augustus Lloyd (1827) and Napoléon Garella (1843), besides the general knowledge of the long-used routes on the Chagres River to the Gorgona or Cruces trails, must have been of first importance in locating the railroad line, for it did not deviate greatly from the lines as previously explored and later adopted.

From the start there was controversy regarding the location of the Atlantic terminus—Porto Bello or Limon Bay (Navy Bay). The rumor at the time was that George Law had bought all the real estate around the capacious and protected harbor of Porto Bello and was holding it at a price too high for the young company to stand, with the result that Limon Bay was selected for the Atlantic terminus in preference to the older and better-known port of Spanish days. Be that as it may, the map and reports indicate that Limon Bay was the preferable location, probably determined by such engineering considerations as the discovery by Baldwin of the mountain pass at Culebra, only 286 feet high, and a survey of the coast line. The railroad route in general followed the route of the present Canal. It followed also the Hughes survey, except south of the continental divide, where it was located more to the west.

Under the leadership of the versatile Stephens and the realistic Aspinwall, the company then looked for engineers familiar with tropical construction and labor. They found in Colonel George M. Totten and John C. Trautwine two of the leading engineers of their time in the United States, who had done important work in Colombia on the canal Del Dique from Cartagena to the Magdalena River and were familiar with construction in the tropics and with the handling of tropical labor. They were given a contract to build the entire railroad.

The first plan was to start work at Gorgona on the Chagres, thirty miles from the Atlantic, a central position that permitted construction toward the Pacific as the best means of quickly eliminating the twenty-mile pack-mule trip from Gorgona to Panamá City, and later to build toward the Atlantic. Trautwine established his headquarters at Gorgona in January 1850 and began the final survey toward Panamá; but difficulties began to appear. He and his officers were prostrated by fever. The two river steamers obtained to ascend the Chagres to Gorgona could not do so in spite of their light draft of 18 inches. After a delay of four months it was decided to begin construction on the Atlantic end.[6]

A sensational event had occurred on January 24, 1848, at Sutter's Mill on the American River in California—the discovery of gold. The news spread around the world with great rapidity despite the relative lack of rapid communication, and almost overnight the Isthmus became the stop-over for the "forty-niners" on their way to riches, but more often to privations. This tide of emigrants on the Isthmus dislocated values and made fulfillment of the railroad contract with Totten and Trautwine impossible. It changed the nature of the undertaking from one based on long-range business planning to one for producing great immediate profits. Also, Trautwine, in his survey in 1850, had found previous surveys erroneous. These factors caused the contractors to refuse to carry out the agreement as based on estimates of the early surveys. The railroad then appointed Totten and Trautwine as associate chief engineers,[7] with Baldwin and John Jay Williams as assistants. Colonel Totten left for Cartagena to procure laborers, and Trautwine remained behind to start work with available help.

GETTING STARTED

One day in May 1850, a *cayuca* approached swampy Manzanillo Island on the eastern shore of Limon Bay. The island was low and flat, about a square mile in area, and covered with jungle. Bordered by mangrove trees from whose trunks and branches pendulous roots descended into black, slimy mud, it afforded a splendid home for alligators, myriads of sand flies,

---

[6] C. T. Lindsay, *A Short History of the Panama Railroad*, p. 8.
[7] *Panama Star and Herald*, Oct. 20, 1883.

and mosquitoes; but to the visitors in the *cayuca* it presented hazardous and almost impenetrable obstacles.

Two North Americans, Trautwine and Baldwin,[8] carrying axes and accompanied by six natives armed with machetes, jumped ashore. The natives, hacking their way into the jungle, cut a path for the axemen, who with rapid blows quickly felled graceful palms, clearing ground in what was described as the "densest jungle, reeking with malaria, and abounding with almost every species of wild beasts, noxious reptiles, and venomous insects."[9] They found it impossible to work unless face and hands were covered with protecting gauze and equally unbearable to reside ashore.

An old brig, anchored in Limon Bay and previously used to bring building materials, was commandeered as a floating barracks to afford relief from perpetual insect attacks. Returning from his Cartagena trip with forty natives from Colombia, Colonel Totten placed them upon this overcrowded brig. Life on board was not easy. Below its decks the vessel was "alive with mosquitoes and sand-flies, which were a source of such annoyance and suffering that almost all preferred to sleep upon the deck, exposed to the drenching rains, rather than endure their attacks."[10] These, added to the nausea created by the ceaseless rolling of the ship in the ground swell, finally caused the purchase of an old steamer, the "Telegraph," which became a more hospitable home for the railroad workers during the rapidly developing rainy season.

Along with Colonel Totten had come John L. Stephens, returning from Bogotá, where, as Vice-President of the Panama Railroad Company, he had negotiated and signed on April 15, 1850, a new contract for the railroad with the Minister of Foreign Affairs, Victoriano de Diego Paredes. Approved by the Colombian (New Granadan) Congress on June 4, 1850, it was the fundamental railroad contract.[11] Among its provisions were

[8] Otis, *op. cit.*, p. 26.   [9] *Ibid.*, p. 21.   [10] *Ibid.*, p. 27.
[11] J. L. Bristow, *Report of Special Panama Railroad Commissioner to the Secretary of War, June 24, 1905*, pp. 296–335 (U.S.).

sections requiring completion of the railroad within six years, granting a monopoly of transportation, including a possible canal and river navigation and provision for free ports at the terminals of the road, and giving the company the right to propose police powers for security of the railroad.

What kind of man was this Colonel Totten who had the responsibility of chief engineer? Of small stature, quiet and reserved, he had the fine qualities suitable for a chief engineer rather than for the go-getter type of general manager. Tracy Robinson described his chief quality as staying power of the first order. "His opinion once formed, there was no more to be said on the subject. Indeed, he was conservative to the last degree. While he was modest and unobtrusive, it would nevertheless have been difficult to move him from a position once assumed. As a military man he would have been an obstinate fighter. As a civilian he was reticent, plain, steadfast, just, and the soul of honor and honesty. He was a superior man without being great . . . ."[12] In short, he was the type required for such an effort as the construction of the Panama Railroad.

After Colonel Totten's return, Trautwine and Stephens left for New York to confer with the directors about plans for the dry season and to recruit more labor, while Colonel Totten and Baldwin continued the work of clearing and tracing surveys, often working waist-deep in mud and water, each taking turns while the other was ill. At Monkey Hill, lumber was dragged through swampland to build construction shanties on high ground. After two miles of location were definitely decided on, work on grading was started in August 1850 near the present Mount Hope Station.

Stimulated by the rapid increase in travelers and the desire for quick financial returns, the "push to completion" became the order of the day. Laborers constantly arrived, natives from Cartagena and Negroes from Jamaica, and each ship from the United States brought construction materials and mechanics who

[12] Robinson, *op. cit.*, p. 33.

hastened the erection of the frame houses sent from New York. As soon as frame dwellings were ready, the floating barracks were abandoned and men were moved ashore to houses nearer their work. Working in mud and water, exposed to rains, oppressed by an appalling humidity, and exposed to diseases, the men formed a fertile field for medical work by Dr. J. A. Totten, the railroad physician and a brother of the chief engineer. It should be observed, however, that contemporary writers did not mention what later became the dread of Panamá—yellow fever.

With Manzanillo Island cleared, the railroad plan decided, and grading begun at Mount Hope, the line was laid southward toward Gatun. There terminal facilities were started, a town laid out, and work begun on the station at Gatun, almost eight miles from Manzanillo Island. The location on the Chagres opposite a native village was convenient for unloading men and materials from vessels for the work of piling and grading toward Aspinwall. Although the total force in August was about 400 men, by December it had grown to 1,000; but the turnover was large, as many were lured from work on the railroad to more lucrative positions on the California transit.

Trautwine returned to the Isthmus in September and remained with the railroad until near the end of the year, when he resigned, leaving railroad affairs in sole charge of Colonel Totten. Returning to the United States, he immediately undertook a defense of the railroad in the press, predicting its "energetic prosecution."

By April 1851 most of the track from Manzanillo Island to Gatun had been laid. Over the lowlands in this section the railroad was built on trestles made with piling "full of pitch,"[13] which even sixty years later, when the North American canal builders excavated north of Gatun Lock site, were found to be sound below sea level. The original rails to Gatun consisted of flat iron bars resting on wood stringers, but these were replaced by wrought-iron U rails in 1853 and these in turn by T rails in

---

[13] *Canal Record*, Jan. 20, 1909, II, 161 (U.S.).

1869. The gauge adopted was five feet, for rail gauges had not yet been standardized.

Meanwhile work was progressing elsewhere on the line. Chief Assistant Engineer J. C. Campbell was extending locations toward Panamá, working at several points. Docks had been constructed on Limon Bay, permitting ships to discharge railroad supplies and laborers. Even so, progress had not been rapid enough to offer competition with the regular travel advertised in the papers of the day. For example, in a Panamá paper the advertisement of R. A. Joy's Transportation Line described the route of the mule-pack trains as from Panamá to Gorgona in the dry season and to Cruces in the rainy season for "passengers, baggage, and merchandise" on good English saddles with everything necessary for comfort. It lamented, however, that one of the greatest causes for delay and annoyance lay in the large packages "totally uncalculated for the transit through the narrow passes of the road" and announced that these "should not weigh more than 100 lbs., gross, or measure more than four cubic feet" and should "be well protected from the wet by tarpaulins."[14] Another writer advised all passengers to provide themselves with "good hams, smoked tongues or sausages, pickles, good coffee, and their accustomed drink; a good blanket, if in the rainy season, a light India rubber overcoat and leggings, also an umbrella."[15]

With only that limited system of travel on the Isthmus, it was natural that the progress of the Panama Railroad should become the byword of the day, with everyone looking for its earliest possible completion. When the survey advanced almost to Panamá the local press howled for passenger trains for "even so short a distance as that between Navy Bay and Gatun."[16] But that required more than wishing. So traffic continued by the picturesque Chagres, whose fullest beauty can be appreciated only

[14] *Panama Herald*, May 26, 1851, p. 3.

[15] E. L. Autenrieth, *Topographical Map of the Isthmus of Panama*, p. 5.

[16] *Panama Herald*, May 19, 1851.

from a boat; and by mule-pack trains, which frequently met disaster by robberies and murders when miners from California were returning with their gold dust.

Nor was the trans-Isthmian river traffic always tranquil. For example, on June 10, 1851, as the steamer "Aspinwall," with passengers on the way from Chagres to Gorgona, and the iron steamer "Gorgona," en route to the sea, were approaching a curve in the river near Gatun, they collided with a shock described as "terrible, breaking off and tearing away the guards of the 'Aspinwall,' bending and wrenching her piston rod, and nearly cutting her in two."[17] Although the passengers and officers of the ship feared an explosion, the ships were separated, and the "Aspinwall" continued on her way with an estimated damage of only $500.

FIRST TRAIN TO GATUN AND THE NAMING OF ASPINWALL

With less than eight miles of road built after more than two years since the granting of the charter, the confidence of distant investors in New York weakened, though they well knew the dangers of the work and the difficulty of competing for labor in a market upset by the feverish gold rush to California. The original subscription of $1,000,000 was about expended, and the market price of the stock tumbled. Work on the railroad and the terminal at Manzanillo continued, and by the first of September there was only one mile to complete before the railroad would reach Gatun, but that was through "one of the worst and most ugly pestiferous marshes on the Continent." The writer in the *Panama Herald* recorded his impressions of this preparatory activity as including, at Navy Bay, "the air of a Commercial City . . . . the shipping discharging at the dock, the large warehouses belonging to the Company, the houses for the officers and men, the machine shops, the splendid new passenger cars, all ready for the road; besides the number of freight and baggage cars building, and that have been built, the locomotive

[17] *Panama Herald,* June 16, 1851.

puffing along with dirt cars."[18] Meanwhile in Panamá City the
people awaited the news of the first train with great expectations,
in the general belief that completion of the railroad would be
the panacea for all the Isthmian economic ills, the basis of a
permanent prosperity, and a quick road to personal fortune.
Many thought of the Isthmus as the cynosure of the whole commercial world.

The tracks to Gatun were then ready for test, and on October 1, 1851, a train of work cars traveled from the terminal to
Gatun—the first Isthmian train; but it would take a little more
time before passenger traffic could be stimulated, as steamers
continued to use the Chagres. The railroad advanced, reaching
Miller's Station, three miles beyond Gatun, about the middle of
November—a month that for the Isthmus has been described as
a month of northers.

Two ships, the "Georgia" and the "Philadelphia," with passengers from the United States, arrived at the open roadstead off
Chagres but were forced by the extremely heavy weather to take
refuge in Limon Bay, where the passengers were landed. The
situation thus created practically forced the railroad in early
December to haul passengers to Gatun—an event heralded far
and wide, for it established Limon Bay as the normal port of
call, forever replacing Chagres. In New York the confidence
of investors was restored, and financing was resumed. Among
the Isthmians there was great joy, for by the starting of railroad
passenger traffic there had come at last the partial realization
of the dream of Spanish leaders who, from the time when Vasco
Núñez de Balboa viewed the Pacific, had striven for a highway
across the Isthmus.

What the Atlantic terminus should be called became a moot
question. The opportunity for naming it came on February 29,
1852, at the ceremony for laying the cornerstone of the company's new office building—the first brick building on the island,
fireproof and containing a specie vault. It was a gala occa-

[18] *Panama Herald*, Sept. 8, 1851.

sion on Manzanillo Island. Railroad employees and residents thronged around. Among the distinguished guests were George Law, owner of the Atlantic steamer line and a director of the railroad; Minor C. Story of New York, one of the largest railroad contractors of his day; John L. Stephens, then President of the Panama Railroad; R. Webb of Manzanillo Island; and Victoriano de Diego Paredes, ex-Minister of Foreign Affairs of New Granada, who was then on his way to Washington as Minister to the United States. As Paredes had negotiated the railroad contract of 1850 with Stephens in Bogotá, he was selected to lay the cornerstone and to proclaim the name of the new city.

Introduced by Stephens, the diplomat explained his part in the negotiations and how elated he was at the progress of the road and the obstacles overcome and predicted early completion of the railroad, as progress was already ahead of stipulations in the contract. When he gave credit to the individuals involved in securing these results, at the suggestion of Stephens he singled out the name of William H. Aspinwall for honoring. Describing the new town as destined to become the "commercial emporium of America and perhaps the whole world," he proposed that "we call this town Aspinwall, as a slight homage to so respectable a person." He did not foresee the repudiation of this gracious act by his own Government, which later changed the name of Aspinwall to Colón, in honor of the discoverer of America.

Replying to this diplomatic accolade, Mr. Webb in behalf of the citizens graciously accepted the proposed name of the terminal city. President Stephens also replied, stating that "no name could have been selected more proper, or which would give more general satisfaction."[19] Dr. Paredes then placed in the cornerstone a copper box containing a memorandum describing the ceremony, a copy of the contract with the Republic of New Granada, a copy of the *New York Herald* of February 9, 1852, and a coin each from the United States, France, England,

[19] *Panama Herald*, March 9, 1852.

Courtesy of the *Panama Star and Herald*

FIRST PUBLISHED TRAIN SCHEDULE OF PANAMA RAILROAD

The Panama Herald, March 23, 1852

and New Granada—a signal for cheers—cheers for the new
city of Aspinwall, cheers for President Stephens, cheers for Mr.
Law, and cheers for New Granada.

DIFFICULTIES MOUNT HIGH

Activity continued to accelerate in Aspinwall, and railroad
line progress became more evident. Hotels and warehouses were
built, and large docks were constructed to accommodate ships
of twenty-foot draft. Some vessels discharged at docks and
others at anchor. Trainloads of rock and earth were constantly
on their way to be dumped from trestles where the railroad
crossed the lowlands.

Work was pushed until the railroad was completed to Bohío
Soldado—a section of track that passed through Black Swamp
in a 3,000-foot stretch of "silt and water"[20] between Lion Hill
and Ahorca Lagarto, where Colonel Totten could not find bottom
at 180 feet. It was at this critical time, in a notice signed March
12, 1852, and effective March 15, that the Panama Railroad
Company published its first train schedule in the *Panama Herald*
March 23, announcing daily train departures from Bohío Soldado to Aspinwall, fare to be $2.00 per passenger.

The road was then sixteen miles from Aspinwall, with thirty-
one miles left to complete. The passengers, after leaving the
train, still had to pole their way in native bungos to Gorgona or
Cruces before shifting to the final lap of discomfort on pack
mules to Panamá. At Bohío Soldado a sandstone quarry was
established. Although the rock was soft, it was sound and
quarryable in large sizes. Used in abutments, piers, drains, and
wharves, there was no evidence of deterioration after twenty
years of service.[21]

Another section was opened to Frijoles about May 1, but the
rainy season was setting in again and, as usual in Panamá, out-
door work slowed down. Even so, by the end of the month it

[20] *Canal Record*, July 29, 1908, I, 377 (U.S.).
[21] *Panama Star and Herald*, Sept. 4, 1879.

was announced that trains would leave Tavernilla—still further reducing river travel. The company planned to carry on to Barbacoas, a place named after the Indian word for "bridge." There the railroad would cross the Chagres. From that point it was decided to complete the railroad by contract with M. C. Story, who was to start by building the Barbacoas bridge and to complete the road in one year.

In July the company advertised that trains would leave for Aspinwall from Barbacoas daily. With twenty-three and one-quarter miles constructed and twenty-five still unfinished, so strong was the desire to eliminate the boat trip on the Chagres that there were great hopes of completing the bridge and running trains to Gorgona by September.

Hardly had train service been extended to Barbacoas when the railroad received its first military test by the United States. On July 16, 1852, eight companies of the Fourth Infantry, United States Army, numbering about 700, including the families, together with some 300 passengers additional, arrived at Aspinwall on the United States mail steamer "Ohio," en route to California for garrison duty. Landing too late for that day's one train, the regiment remained in Aspinwall overnight at a time when the rainy season had set in, flooding the streets, and when cholera was epidemic on the Isthmus. By the next morning most of the baggage had been loaded on cars, but the locomotive proved too light to carry more than half the troops, and two trains had to be dispatched at one-hour intervals, baggage being left for a later trip.

Arriving at Barbacoas, where the railroad's facilities for transit to Panamá City ended, the regiment was divided, the main body going to Gorgona by the slow method of pole-propelled boats and thence marching to Panamá. One company under the regimental quartermaster, Captain U. S. Grant, with the sick, the women and children, and the baggage, was ordered to Cruces, a few miles beyond Gorgona. There mule transportation to Panamá was supposed to be ready, under the terms

of a previous army contract by which the steamship company
assumed the entire cost and responsibility for the regiment's
transportation to California by both land and water, acting
through its agents along the route. But the company's local
agent could not obtain mules for the troops because of higher
prices paid by the civilian passengers. Grant waited three days;
then he himself hired mules at double the agent's price, charg-
ing it to the shipping company, and resumed the journey to
Panamá.

Because of this delay and the exposure to rains at Cruces and
the inability of the Gorgona troops to make headway in the mud
the transit was not executed as planned. Cholera and jungle
fever attacked the troops along both routes, so depleting the
small guard at Cruces that baggage had to go unprotected, subject to native thievery and to local infection that later compelled
some of it to be destroyed. In addition, the troops ate contami-
nated local fruits and drank indiscriminately along the way,
thus adding to the sickness. Order or organization en route became impossible and the movement developed into a straggle,
each one for himself. The troops arrived at Panamá wet and
muddy, tired and hungry. Some arrived drunk, some sick, and
some did not arrive at all, having died in the mud along the way.

When the regiment, after four weeks' delay on the Isthmus,
finally reached California late in August, about eighty of the
men had died, besides nearly as many of their women and children. The experiences encountered on the Isthmus have been
told by the regimental surgeon,[22] who lived constantly in vital
and responsible contact with the officers, the men, and their
families.

As a result of these unfortunate delays, Captain Grant, later
to become General of the Armies and President, obtained some
very unfavorable local editorial publicity—interesting in the
light of his subsequent distinguished career. The comment

[22] Dr. C. S. Tripler, *Report of the Regimental Surgeon, Fourth Infantry, to Surgeon General, Sept. 14, 1852*, pp. 454–58 (U.S.). A. D. Richardson, *Personal History of Ulysses S. Grant*, chapter 10.

states: "Unfitted by either natural ability or education for the post he occupied, he evinced his incapacity at every moment."[23]

Captain Grant's experiences on the Isthmus must have impressed him deeply, for early in his first term as President of the United States he secured from Colombia and from the United States Congress the authority which enabled the United States Navy to conduct the first comprehensive survey of Isthmian canal routes, 1870–1875.

On the part of the railroad, little time was lost in starting the bridge across the Chagres at Barbacoas, where the river was about 300 feet wide and subject to great changes during the heavy rains, becoming then a destructive torrent. When the bridge was nearly completed, a sudden freshet of the raging Chagres swept away one span—an accident which prevented continuation of the railroad to Gorgona during the dry season of 1852.

Another great loss came to the company in the passing of its president, John L. Stephens, who had been the dominating genius in the enterprise. After having been exposed to great hardships and diseases he returned to New York, where he died October 13, 1852, from a malady contracted on the Isthmus. He was succeeded by William C. Young.

The collapse of the bridge, the death of President Stephens, the illness and death of many workmen—all added to the difficulties of the company, and work bogged down. Although the railroad was supposed to be completed by the contractor in October 1853, not only was the Barbacoas bridge still unfinished but only about a tenth of the contract work had been accomplished.

The Isthmians lamented the lack of the railway, they lamented the lack of activity, and they regretted the setting in of the wet season with so little being done except surveys by the engineers, "who perform mysterious evolutions . . . . looking through complicated instruments at long staffs, driving stakes

[23] *Panama Herald*, Aug. 17, 1852.

into the ground, rushing about woods and . . . . swamps in all directions . . . . and then disappearing as secretly as they arrived." There were no "stalwart laborers" clearing the soil or making the forest ring with the "stroke of the axe." The Isthmians thought that thousands of workers should have been engaged in constructing the railroad. Instead, the line was still the "birthplace of tropical vegetation and the haunt of the beast of prey."[24]

Complaints from passengers about the loss of baggage also received public notice. The inefficiency, the risk, and the uncertainty of the baggage service combined to cause discontent among the riding public and often forced passengers to wait in Panamá for delivery of their valuables and to miss their ships, or to sail, leaving valuables behind. With rates for passengers from Cruces to Panamá by mule at $18 per person and 17 cents per pound for baggage, it is not strange that complaints concerning the poor service were so numerous.

Again a reorganization occurred. The contractor, unable to handle his contract within the price limit, was relieved and the work taken over by the company. President Young resigned and was succeeded by David Hoadley.

A NEW LEADERSHIP

Among the first activities under the new leadership was the recruiting of more labor. Men came from all over the world— Ireland, Hindustan, China, England, France, Germany, and Austria—in all, more than 7,000 men. Selected because they were able-bodied, many of the workers did not thrive in Panamá because of the vast difference in climatic conditions. The company tried hard to meet their special needs, even going so far in the case of the 1,000 Chinese as to provide them with "hill-rice, their tea, and opium."[25] But so unhappy were the Chinese that many committed suicide—a fact which gave rise to the

[24] *Panama Herald*, March 11, 1853.
[25] F. N. Otis, *Isthmus of Panama*, p. 35.

curious fable that Matachin was so named to commemorate dead Chinese, since in Spanish *mata* means kill and *Chino* means Chinese. As a matter of historical interest, Matachin is shown on maps of this region published as early as 1678.[26]

Disease became so rampant and desertions so common among the workers that it was necessary to import large numbers of Jamaicans as replacements, and construction was on again.

Reconstruction was started on a new Barbacoas bridge across the Chagres, to be 625 feet long and 18 feet wide, to be made with wrought-iron girders, and to stand 40 feet above the water. It was to be one of the "longest and finest iron bridges in the world." Actually the bridge was rebuilt so strong that it lasted more than half a century and was used by the railroad even after the United States occupied the Canal Zone. The iron girders, supported by rock masonry piers and abutments quarried at San Pablo, gave the appearance of strength and durability, while the American pine in the bridge, imported from Darien, Georgia,[27] suggested a linking of the oceans. Along the rest of the road many temporary bridge structures were replaced with permanent culverts or bridges, using "masonry abutments, and iron superstructures." Original soft-wood crossties were replaced with lignum vitae ties, which were so hard that holes had to be bored before spikes were driven and so durable that when sections of track were taken up in 1910 the ties were still unrotted.

From Panamá, construction became active, pushing toward the Atlantic. In June 1853, the railroad company erected buildings near the north city gate on the Playa Prieta for use of workmen and started clearing the right of way at Panamá. It was rumored that the company had bought Flamenco, Perico, and Naos Islands. It should be remembered that access to deep water at Panamá City was long the primary aim of those engaged in shipping, as the large tidal range on the Pacific caused vessels to ground at low tide in the harbors.

[26] G. W. Davis, article quoted in *Canal Record* (Dec. 25, 1907), I, 133 (U.S.).
[27] Robert Tomes, *Panama in 1855*, p. 82.

In August, conditions once more looked promising. Colonel Totten, the experienced chief engineer, took charge again after failure of the contractor and pushed work with his characteristic force and determination. Gleefully it was announced that contractor Story had been pushed overboard and that the increase in activity had had a "magical effect"; the faces of the merchants "shortened and their purse strings . . . . loosened," many betting that the road would be completed within ten months—the completion, of course, being the omen for a "glorious future."[28]

Progress everywhere was reported, hills were leveled, and ravines were filled with the spoil as preparation of the right of way continued. It was expected that the railroad would be completed all the way by August of the next year. "Where would the Nicaragua transit be then?" asked the elated Isthmians. But in spite of their wishful thinking, nothing had been done to repair the muddy Cruces road so that transit from Aspinwall could be made in one day. The transit continued to be an arduous undertaking in spite of the screams of locomotive whistles frequently heard in Panamá. Even in early September, passengers required thirty-six hours to cross the Isthmus!

But events were developing rapidly to speed up Isthmian transit. The Barbacoas bridge was nearing completion. The Cruces road, long a difficult and muddy trail, was being repaired by young Ran Runnels, former Texas ranger, and in September a mail transit of twelve hours was made while the railroad was being pushed with the work of 1,000 men.

Trains had been running for about two years when, on October 1, 1853, the 3:30 P.M. train pulled out of Aspinwall with 600 passengers. Passing the Monkey Hill Station, it slowly approached Tavernilla, where a sharp curve in a cut contained a bridge, the view of which was obscured. A bull was sighted on the bridge, but the train was too close to stop before colliding with the beast in what was the first fatal accident on the Panama Railroad. The locomotive, four baggage cars, and two crowded

[28] *Panama Star*, Aug. 21, 1853.

passenger cars plunged into the valley, killing two—a native and a North American on his way to California. But this accident did not delay the railroad work.[29]

Accidents were not the only difficulty to distract Colonel Totten. Repair of the Cruces road was nearing completion, with workers paid at the rate of 80 cents per day. To stimulate efforts and to reduce turnover among employees, Colonel Totten authorized a bonus of an additional 40 cents a day to all workmen who remained until the work was completed. This satisfied the men at first, but the local judge at Cruces saw a financial opportunity for himself. He told the workers, 150 strong, that if each of them would pay him a dollar he would require their superintendent to pay the full $1.20 a day, regardless of whether they remained with the railroad or not—a proposition readily accepted. The judge, accompanied by a group of soldiers, then arrested the superintendent, placed him in irons like a criminal, and dragged him through the streets to the prison, where he was told he would not be released except on payment of some money. After a few days, friends interceded and obtained release but not redress. The only result of the entire episode was to delay the work of completing the Cruces road.[30] Even with the repair work already done, it still required seven to eight hours to reach Cruces from Panamá.

COMPLETION OF THE RAILROAD

In November 1853, Colonel Totten could clearly foresee the future problems involved in completion of the railroad. To prepare for the approaching dry season he reported the conditions to the directors. Over seven miles of grading from Chagres River to the Obispo was nearly finished, with about three miles of track laid. He expected the Barbacoas bridge to be completed by December 1, and that would have permitted the running of trains to Gorgona and to the Obispo River by the next January 1. With the Cruces road repaired and with the completion of a

[29] *Panama Star*, Oct. 8, 1853.   [30] *Ibid.*, Oct. 29, 1853.

branch road extending from it to the Obispo, it was planned to transfer passengers and freight directly from the steam train to the pack mules when the trains reached the latter place. This connection would have enabled transit in twelve hours without a boat ride.

Grading and clearing the right of way along the Obispo and at Panamá had already started. Of the 48 miles in total length of road, about 23 were in operation to Barbacoas and it was expected that 30 miles would be in operation by January 1, so that only 18 would remain to be completed. It was in this remaining portion, Colonel Totten stated, that the summit ridge had to be crossed at an elevation of 250 feet above Pacific high tide. He considered the ground favorable, with the largest cut at the summit 1,300 feet long by 24 feet deep and the total excavation about 30,000 cubic yards. On the basis of performance by Mr. Story, he estimated that with 4,570 men the road could be completed to the Pacific within six months—that is, by August 1854. But he was hesitant in giving an exact prediction, for he had had too much experience in the Isthmian area to venture definite forecasts. He did point out, however, that all materials had to be imported, even timber for ties, which were obtained from either the United States or New Granada. As for workers, they also had to be imported, at a cost per worker varying from $15 to $50. As to sickness, although it was an important item, he emphasized its exaggeration by showing that it was actually less than the average of public-works projects in our Western States. Iron for the entire railroad was on the Isthmus, and the remaining expenditure to complete the railroad was estimated at $1,426,800.[31]

The Panama Railroad at this time had eight locomotives, twelve first-class cars, 100 platform cars, and 100 dirt cars, one foundry, one carpenter shop, and one blacksmith shop; the entire road was employing 1,400 men and had main offices and repair shops located at Aspinwall. It is no wonder that Colonel

[31] *Ibid.*, Dec. 22, 1853.

Totten proudly considered his railroad "as perfect a road as can be found in the United States." He felt secure, with iron for the rest of the railroad on the Isthmus ready for use. The entire railroad force had grown to 2,500, with 1,200 on the Obispo section.

But already visitors to hotels had begun to complain of the noise so suggestive of present-day life on the Isthmus. After a visit to Aspinwall one writer wrote that "the 'snorting of the iron horse' as it coursed up and down the railroad in front of the Hotel"[32] had awakened him early.

On November 24, 1853, another milepost was passed in the history of the railroad. One witness of the event wrote: "The Rubicon is passed. The great obstacle is overthrown. This day at 11 o'clock A.M. precisely, the pilot train passed over the great bridge at Barbacoas with flying colors. There were one locomotive and nine cars, heavily laden with freight and passengers."[33] Of course there was a celebration!

Nicaragua, the ancient Panamá competitor for interocean traffic, was at this time also very active as a highway of travel. To offset the competition the press announced that after January 1, 1854, trains would run from Obispo to Aspinwall, that the road from Obispo to Cruces was open, and that a trip between the two oceans could be made in eight hours. Appealing to the prospective traveler for confidence and imploring him not to credit false rumors, the announcement concluded: "As to all the nonsense about malaria, fever, pestilential swamps and the thousand other ills that are charged to the Isthmus, we repeat again, they exist no more than in any other tropical climate, and that prudence and ordinary precaution is all that is required on the part of unacclimated passengers."[34]

In January 1854 the working forces were augmented by the arrival of 360 Irish railroad laborers—all young men about twenty years old, healthy and able-bodied, but not so efficient on

---

[32] *Panama Star*, Nov. 8, 1853.
[33] *Ibid.*, Nov. 30, 1853.   [34] *Ibid.*, Dec. 24, 1853.

the Isthmus as in the cooler climates. Even so, Colonel Totten estimated that they would do a fair amount of work during the first four or six months. The next month about 3,000 workers were engaged on the eighteen miles between Obispo and Panamá, presenting the energetic activity which so often has appeared to Latin Americans as the chief characteristic of the Anglo-Saxon race. To Colonel Totten this activity gave rise to the hope that the rails would join the oceans in August, and the progress was shown by changing the daily advertisement in the Panamá papers as each completed section advanced toward the Pacific. On February 14 it was advertised that trains ran daily from Aspinwall to Obispo, leaving Aspinwall at 9 A.M. and reaching Obispo at 2 P.M. Fare was $12.50 one way for one passenger and 100 pounds of baggage.

The young Irishmen from Cork proved better than expected and were reported becoming more useful daily and enjoying "generally excellent health," as the work on the railroad was being pushed toward the summit and while Panamá was waiting anxiously to have the "iron horse snorting"[35] near by. On March 30 came the announcement for the particular benefit of the California public that transit time was now six hours, and on July 13 trains ran to within one mile of Summit—only eleven and one-half miles from Panamá.

One day near Summit a wounded Irishman, John McGlynn, was attacked, robbed, and left to die. He was discovered by the former Texas ranger, Ran Runnels. With the local government impotent to enforce law and order in this area, which so often had been subjected to unrestricted robbery and murder of travelers, it was necessary to take prompt measures. Ran Runnels offered to organize a mounted guard of twenty men to clear the Isthmus of murderers and robbers, and it was published that foreigners would be protected whether the impotent local government liked it or not.[36] Runnels was vested with complete authority by the

[35] *Ibid.*, March 29, 1854.
[36] *Panama Star and Herald*, July 18, 1854.

railroad and the government. He proceeded to hunt down the murderers and robbers, using the very efficacious method of "whipping, imprisonment, and shooting down in emergency."[37] It was not long before there was a "regular stampede among the undesirables" to leave the Isthmus without saying goodbye.

When the government no longer feared its incapacity, after the expulsion of the criminals, the authority of Ran Runnels was revoked, although the excellent quality of his work was greatly appreciated. The protection of the railroad then returned to the feeble hands of the New Granadan Government.

Late in September the railroad was completed to Summit, and of the remaining part to Panamá only four miles of grading and seven miles of rail were uncompleted. For some time in 1854 the terminus was at Culebra, a little native village beyond Empire. There sprang up a thriving village which boasted of its hotels that had been "imported ready-made from the United States, into which often more than a thousand men, women, and children were promiscuously stowed"[38] for a night stopover on the transit trip. As the completed section of the railroad advanced, the terminus shifted southward with its activities. Construction gangs worked from both ends to hasten the day of joining the rails. On October 28 another advance was marked when the Panama Railroad advertised train schedules from Aspinwall to Summit.

Colonel Totten then estimated the railroad would be completed in January, and he wanted to make a ceremony of the event. On November 15, 1854, he wrote to one of the directors, Gouverneur Kemble, suggesting that as many directors as possible attend the celebration and look over the work. He alluded to the "difficulties overcome" but which did not impress him. Not boasting, he expressed quite opposite feelings: "I am ashamed that so much has been expended in overcoming so little, and take no credit for any engineering science displayed on the work. The difficulties have been of another nature,

[37] Tomes, *op. cit.*, p. 124.   [38] Otis, *op. cit.*, p. 121.

and do not show themselves on the line."[39] Perhaps he was too modest in this statement, for it was his determination that pushed construction to completion, and his achievement is recognized today by a suitable memorial plate in the Panama Railroad Station at Panamá City.

Conversation in Panamá next centered around the plans for the inauguration. Some wanted a parade, some a dinner, and others a ball. But the *Star and Herald* characterized a parade as a funeral, feared a dinner would be dry, and did not like a ball because it had another plan. It was for a picnic trip by the railroad to the bank of the Chagres: "A trip to the Chagres and back, a breakfast, dance and lunch on its banks, all in one day: why, such a thing was never heard of before, and the mention of it would have been laughed at as ridiculous five years ago."[40]

At last on January 27, 1855, rail-laying gangs were in sight of each other, and at midnight at Summit in "darkness and rain, the last rail was laid,"[41] at a point thirty-seven miles from Aspinwall and ten and a half from Panamá. The next day was Sunday. Large crowds gathered along the line to see the first trans-Isthmian train. Warning of its approach by the shrill sound of the whistle, it came "thundering over the summit, and down the Pacific slope" as a "chariot of fire" on what to them was a "perilous journey, over fearful chasms, through mountain gorges, along pleasant valleys, winding around hoary mountain tops, perched upon a narrow shelf of rock in mid-air."[42] It had also passed through jungle and forest and crossed swamps and rivers as it carried distinguished guests, headed by Colonel Totten and Vice-President Alexander J. Center, on the historic ride.

As the "iron horse" rattled along cautiously into Panamá, the people, impressed by the appearance of the train and the "facility with which the wild creature was handled,"[43] gave hearty cheers. They felt that at last the great panacea for all

[39] *Panama Star and Herald*, Dec. 19, 1854.   [40] *Ibid.*, Jan. 23, 1855.
[41] Otis, *op. cit.*, p. 36.   [42] *Aspinwall Daily Courier*, Feb. 24, 1855.
[43] *Panama Star and Herald*, Jan. 30, 1855.

their troubles had come. They saw the end of mules and saddles as well as the muddy and difficult Cruces road, with a capacious railroad car as a welcome substitute. They hailed the "Yankee enterprise" which in five years had completed what the British and French had been unable to carry through.

It was not long before the Isthmians realized that the millennium was not at hand. Those who formerly had been in the pack-mule business were thrown out of work. Business did not increase overnight to offset the effect of the losses. To this disappointment was added the dissatisfaction with trans-Isthmian rates, which were advertised as $25 each way, although monthly commutation tickets for $50 were allowed to residents.

Why this railroad had such high rates is not clear. The Superintendent, Colonel Center, said that they "were intended to be, to a certain extent, prohibitory, until we could get things in shape,"[44] after which it was apparently his idea to reduce rates. But the high rates were retained for many years, during which the road established its great reputation as a dividend payer.

Finally the time of formal celebration arrived, as the distinguished guests collected at Panamá. It began with the arrival of the dignitaries on the steamer "George Law" at Aspinwall on February 15, 1855, with almost five hundred passengers on the way to California but just in time to join the celebration.

The next morning, as their train proceeded, there were demonstrations along the line, made effective by inscribed floral arches over the road. Upon reaching Matachin the train stopped. The crowd alighted and went to a nearby hill to dedicate a monument amid a deluge of perfervid oratory.[45] The journey was just as quickly resumed to Panamá. The gold seekers sailed for the West without delay, but the program for the celebrants was only started.

[44] Tracy Robinson, *Panama: A Personal Record of Forty-six Years, 1861–1907*, p. 24.

[45] *Aspinwall Daily Courier*, Feb. 24, 1855.

On the following day, Saturday morning, February 17, 1855, directors and stockholders, steamship agents, and guests embarked on the "Columbus" for a trip to Taboga Island. Landing amid the roar of guns from all the ships in the harbor, they were entertained at lunch by Captain Wild of the British ship "Bolivia," with the "substantiality and cordiality of a good old English welcome."[46] Then there was a visit to the steamer "John L. Stephens," which had gone around the Horn, and for an interlude in the afternoon there came a tropical shower and a good drenching for many. In the evening Colonel Totten entertained eighty guests at dinner at Aspinwall House. Toasts were made to the President of the United States, to the Governor of Panamá, to the President of the Panama Railroad, to the press, and to the agents of the shipping companies at Panamá. On the following Tuesday the exhausted guests returned to Aspinwall to embark for New York, and the railroad people returned to normal. The period of construction was over, and the Isthmus gradually slumped back into its monotonous existence.

The road as completed in 1855 was about forty-seven and a half miles long. Starting at Aspinwall on Manzanillo Island, the road followed Limon Bay, crossed the Mindi River, and reached the Chagres at Gatun. Then, following the valley of the Chagres, it crossed the river at Barbacoas and continued along the Chagres to the Obispo River, the valley of which it followed on its way to Summit. After passing the summit of the Isthmian cordillera the road descended along the valley of the Rio Grande to Panamá City. The total length of the railroad was 47 miles and 3,020 feet. The total cost of the railroad until completion of the construction in 1859 was about $8,000,000.

Loss of life among construction laborers was not large, except in the case of the Chinese. They resisted medical treatment, exposed themselves to bad weather, used opium, became panic-stricken, and committed suicide. Out of a total force estimated by Colonel Totten to have been about 6,000, deaths numbered

[46] *Panama Star and Herald*, Feb. 20, 1855.

835 (whites 295, blacks 140, and Chinese 400). In constructing the road, about 140,000 ties were used.[47] When the number
of ties used is compared with the actual number of deaths, we
have facts which throw into irrefutable discard the widely quoted
and alluring fable of a "dead man for every tie."

Furthermore, it was demonstrated quite effectively that the
Isthmus possessed no important resources in labor, capital, material, food, or clothing, but required importation of all these
essentials. From the United States came the leaders—the "capitalists, the men of science, the engineers, the practical business
managers, the superior workmen, the masons, carpenters, and
forgers of iron."[48] Ireland, Jamaica, India, China, and Colombia supplied the bulk of the labor. Even Colonel Totten himself
said the Isthmus afforded nothing which could be used in the
construction of the railroad, necessitating the importation of
all materials, even crossties, which had to be brought from
Cartagena or from the United States. Was this condition prophetic of future difficulties when the time for greater construction projects should arrive?

The completion of the railroad across the Isthmus was for
many the realization of an age-old dream. For the promoters
it was the launching of a singularly profitable business enterprise. For those with greater vision, to have an operating railroad practically running along the line of the future canal,
ready for use when the day of canal construction should come,
was an essential prerequisite for digging any canal. The railroad stimulated United States commerce and hastened the settlement of the West. It gave to Panamá a tremendous advantage
in the choice of a route for the first canal. It educated engineers
in the geography of the Isthmus and interested them in the problems of an Isthmian canal. It was the first step in constructing
a waterway, forever placing the builders of the Panama Railroad as the real pioneers of the Panama Canal.

[47] G. W. Davis, article quoted in *Canal Record* (Dec. 25, 1907), I, 133.
[48] Tomes, *Panama in 1855*, p. 112.

Panama Railroad Bridge over the Chagres at Barbacoas

From F. N. Otis, *Illustrated History of the Panama Railroad*, 1861

FERDINAND DE LESSEPS, 1805–1894

From statue in the Plaza de Francia, Panama City

CHAPTER II

FROM SUEZ TO PANAMA

I have never been alarmed by the obstacles thrown in the path of a great enterprise, nor by the delays which discussion and contradictory arguments entail, my experience having taught me that what is accomplished too quickly has no deep roots.—FERDINAND DE LESSEPS, builder of the Suez Canal.[1]

PRELUDE TO THE PARIS CONGRESS

While Colonel Totten was completing the railroad across the Isthmus of Panamá, another man, inspired by the efforts of Egyptian rulers for over 3,000 years, was starting a great project destined to realize the dream of the Pharaohs. Overcoming incredible difficulties, hardships, and determined opposition by the rivals of France, he succeeded in opening the Suez Canal to the commerce of the world on November 17, 1869, obtaining such rare distinction in the eyes of the French nation that he was universally acclaimed as "The Great Frenchman." That man was Ferdinand de Lesseps.

But he did not rest. In the following years he began to think of the Isthmus of Panamá, which he studied seriously. Then came the devastating defeat of France in the Franco-Prussian War, 1870–71. This in turn was followed by the natural desire of the French nation to offset its defeat by a great project of peace as the first step in revival of its position of power and prestige. The Panama Canal was a great concept that would rank with Suez. When the name of De Lesseps was associated with Panamá, the idea of the Panama Canal attained universal appeal.

The concept of a canal at Panamá was posed in 1871 at the International Geographical Congress at Antwerp, as a result of many explorations in Colombia by Anthoine de Gogorza, who was born in the United States of French parents and had lived

[1] De Lesseps, *Recollections of Forty Years*, II, 202.

31

for years in Colombia. But it was not until 1875, when De Lesseps was presiding over the Geographical Society of Paris, that the subject received wide public attention. Until then De Lesseps had preferred the project of a lock canal at Nicaragua but had to give up the idea because of the predominant interest of the United States in that field. He had experienced the tremendous success of his sea-level canal at Suez, which was paying dividends to small shareholders rather than to powerful financiers. Because of its success the canal at Suez became to the French people the idealized type, and therefore they called for a sea-level canal at Panamá.

At this 1875 meeting there was insufficient knowledge to permit detailed discussions; but De Lesseps, reflecting the trend of the times, claimed a sea-level canal was the only one capable of meeting the needs of navigation and that failure of the early planners to examine the matter of a sea-level route, as well as a lock-canal route, was a great error. The result was a resolution calling for an international congress to collect evidence and evaluate all information and then to make definite recommendations for a canal. A Committee of Initiative, with De Lesseps at its head, was formed and made efforts toward securing international co-operation in conducting surveys. De Gogorza was sent back to Colombia.

Meanwhile the efforts of the United States to secure canal rights, which had been interrupted by the Civil War, were resumed under President Johnson; but the treaty signed with Colombia in January 1869 was rejected by the Colombian Senate. The succeeding administration of President Grant continued negotiations, and a treaty was signed on January 26, 1870; but this was so amended by the Colombian Senate as to make it unacceptable to the United States Government. Because of the undeveloped means of communication of that day and the consequent delay of messages, further canal negotiations were transferred in 1873 from Bogotá to Washington, where they likewise failed.

During this period the explorations and surveys authorized by Congress in the early part of Grant's first term had been progressing over the various routes—Darien, Tehuantepec, Nicaragua, and Panamá, 1870–1875—with a thoroughness and precision unequaled by previous explorers and civil engineers. In March 1872, Congress authorized the President to appoint an Interoceanic Canal Commission to study and evaluate the reports of these surveys and other reliable material, with a view to determining the most practicable route for a waterway between the two oceans. In February 1876 the Commission made its report, recommending the Nicaragua route. Any further attempts by the United States to renew negotiations with Colombia were thus rendered useless, and attention was directed toward Nicaragua.[2]

Moreover, the United States Congress, under pressure for strict economy in the country-wide period of drought and depression, by its Appropriations Act of August 13, 1876, cut out all provisions for the legations in Bolivia, Colombia, and Ecuador, in addition to many in Europe. Grant, under protest, was thus forced to withdraw the ministers and close these legations for the rest of his term.[3]

Fortunately for the French, these events left the way open for De Gogorza to work unopposed in Bogotá. He convinced the Colombian Government that he knew a practicable route in the San Blas region where the Atrato and Tuyra rivers could be utilized, and on May 28, 1876, obtained a contract which required a report on explorations within eighteen months. He then returned to France.

In Paris the Geographical Society had organized the Committee of Initiative to examine the subject of an interoceanic canal, with De Lesseps as its president and with Admiral Baron

---

[2] S. F. Bemis, *The American Secretaries of State and Their Diplomacy*, VII, 206–9. Allan Nevins, *Hamilton Fish: The Inner History of the Grant Administration*, Appendix I, pp. 913–15.

[3] State Dept., *Register, 1876–1878* (U.S.). *New York Tribune*, Aug. 16, 1876, p. 1; Aug. 12, p. 1.

de la Roncière-le Noury, president of the Georgraphical Society, and J. L. J. Meurand, Director of Consulates in the Paris Foreign Office, as vice-presidents. But geographical knowledge of the Isthmus was insufficient, and to obtain more information it was necessary to finance additional explorations and surveys. Accordingly, a limited company, La Société Civile Internationale du Canal Interocéanique, was organized by General Istvan Türr, aide-de-camp to the King of Italy; Lucien N. B. Wyse, a lieutenant in the French Navy and a grandson of Lucien Bonaparte; and shrewd Baron Jacques de Reinach, naturalized Frenchman and financier. It was a real "combination of geography and finance," and the society took over the Colombian concession of De Gogorza.

Wyse, a dominant influence in the formation of the society, was authorized to explore the Isthmus. Selecting Armand Réclus, a naval lieutenant, as his chief assistant, he sailed for Panamá; but three of his eight engineers died on the way.

Wyse divided his expedition into groups and explored several routes in the Darien-Atrato regions. Completing his work in April 1877, he returned to Paris with plans which De Lesseps promptly rejected because all required tunnels and locks. So Wyse had to visit the Isthmus again and was able to start his second exploration on December 6, 1877, this time in Panamá. There he examined two routes, the San Blas and the present canal route from Limon Bay to Panamá, and chose the latter. His plan was a sea-level project, conveniently near the railroad and with a 7,720-meter tunnel through Culebra.

Armed with this sea-level plan for the Panama Canal, he left for Bogotá, a trip that required him to spend eleven days on horseback. It was in this isolated South American capital that, in the name of his society, he negotiated what is known as the Wyse Concession and signed it with the Minister of Foreign Affairs, Eustorgio Salgar, on March 20, 1878. That day marks the legal start of the Panama Canal.

Wyse returned to France via New York, where he made arrangements for securing control of the Panama Railroad. He landed in France not only with his reports of explorations and a concession from Colombia but with assurance of control of the railroad that was required as an adjunct to French construction.

With the reports of Wyse available for De Lesseps, together with those of the extensive explorations during Grant's Administration as evaluated by the United States Interoceanic Canal Commission in its report of February 1876, the great canal promoter was in a position to proceed with the next step.

De Lesseps had learned many lessons at Suez. Besides, he was an experienced diplomat, acquainted with the ways of the world. He knew the need for that nebulous thing called international co-operation in the launching of great projects in foreign lands and counted upon this to quiet foreign opposition, the nature of which he fully understood. He did not like engineers; he had had to resolve too many disputes between them at Suez.

Invitations were sent out by the Geographical Society of Paris to "all the savants, engineers, and sailors of the Old and New World,"[4] as well as to chambers of commerce and geographical societies, asking each to send delegates for an international congress to meet in Paris on May 15, 1879.

What were the forces behind all this movement? There were disinterested geographers and also shrewd financiers who owned the concession and who desired to sell their holdings; but these men could not be expected to leave Paris for the frontier life at Panamá. Furthermore, there were many—leaders, engineers, and explorers—who, inspired by the vision of the French nation as the creator of the other great waterway of the world, were willing to follow their calling to the jungles of Panamá. There was De Lesseps!

THE PARIS CONGRESS

The International Congress for Consideration of an Interoceanic Canal (Congrès International d'Études du Canal Inter-

[4] De Lesseps, op. cit., II, 176.

océanique) met at Paris on May 15, 1879, under the temporary
chairmanship of Admiral Baron de la Roncière-le Noury, with
a total of 135 delegates. Its members were celebrated in the
fields of "science, politics, and industry." Seventy-four were
from France. The eleven from the United States included men
interested in Nicaragua and other canal areas. Ferdinand de
Lesseps was chosen for the presidency, which he assumed with
all his characteristic force, enthusiasm, and confidence. Admiral Daniel Ammen[5] was made first vice-president and sat on
De Lesseps' right.

The Congress was organized in five committees. There was
the Statistical Commission, with M. Pierre E. Levasseur presiding, whose task was to determine whether the probable tonnage passing through the canal would be sufficient to provide
expected returns on invested capital. It predicted that 5,250,000
tons would be the normal traffic, that it would be developed
gradually after the assumed opening in 1889, and that 2,000,000
tons would be diverted from the trade then existing between
Europe and Asia.[6] But it would be possible to handle an annual
traffic of even 6,000,000 tons, the Secretary-General of the Suez
Canal advised, provided fifty ships could be transited in a day.
That, De Lesseps said, was the reason that the Suez was a sea-
level and not a lock canal—a view which produced its effect on
the members.

Nathan Appleton, of Boston, headed the Economic Commission. It reported on distances to be saved by use of the Panama
Canal, the new markets to be opened and new traffic created, and
the reductions on freight and insurance to be effected by the
shortening of voyages and the avoidance of dangerous areas like
Cape Horn. This Commission also mentioned the adverse effects
of locks or tunnels in handling the largest ships.

The Commission of Navigation was composed of marine men,

[5] Ammen to Secretary of State, June 21, 1879, *Sen. Doc. 102*, p. 2, 58th Cong.,
2d sess. (U.S.).

[6] Isthmian Canal Commission (hereafter designated as I.C.C.), *Report, 1899–
1901*, II, 6 (U.S.).

with Dr. O. J. Broch, an ex-minister of Norway, presiding. It studied the questions of winds and currents and the canal's probable effect on shipbuilding, and considered a lock canal acceptable only if a sea-level type were proved impossible. In the event a lock canal were adopted, it reported that expected traffic would require "double locks, side by side, one for vessels going west and the other for vessels going east."

Most fundamental of the committees was the Technical Commission, to which were assigned men who were the most eminent engineers of their time, including Alexandre T. Lavalley and Abel Couvreux, Jr., the dredgers of Suez.

Advocates of the various canal ideas submitted their plans. Francisco de Garay, Mexican delegate, championed Tehuantepec, which was summarily rejected because of its one hundred twenty locks plus twelve days required for transit. United States representatives, Admiral Daniel Ammen, Commander Edward P. Lull, and Civil Engineer A. G. Menocal, proposed a Nicaragua lock canal. The French naval officers, Wyse and Réclus, offered their plan for a sea-level canal at Panamá. Nathan Appleton advocated the thirty-three-mile San Blas route, but it contained a nine-mile tunnel and was rejected. Commander Thomas O. Selfridge suggested a project by way of the Atrato River, and that was rejected. Altogether fourteen plans were submitted. These were sifted down by a subcomittee to two: Nicaragua and Panamá, each with its adherents.

The Technical Commission of the Congress checked upon the distinctive features of these two routes, weighing the merits of the sea-level plan at Panamá and the lock plan at Nicaragua. The inspiration and will of De Lesseps were reported as predominant, and the discussions "long, and sometimes very heated." At its last meeting on May 28 the Technical Commission adopted its findings by vote, recommending a sea-level canal in a route from Colón to Panamá. The vote, however, was not unanimous, and opposition to De Lesseps' sea-level ideas was indicated by abstentions as well as by nays.

With four reports completed, the Ways and Means Commission under the presidency of M. Paul Cérésole, ex-President of the Swiss Confederation, was able to report the "sum of elements of transit" as sufficient to pay the cost of the canal and that it would expand to "an incalculable extent." The transit dues were placed at 15 francs per ton, and an annual net profit of 1,680,000 francs was predicted. This Commission also hoped with the others that, even at a cost of more time and money, the canal could be constructed "without locks or tunnels."

Though all the Commissions reported for a sea-level canal, there were marked differences of opinion, particularly among the engineers. One of them, Adolphe Godin de Lépinay, made a strong plea for a lock-type canal. Of the French members he was the only one who had supervised construction work on the Isthmus. He knew its topography, the nature of the torrential Chagres and the necessity of controlling it. He understood the problem of labor in the tropics and had seen the effects of tropical diseases.

De Lépinay explained that there was a central highland to be crossed by the canal and that excavating a sea-level canal through that mass of land would be too vast a project to undertake in any country, but especially in Panamá where there was yellow fever. He had a simpler and less expensive solution for building the waterway. He knew that the headwaters of the two important Isthmian rivers approached each other near Culebra. The Rio Grande drained southerly into the Pacific; the Obispo drained northerly into the Chagres, which in turn drained into the Atlantic. The valleys of these rivers were bordered by ranges of mountains and hills that provided natural impounding perimeters for the formation of lakes. That was the key to the problem.

It was not strange that, in arriving at his solution for constructing a canal across the mountains, De Lépinay should have utilized the contours of the land and the water supply of the rivers as offering the best means of overcoming the greatest

problems—the control of the Chagres River and the excavating
of a channel across the mountains. He was confident of the
soundness of his plan, which he had first thought of as early as
1859.[7]

De Lépinay's concept of the Panama Canal was of unbeliev-
able simplicity. He proposed the creation of a large lake on
each side of the continental divide by erecting a dam across the
Chagres River and another across the Rio Grande, as close to
the seas as configuration of the land permitted. The water in
each lake would be allowed to rise to the approximate level of
80 feet, the two lakes would be joined by a channel across the
divide, and on each side of the Isthmus locks would be constructed between the lakes and the sea level. His concept is
clear, simple, and definite—a high-level lake on each side of
the Isthmus, joined by an open channel through the mountains,
and each lake connected by locks to the seas.[8] That was the
terminal-lake conception. It was the fundamental plan for
constructing the Panama Canal that has immortalized its origi-
nator.

Unfortunately, the members of that Congress did not understand his prophetic words. In their ignorance of the problem
involved, they could not understand. To them these prophecies
were probably nothing more than engineering abstractions. De
Lépinay's proposal was not even discussed seriously. But failure to understand and approve deprived the French of the only
plan that would have been feasible.

When the voting came, De Lépinay was much perturbed and
rose in protest. He did not want his name linked with what he
called the disastrous measure of the sea-level canal. Defeat could
not shake his confidence in his own concept; for, he said, "If I
have not known how to make my advice triumph, I cannot let it
be believed that I abandon it, all unknown though I am."[9]

---

[7] L. W. Bates, *Statement,* March 10, 1906 (Hearings No. 18, II, 1666) (U.S.).

[8] Bunau-Varilla, *Panama: the Creation, Destruction, and Resurrection,* p. 26.

[9] De Lépinay; quoted in Bates, *op. cit.,* pp. 1666–67.

He stated the advantages of the lock canal as costing 500,-000,000 francs less than the sea-level, as affording more rapid transit than the sea-level canal, and as avoiding the unnecessary sacrifice of thousands of men. Then he added: "In order not to burden my conscience with these useless deaths and with the loss of a large capital, I abstain from voting, or I vote *No*."[10]

Read today in the light of greater general knowledge, De Lépinay's plan seems so sound and so simple that it is hard to understand how it could have been so completely ignored. Its adoption would have eliminated almost all excavation in the valleys of the Chagres and Rio Grande for the French Canal, except in the sea-level sections. It would have tremendously reduced the quantity of excavation in the Obispo valley and in Culebra Cut. It was, in the main, the canal plan finally adopted in 1906 by the United States.

In a hall crowded with enthusiasts, a vote was taken on the final resolution on May 29 in full session. Summarized, it called for a "one level"[11] canal from Limon Bay to the Bay of Panamá. The vote on this resolution was significant. Of the 135 members, 37 were absent; of the remaining 98, the vote was: ayes 78, nays 8, and 12 not voting. Admiral Ammen refused to vote, on the ground that only engineers should vote. Of the members, 74 were French and 11 were from the United States; 42 were engineers. Of the 78 ayes, 20 were engineers, but only one of them had visited Panamá. Of the 11 United States delegates, 4 were absent, 4 did not vote, and 3 voted for Panamá, Commander Selfridge among the last.

By this vote the Congress had approved a sea-level canal on a location from Limon Bay to Panamá, along a route "traced by Lloyd, Totten, Garella, Wyse and Réclus," at a cost of 1,070,-000,000 francs ($214,000,000), with twelve years' time to complete it. But even so, it appears that a majority of the engineers were skeptical of the sea-level idea. One of them, M.

[10] Congrès International d'Études du Canal Interocéanique, *Compte Rendu des Séances*, pp. 658–59 (tr.).

[11] De Lesseps, *op. cit.*, II, 198–99.

Charles Kleitz, supported his negative vote with the statement that the resolution submitted was "too positive and too absolute." He agreed that the canal should run from Limon Bay to Panamá, but considered the surveys insufficiently thorough to make a choice of type "based upon reasons and proofs."[12] Although he admitted the desirability of a sea-level canal, he considered a lock canal would meet requirements. But of course it would have taken more than the cautious analyses of a few keen engineers to stem the tide in such a well-managed affair.

De Lesseps had lent the full force of his high prestige toward securing a vote for the sea-level canal, deliberately ignoring the technical advice of the well-informed engineer, Godin de Lépinay; but he was supported in his stand for a sea-level canal by the other engineers. Even so, it was at this point that he made a fundamental error in launching the vast program based upon false assumptions.

De Lesseps must have had a sense of high elation as the results were announced. He commended the Congress for its work with highest praise, and yielded the chair to Admiral Baron de la Roncière-le Noury. The Admiral ended an effective closing speech with the hope that "the illustrious gentleman who had been the soul of the deliberations, who was the personification of grand enterprises, and who had charmed all by his courtesy and dignity, might live to witness the completion of the great work to which his name would remain forever attached, and of which he could not refuse to take the direction."

The Great Frenchman could not resist this stirring accolade and replied that "a general who has once gained a battle never refused to engage in another."[13]

ORGANIZING THE PANAMA CANAL COMPANY

In Panamá the people were overjoyed at the news of the approval of the Wyse-Réclus route by the Paris Congress and

[12] I.C.C., *op. cit.*, II, 7 (U.S.).

[13] *Panama Star and Herald*, June 10, 1879.

that De Lesseps had proclaimed he could raise $100,000,000 in thirty days to commence work.

In the United States, part of the press assumed an ominous tone, threatening to apply the Monroe Doctrine—a tone which was reflected very soon in the Congress of the United States by the introduction on June 25, 1879, of a joint resolution by General Ambrose E. Burnside, "That the people of these States would not view without serious disquietude any attempt by the powers of Europe to establish under their protection and domination a ship-canal across the Isthmus of Darien" and that it would be regarded "as a manifestation of an unfriendly disposition toward the United States."[14]

In France the idea of building another great canal fitted in with the spirit of the time, dimly persistent from the doctrine by Saint-Simon, "social regeneration through work, and universal peace through great public undertakings, and particularly by developing communications between the peoples of the world."[15] There was also the natural desire for a peaceful revenge against the Germans, who had defeated the French so decisively in the Franco-Prussian War.

But how to organize and finance an enterprise so great? Suez had been financed through subscriptions. De Lesseps decided that the same method was best for Panama. This way was independent of capricious government policies, "leaving the enterprise its purely industrial character, and avoiding anything like dabbling in politics."[16] In his efforts to finance Suez he "had walked out on Rothschild," but he had succeeded. Could he repeat it here?

De Lesseps was no longer a young man, having passed his seventy-third birthday. Friends and family tried to dissuade him from heading an undertaking that would require such tremendous efforts and so much time. The difficulties were fore-

[14] Burnside, "Joint Resolution (Sen. Res. No. 43)." *Congressional Record*, IX, Pt. 2, p. 2312 (46th Cong., 1st sess.) (U.S.).

[15] André Siegfried, *Suez and Panama*, p. 239.

[16] De Lesseps, *op. cit.*, II, 178.

seen, and he was warned by the leaders of the risks to be run. For him money was not a motive, as he had sufficient; but it was the glory of a second great victory. His son, Charles de Lesseps, asked ". . . . for us who have worked at your side, are we to have no repose?"[17] But to all who opposed his assumption of leadership, Ferdinand de Lesseps was deaf. He was confident of success at Panamá, publicly stating that the canal would be completed in eight years at a cost of about $50,000,000 and that the difficulties were "not so formidable as those which had to be overcome in the construction of the Suez Canal, as a railway already exists along the course . . . . with a large town at each extremity."[18] Some of his statement was true!

To launch such an enormous undertaking the force of a great prestige was needed. In France De Lesseps was regarded as one who had held aloof from the controversies of the canal until he was certain and who would not attempt anything not genuine or feasible beyond a doubt. He would expect to make money, but being rich already he needed no more; besides, at seventy-four a man with his record could not be moved by a financial consideration. The motive was "fame rather than greed for gold."

The Universal Interoceanic Panama Canal Company (Compagnie Universelle du Canal Interocéanique de Panama), now known as the Old Panama Canal Company, was started with a capital stock of 400,000,000 francs ($80,000,000)—800,000 shares at 500 francs each; and it was speedily announced that De Lesseps would dig the first spade of earth on January 1, 1880. De Lesseps at first proposed General Grant as the first honorary president, while he himself would serve as general manager; but opposition in the United States did not permit, and De Lesseps was made president.

It was necessary to obtain money for organizing the new company. This was done by selling 400 founders' shares of 5,000 francs each to persons "interested in the creation of great enter-

[17] Siegfried, op. cit., p. 237.   [18] Panama Star and Herald, July 22, 1879.

prises,"[19] to each of whom were given free 100 additional shares. Thus was obtained 2,000,000 francs ($400,000). De Lesseps then acquired the Wyse Concession from the society headed by General Türr, for the high price of 10,000,000 francs ($2,000,-000). A public subscription was arranged for August 6 and 7, and circulars were sent out to Europe and America announcing the formation of the company, with an expected annual income of 90,000,000 francs and dividends at the rate of 11.5 per cent.

Strong political attacks on the effort marked the opening of the campaign. The cost estimates were considered too small and estimated receipts too great. Both the press and the high financial circles in France were hostile. The subscription tended to arouse fears in the United States, which were increased by the campaign for Nicaragua by Admiral Ammen and Civil Engineer Menocal. De Lesseps was represented as a Bonapartist seeking power.

Why all this opposition arose was not clear at the time; but many years later, after the collapse of the company and when Charles de Lesseps was being prosecuted, he claimed that his father succeeded in stopping the clamor of the opposition by placing the financial management of the company in charge of a small group associated with "journalism and finance, who undertook to render public opinion favorable to the enterprise."[20] That was the price De Lesseps had to pay for the privilege of being left alone.

The result of the first campaign was almost a complete failure, with only 30,000,000 francs ($6,000,000) subscribed; but it did not deter De Lesseps. In August, although admitting the failure, he called for new surveys and the sending to Panamá of an International Technical Commission of celebrated engineers, which he would accompany, to check the Panamá location as the most practicable route. Then by visiting the United States in person he would "silence the clamor of opposition raised by hostile America." It should be remembered that the press in the United

[19] Siegfried, *op. cit.*, p. 244.   [20] I.C.C., *op. cit.*, II, 8 (U.S.).

States had become so active as to surprise and startle not only France but also Panamá, where the people thought the United States was playing at Panamá the part played by England at Suez when De Lesseps was so bitterly opposed. But they hoped he would be equally successful in his second battle. They believed the "reckless adventurer condemned by the English Press is today the great genius whose energy and foresight have carried out the greatest work of our country, in spite of a seemingly insurmountable opposition."[21]

To assist in overcoming opposition to the Panama Canal idea, De Lesseps started a fortnightly bulletin on September 1, 1879, entitled *Bulletin du Canal Interocéanique,* which was published until February 1889. It issued promotional propaganda and reports on construction during the French effort and probably inspired later the starting of the *Canal Record* by the Isthmian Canal Commission in 1907. The result of the opposition was to delay, but not to defeat, the French efforts.

ECHOES IN THE UNITED STATES AND PANAMA

At regular intervals during these early promotional periods there appeared some strongly realistic persons. They had spoken during the Paris Congress in May. From New York came ideas from Colonel Totten, then an old man. After completing the Panama Railroad, he had studied the canal problem and submitted a plan in 1857 for a lock canal from Limon Bay to Panamá Bay. Its main features called for a bottom width of 150 feet, a depth of 31 feet, locks 400 by 30 feet, and a summit level of 150 feet supplied by a 24-mile feeder from the upper Chagres. The estimated cost was $80,000,000.[22]

Naturally he watched the Paris proceedings intently and published his views. Writing in October 1879, he pointed out that up to the end of the Congress the type of the canal considered necessary was doubtful, that is, whether it should be sea-level,

[21] *Panama Star and Herald,* Sept. 7, 1879.
[22] J. E. Nourse, *The Maritime Canal of Suez,* p. 142 (U.S.).

lock, or tunnel, but it had been decided that Panamá was the most advantageous route. At this time Colonel Totten considered a sea-level canal impracticable from the business standpoint. He did not mean, however, that with enough "money, science and perseverance" it could not have been accomplished.

The sea-level plan of Wyse and Réclus provided a dam for the Chagres—the river whose sudden floods created the greatest of problems for the sea-level plan. This problem, he thought, could be handled only by diverting the Chagres in a "radical removal," for damming the river was considered too dangerous. Totten was familiar with the features of the country and had no illusions. Based upon a bottom width of 105 feet in earth and 120 feet in rock, he estimated a cost for a sea-level type at $344,000,000 without a tunnel. To this he added $85,000,000 for diverting the Chagres to Las Minas Bay, bringing the total to $429,000,000—a cost so great as to cause him to consider a sea-level canal impracticable.[23]

In the meantime plans went forward for the approaching visit to Panamá of the International Technical Commission. De Lesseps conducted a lecture tour of France, and every mail to the Isthmus brought news from France of new indications of the "earnestness and sincerity" of De Lesseps in his great work of uniting the oceans. In November word came that he expected to arrive late the following month.

The program of opposition in the United States continued undiminished, but United States citizens in Panamá remained sympathetic to the French. All looked forward to the coming visit of De Lesseps, predicting that the "intelligence, energy and good faith" which he had used in "making the Panamá route known to the world, and of inaugurating actual work in the enterprise" would prove of "more value than the lucubrations of a dozen politicians, presidents though they be."[24]

During the fall of 1879 a party of engineers from France ar-

[23] *Panama Star and Herald*, Dec. 9, 1879.
[24] *Ibid.*, Dec. 4, 1879.

rived at Panamá with drilling machines. They began a series of borings and surveys in preparation for the consulting engineers. A special reception committee arranged a schedule of entertainment for the distinguished guests, among whom were expected Wyse and Réclus, and Colonel Totten, the builder of the Panama Railroad.

As the time for De Lesseps' arrival approached, the Isthmians increased their confidence in the future as well as their disdain for North Americans. The latter had been "maundering and drivelling over their Monroe Doctrine, and the necessity of American supremacy in a part of the world where their interests are fifth rate," while De Lesseps was "working quietly and practically, demonstrating the first part of the great problem,"[25] that is, the practicability of the route from Limon Bay to Panamá and the cost of construction. That was the spirit at Panamá almost on the eve of the arrival of the Great Frenchman.

DE LESSEPS ARRIVES AT PANAMA

On the afternoon of December 30, 1879, an excited crowd was waiting on a wharf in Colón. The city was decorated with flags of all nations except the United States. A band was playing "soul-stirring airs," and the reception committee gathered as the "Lafayette," flagship of the French West Indies Squadron, approached her berth. As soon as the gangway was rigged the reception committee went to the saloon and greeted Ferdinand de Lesseps. With him were his young wife and three young children, whom he had brought as the best way to discredit the accepted rumors about the dangers of the Panamá climate. Also there were eminent engineers of the International Technical Commission, who had come with him from France, and a group from the United States, which included Nathan Appleton, of Boston; Trenor W. Park, President of the Panama Railroad; and Colonel Totten, who served as the important connecting link between the building of the railroad and the French canal effort.

[25] *Ibid.*, Dec. 25, 1879.

An address of welcome was made by J. A. Céspedes, with a gracious response by De Lesseps, and afterward came the usual cordialities and convivialities. Tracy Robinson, a member of the committee and long a resident of Colón, has left his impressions of the seventy-four-year-old canal builder. He was "still active and vigorous; a small man, French in detail, with winning manners, and what is called a magnetic presence." He was confident and convincing, answering all questions about the canal with facility and amiability. Robinson asked him, "What will be done with the Chagres River?" Without hestitating he replied, "It is the intention to turn the upper river into the Pacific Ocean, thereby relieving the lower valley of all danger of floods."[26] This conversation made a great impression at the time. It was a new idea.

In the evening there was a display of fireworks from the ice-house, the most popular institution of those days. Later in the evening De Lesseps, with a few friends, went ashore for a stroll around the streets of Colón, among throngs of enthusiastic Isthmians.

The next day was one for work. De Lesseps and the engineers inspected the Pacific Mail wharf. He asked about the force and nature of northers which, because of the northern exposure of Limon Bay, so often had made that anchorage unsafe. He indicated the location of a breakwater and the probable canal entrance on a chart and evidenced complete satisfaction in the prospects for the successful completion of the canal. He recognized only two great difficulties: the Chagres River and the cutting of the canal through the summit at Culebra. The first problem would be overcome by diverting its headwaters "into another channel, and the second will disappear before the wells which will be sunk and charged with explosives of sufficient force to remove vast quantities at each discharge."[27] Landing for the first

---

[26] Robinson, *Panama: A Personal Record of Forty-six Years, 1861–1907,* pp. 139–40.

[27] *Panama Star and Herald,* Jan. 1, 1880.

time in that region of luxuriant vegetation, just at the beginning of the dry season, before plants had begun to fade, he must have compared the scene with the desert of his former endeavor at uninhabited Suez. It is no wonder that the very existence of the railroad impressed him and that he expected work to start without much delay.

With the visit at Colón completed, he left for Panamá City on the 11:30 A.M. train, and all along the line met scenes which he called "indescribable ovations." When halfway to Panamá, at Barbacoas bridge, the President of the State of Panamá boarded the train and entertained at dinner on the way to Panamá City, where elaborate preparations had been made to honor their illustrious guest.

When the train stopped, the party stepped off into an open tent where the "great impresario" was introduced to all the local dignitaries; from there they were taken in carriages to the Grand Hotel, along the Avenida Central, between lines of Colombian troops. The Avenida Central and connecting streets were profusely decorated, with the flags of France and Colombia prevailing. At intervals were mounted shields, each bearing the name of earlier Isthmian explorers—from Balboa in 1513 to Wyse, Réclus, and Pedro J. Sosa in 1877 and 1878. On arches were salutations—at Santa Ana Plaza one which read "Colombia salutes Ferdinand de Lesseps"; at the Grand Hotel another reading "Panama salutes her illustrious guest, Ferdinand de Lesseps."[28]

His work for the next decade was to be the dominating subject of conversation and thought on the Isthmus and the cause of endless discussion in the United States.

[28] *Ibid.,* Jan. 1, 1880.

CHAPTER III

PROMOTING THE PANAMA CANAL COMPANY

The United States have, by right, the pre-eminence in this enterprise and it is my conviction they will secure it. Science has declared that the canal is possible, and I am the servant of science. I will carry this work to a successful result, and it will make America queen of the seas.—FERDINAND DE LESSEPS, builder of the Suez Canal.[1]

DE LESSEPS INAUGURATES THE PANAMA CANAL

During the preceding June, De Lesseps had promised to dig the first spade of earth for the Panama Canal on January 1, 1880. When that day arrived he was at Panamá, ready to carry out his promise in the manner that only a distinguished graduate of the Suez undertaking could have managed. He planned to move the first ground at the mouth of the Rio Grande, the future canal entrance, with his young daughter Ferdinande de Lesseps turning the "first sod."[2]

De Lesseps and his party of distinguished guests boarded the steam tender "Taboguilla" to make the three-mile trip to the Rio Grande, with the intention of landing for a ceremony after a reception and feast on board. The departure was delayed by late guests, and by the time the "Taboguilla" arrived near her destination the waters of the Pacific had receded so far as to prevent the vessel from approaching the desired spot. De Lesseps rose to the occasion and broke out his ceremonial shovel and pickaxe, which he had brought from France especially for the inauguration of the Canal. Announcing that the ceremony was only symbolic, he proceeded to conduct it on board with a champagne box filled with earth. Amid much applause, young Ferdinande struck the first blow with the pickaxe. Then followed

---

[1] *Addresses at the De Lesseps Banquet, March 1, 1880*, p. 24.
[2] W. C. Haskins, *Canal Zone Pilot*, p. 180.

other symbolic blows by the guests to show, as De Lesseps explained it, the "alliance of all peoples in the work of uniting the two oceans for the good of mankind."[3]

De Lesseps then proclaimed the fulfillment of his promise to begin practical work on January 1, 1880, expressed confidence of success in the task to which he had dedicated the closing years of his life, and said he had no fear of lack in financial assistance for the opening of another great highway of world trade. There were more speeches, and the exercises were concluded with a benediction by Bishop José T. Paúl of Panamá, who extended the blessings of the Universal Church. And the party returned to Panamá.

The third day of the De Lesseps reception was relatively quiet. There was only an exhibition drill by a battalion of the Colombian Army. Behind the scenes of gaiety, however, the International Technical Commission began its laborious work of exploring and examining the canal route.

The last celebrations for De Lesseps were held on Sunday, January 4, 1880. There were a military display, some bullfights in the Plaza Santa Ana, and finally an elaborate banquet for one hundred forty at the Grand Hotel (now the Panamá Post Office). There Dr. Antonio Ferro presided, with Madame De Lesseps sitting on his right and Ferdinand de Lesseps to the left. Among the guests were the illustrious Bishop Paúl of Panamá, Lucien Wyse, and Colonel Totten. After replying to the toasts made to him, De Lesseps observed the presence of newspaper men. Knowing how closely the United States was watching and how much public opinion there was created by the newspapers, he proposed a toast to the press—"The representatives of public opinion, the greatest force of our epoch, with the assistance of which the great commercial and interoceanic highway for the benefit of the world would be made in Colombian territory, under the protection of the Colombian Government, and of the great powers of the world."

[3] *Canal Record*, July 29, 1908, I, 383 (U.S.).

Later, De Lesseps announced that the International Technical Commission had completed its organization, under the presidency of Colonel Totten and the distinguished canal engineer, Jacob Dirks of Holland. The canal line from Colón to Panamá had been divided into five sections, each with a brigade of engineers to conduct surveys. De Lesseps ended by referring to the important work done for the canal by Wyse, who had negotiated its concession and explored the route.

Wyse did have firsthand knowledge. He knew how the work would have to be done in the Panamá climate and, after acknowledging the unusual recognition by his chief, he proposed the health of "the humble laborers, without distinction of race or nationality, who in the future may be the useful but modest instruments"[4] to bring the great work to completion. It was evident to him then that the black man would perform the hard labor in that climate.

All of this prelude appears characterized by a lamentable artificiality and lack of reality. Some of it was induced by ignorance of the country—its geography, its geology, its climate and health conditions and resources. Part was due to incorrect conclusions drawn from the experience of Suez, which unfortunately did not apply at all to the Isthmus of Panamá—a land which John F. Stevens, as chief engineer of the Panama Canal for the United States, described about twenty-five years later as "one of the most forbidding spots on earth"[5] from a construction viewpoint. Above all, it should be remembered that De Lesseps was not an engineer but a trained diplomat, that he was the promoter of the most gigantic commercial enterprise in the history of the world and had taken on himself the task of financing it by private subscription. Notwithstanding his advanced age, he had proved himself a gifted propagandist and promoter. By his selection of the Panama route he had determined the location of the trans-Isthmian waterway and had started one of the greatest works of man.

[4] *Panama Star and Herald,* Jan. 6, 1880, p. 2.
[5] J. F. Stevens, *An Engineer's Recollections,* p. 40.

SURVEY BY DE LESSEPS AND
INTERNATIONAL TECHNICAL COMMISSION

January is a pleasant month in Panamá, with refreshing trade winds during the day and little or no rain. The rainy season ends in December, and in January the dry season is not advanced enough to present the parched appearance of April; instead, the landscape retains much of the luxuriant green of the rainy days. It was an ideal month for the Technical Commission to start its labors.

This exploring effort was considered in Panamá as the "largest, the most efficient" with respect to experience and practical knowledge of members, "the most completely equipped, and perfectly organized." Besides, it had the "advantage of being under the leadership of a veteran campaigner, whose name is a guarantee of success."[6]

The exploring parties, at first organized into five groups, were changed later to eight, each under a competent engineer. Reports of observations made in the field were forwarded to the commission headquarters in Panamá, where they were classified by a committee consisting of Colonel Totten, Mr. Dirks, and General W. W. Wright, for use in the final report. De Lesseps remained conveniently near in Panamá with Wyse and kept in close touch with the progress of the survey.

De Lesseps had already inaugurated the canal at the mouth of the Rio Grande. He next decided to inaugurate the excavation of Culebra Cut on January 10, 1880, and went to Cerro Culebra (afterward known as Gold Hill) for the ceremony. A mine, fitted with an electric firing device, had been laid in the hard basalt formation a few feet below the summit and was ready. Proceeding with some celebrities, including Bishop Paúl and little Ferdinande, he again selected the daughter to render the honors. The Bishop extended his blessing, and Ferdinande pressed the button. Large masses of rock were hurled into the

---

[6] *Panama Star and Herald*, Jan. 7, 1880. Jan. 29, 1880.

air, and the party returned to Panamá enthusiastic for the "perfect success."[7]

The work outlined for the International Technical Commission was large. It comprised a verification of all previous surveys, including those of Lull and Menocal and also of Wyse and Réclus, the making of necessary additional surveys, and the final determination of the line of the canal. Borings had to be made to determine the nature of the earth along the canal line and at terminal ports. Calculations of quantities to be excavated and classification of materials were required, along with cost estimates. All of this was necessary to enable preparation of working plans for the Wyse-Réclus sea-level canal, which De Lesseps unfortunately thought feasible at a much smaller cost than was estimated originally. Special attention was paid to the Chagres and to the geology of the Isthmus. The earth depth was found to be greater and the rock softer than at first supposed. The Technical Commission also re-examined the project of erecting a dam at Gamboa and the diversion of the Chagres. It hoped by investigating and reporting on these matters that De Lesseps, when he arrived in New York, would be supplied with information to refute charges that he was simply a "promoter of a work hastily conceived, whose difficulties are but half understood, whose plans are imperfect, and its estimates of cost unreliable."[8] All this was necessary to combat the propaganda for Nicaragua, headed by Ammen and Menocal in the United States, and also for use in later financial campaigns. Even so, the few weeks' time allowed for the survey was too short for an investigation of such vast importance.

Like the sudden influx of canal workers in later years, the arrival of the French engineers in the small community of the Isthmus had its effects. Prices advanced suddenly. Merchants were seized with a "mania of sudden riches." Rent soared from $40 per month to $80. Vacant lots formerly priced at $1,000

[7] *Panama Star and Herald*, Jan. 12, 1880.
[8] *Ibid.*, Jan. 29, 1880.

sold at $4,000. People thought that the French had come with pockets bulging with gold and willing to give without receiving any value.

The rise in prices was reported to the home office of the company. As a result, ready-made houses were ordered from Chicago, and the Canal Company embarked on a policy of establishing its own towns. The dangers to the business interests of Panamá then were recognized by the press, which previously had accepted the canal work as an assured fact with a great expenditure of money certain. It warned, however, against expecting a "reckless expenditure," frankly stating that if the Panamanians would give real value then "well and good, if they will not, then this immense company can easily and will readily provide for themselves."

The report of the International Commission was ready on February 14, with replies to the questions which De Lesseps had asked of them. The line of the canal recommended by the Paris Congress was verified, and slight changes were made to reduce curvature. Borings to depths of 12 to 21 meters had been taken along the line of the canal and at the Gamboa Dam site. To produce stable banks on the sides of the canal the Commission adopted a slope of 1 to 1 for all excavations, except the summit division, where a slope of ¼ to 1 was recommended.

In general the canal was to be a trench 72 feet wide at the bottom and 27½ feet deep, on a route following the Panama Railroad. Starting at Colón, the canal would pass through six miles of lowlands to the Chagres valley at Gatun. It would then follow the valley for about 21 miles to Gamboa, where it would curve right and follow the valley of the Obispo, cross the continental divide at Culebra, and join the Pacific by following the valley of the Rio Grande.

Unless something was done to control the Chagres, a sealevel canal would have caused a huge waterfall from the higher bed of the Chagres into the canal at Gamboa. Accordingly there were planned a giant dam 40 meters high to retain its waters in

a large lake, and a new channel, the east diversion, to carry its
waters to the Atlantic. For drainage on the opposite side there
would have to be a west diversion. South of the cordillera an
east and a west diversion would have to be constructed, thus
making a total of five canals—one main canal and four diversion channels. For terminal facilities no work was considered
necessary, except a tidal lock at the Pacific where the tidal range
was great, and a breakwater at Colón where the anchorage was
subject to heavy northers. The grand total excavation was estimated at 75,000,000 cubic meters, and the estimate of total
cost was 843,000,000 francs ($168,600,000), a much higher
figure than that of the Paris Congress, which did not cover items
for interest and miscellaneous expenses totaling 409,000,000
francs. The report, signed by all members with Colonel Totten's name at the head of the list, was later described by J. B.
Bishop as thorough and scientific. It declared that with "good
and judicious management"[9] the canal could be completed within
eight years.

With completion of the survey, the time for De Lesseps' departure had arrived. During his visit he had endeared himself
to the people of the Isthmus. Gracious, affable, and courtly, he
was well liked and he liked people. A splendid horseman, he
was admired as he rode over the trails on his inspections. At
no time did the volume or importance of his work prevent him
and his wife from infusing "new vigor and animation" into the
dull life of the Isthmus. He cultivated his Panamá friends. He
attended their churches and social affairs. He sympathized with
them in sorrow and became the godfather of their children. He
worked all day and danced all night with the energy of a youth,
one time even crossing the Isthmus with Colonel Totten to attend
a ball given in their honor.

It was only natural, when the time came for De Lesseps to
leave Panamá, that the departure of this extraordinary man was
as spectacular as his arrival, the same state committee accom-

---

[9] *Panama Star and Herald*, Feb. 16, 1880.

panying him across the Isthmus. While at Colón he selected the permanent site for the statue of Columbus, presented to Colombia by Empress Eugénie of France, and received new ovations and honors.

When mentioning the work of his International Technical Commission, he declared that with its report in his hands the raising of the necessary funds in France would be "less onerous than the labor of gathering together the millions which gave the Suez Canal to the commerce of the world."[10]

On Sunday, February 15, 1880, shortly after the ceremonies for the Columbus statue, he boarded the "S.S. Colon" and left for New York, having been on the Isthmus one month and seventeen days.

DE LESSEPS VISITS THE UNITED STATES

On the voyage to New York De Lesseps studied the report of the engineers and revised the estimates of construction costs downward from their 843,000,000 francs ($168,600,000) to 656,000,000 francs ($131,200,000).[11] Having just seen the problems of the Isthmus by personal observation and received the technical report of the survey by his Commission, he must have known that great difficulties were ahead. His action in reducing the estimates is hard to understand except on the basis that he was preparing a promotional campaign which he wanted to wage in the United States. The object was success, not accuracy.

His arrival in the United States was anticipated with a tremendous, but somewhat hostile, public interest. A committee met his steamer and escorted him to his hotel for too brief a rest; and he was again on his campaign, opened by an address on March 1, 1880, before the American Society of Civil Engineers.

As he started to explain the canal, his map fell suddenly to

10 *Ibid.*
11 J. B. Bishop, *The Panama Gateway,* p. 75.

the floor. Quickly he exclaimed: "Oh, there's my canal gone to the ground!" It was picked up immediately and replaced. De Lesseps, gracious and quick, remarked: "But America has restored it to me," and continued unperturbed. Though pleased to be received and acclaimed as an engineer, he did not want any misunderstanding about himself or his background and explained that his training had been as a diplomat and not as an engineer.

As to the original capital of the company, he wanted it understood that one-half could be subscribed in the United States, as he knew that the interests of the United States in the canal were vital, equaling "all the rest of the world put together."

De Lesseps' determination for a sea-level canal came out strongly on this occasion. Someone in the audience asked why a lock canal should not be constructed instead of a sea-level canal as recommended by the Commission. The response was instant: "If the committee had decided to build a lock canal I would have put on my hat and gone home."[12] This won the audience, and he ended the meeting with new friends created for Panama.

The same evening he was lionized in the typical North American way at a banquet at Delmonico's, the most famous New York restaurant of the time. Adorned with flowers and flags, the dining room made an effective setting for the coats of arms of the United States and France as well as the models of Suez and Panama. The guests numbered 253 carefully selected leaders and their ladies, from the financial, religious, diplomatic, and political fields in the United States.

In an eloquent and interesting speech of welcome, the distinguished clergyman, Richard S. Storrs, presented a word picture of the importance of communications in the cause of peace, telling how De Lesseps had planned not only the Suez Canal but the Corinth Canal and the railroad from Europe to India. He mentioned the German geographer, Johannes Schoener, the namer of America, who constructed a globe in 1520 clearly

[12] *Panama Star and Herald*, March 12, 1880.

showing the Isthmus of Panamá with a line drawn across it as if to represent a future Strait of Panama[13]—probably the first map of its kind. He was impressed at the sight of that man of seventy-four setting forth to realize the dream of three and one-half centuries as the crowning achievement of his long life.

The distinguished diplomat, John Bigelow, likewise supported De Lesseps as the natural leader and ridiculed the idea of the French effort being a violation of the Monroe Doctrine. If aiding commerce by digging a canal were a violation, he said, "we are violating it every day in permitting our railway bonds to be sold abroad and foreign steamers to land and unload at our wharves."[14]

De Lesseps replied in French. Realizing the nature of opposition which had been rising in the United States, he endeavored to remove its cause. He explained that in negotiating with Colombia he had announced that he had no political interest, nor did he seek to advance the interests of France. If the canal should become a political issue he declared he would be "very happy to have recourse to the protection of the United States."[15] This same declaration, he said, would be made also to the President of the United States when he visited Washington.

There were many other speeches before the close of that long evening. The guests were interested in Panama, but more interested in De Lesseps. They were struck with the "magnificent freshness, enterprise, and youth" of the man who sat there "crowned with the triumph of a desperate but successful victory,"[16] in overcoming deserts of Africa and joining the waters of the Mediterranean with those of the Red Sea. They wanted to see that ability and experience applied to Panama.

In Washington, De Lesseps called on President Hayes. In an interview afterward he reported the meeting as having been highly satisfactory; but soon afterward President Hayes, not in-

---

[13] *Addresses at the De Lesseps Banquet, March 1, 1880*, p. 15.
[14] *Ibid.*, p. 20.   [15] *Ibid.*, p. 24.
[16] Address by H. W. Bellows, *ibid.*, p. 46.

fluenced by De Lesseps' call nor by the speeches at Delmonico's, sent a strong message to the Senate on March 8, 1880, calling for a "canal under American control," and declaring that the United States could not consent to "the surrender of this control to any European power or to any combination of European powers."[17] The Government of the United States had not forgotten the ill-fated dream of an empire in Mexico which France had attempted to realize only twenty years before in the tragic episode of Maximilian. But, as John Bigelow pointed out in his speech at Delmonico's, if there were any fears of violation of the Monroe Doctrine, the fate of Maximilian in Mexico should have ended them.

While in Washington De Lesseps also appeared before a congressional committee dealing with the canals. He expressed his delight with the presidential message, saying it certainly would be "advantageous to have the protection of the United States during the work and after the opening of the canal."[18] To his *Bulletin* in Paris he telegraphed that the President's message "assured the safety of the canal."

Indications of a favorable public reaction were almost immediate. De Lesseps' visit was hailed as the most publicly appreciated visit of a foreigner in over twenty years. He was acclaimed as a prophet of the incoming era of world-wide commerce and national intercourse. "With the eagle glance of genius he stands upon the summit where the rising dawn casts its earliest light, and sees, in advance of the sleepers in the shadowed valleys below, the illumination which the climbing sun will shed upon them also."[19] The favorable reactions in the United States were most gratifying to those left behind in Panamá and to those who were watching from Paris.

Like so many less disinterested propagandists since that time, De Lesseps toured the United States. He visited San Francisco,

[17] *Messages and Papers of the Presidents*, X, 4537–38 (U.S.).
[18] *Panama Star and Herald*, March 23, 1880.
[19] *New York Herald*, March 3, 1880.

Boston, Chicago, and other cities. In some his receptions were
not so favorable as in New York. In Chicago he met some opposition, which exasperated him. He was addressing a large
crowd at the Exchange when someone confronted him with that
ubiquitous question—the Monroe Doctrine. Boldly he answered
the challenging heckler: "Here are 20,000 of you Americans.
Now explain to me how the Monroe Doctrine prevents my making
the canal." There was silence. He must have known that they
did not have an accurate understanding of that famed doctrine.
He then explained the meaning of the Monroe Doctrine and that
it did not operate against building the canal. He added: "I cannot agree with a town only one-third my own age, though with
400,000 inhabitants, which says that the thing is impossible."[20]

"Hurrah! That's the boy we want!" was the instinctive response of the audience. He had won another victory.

Returning to New York after his wearing trip, he did not
take long for rest. The following morning there was a reception and luncheon at the home of Cyrus W. Field, of trans-
Atlantic cable fame. In the afternoon he was again interviewed
by the press. He announced that shares to the value of 300,000,-
000 francs (600,000 shares at 500 francs) would be offered
in the United States as soon as arrangements could be made in
Paris for the formation of a banking syndicate in the United
States. Should the United States take that amount, De Lesseps
said, she would have a "controlling voice in the enterprise."
But in event no shares at all were sold, he said, he would still
build his canal, for he was confident of his success because he
had a market for his securities in Europe. He declared: "In
France and England I am confident I can place all the shares if
America does not wish to take any; but from my reception here
I am of the opinion that the United States will be inclined to
take a large proportion of them. At any rate I shall proceed
with my canal."[21]

[20] *Panama Star and Herald*, Dec. 28, 1880.
[21] *Ibid.*, April 21, 1880.

The next day, April 2, 1880, the De Lesseps family was taken to the White Star liner "Adriatic" by Cyrus Field. They sailed for France via England, Belgium, and Holland with a send-off that equaled their arrival in enthusiasm. However, De Lesseps had not been able to sell his securities in the country he had just toured and from which he had received such extensive honors and universal genuine admiration. But he had made friends.

THE CAMPAIGN FOR PANAMA IN EUROPE

Upon arrival at Liverpool he reopened the promotion campaign. He proposed the offer of £166,000 worth of shares to the British public and publicly estimated that 8,000 men could complete the work in six years—a rash statement for a promoter of a project of the enormous magnitude of the Panama Canal.

De Lesseps was a captivating speaker. People instinctively believed what he said. While at Brussels he announced that the work of digging the canal would be undertaken by Messrs. Couvreux and Hersent, the contractors who had helped him so much at Suez. Bunau-Varilla suggests that this talk, notable for its large number of errors, gives an interesting insight into the views of De Lesseps, who did not like engineers. He had had to arbitrate their disputes too often at Suez. He did like practical men, and Couvreux was a "practical man." The result was that De Lesseps, overconfident already because of his earlier successes and prestige, was convinced that the building of the Panama Canal was an easy task. Convincing De Lesseps was the same as convincing France. He did not realize that, with "new elements of labour, new sanitary conditions, excess of rainfall, and ground to excavate the nature of which was unknown," serious error could result from the advice of men whose "limited education deprives them of that suppleness of mind needed to foresee and to measure the unknown quantities in a new problem."[22]

De Lesseps was followed by Abel Couvreux, Jr., who said

[22] Bunau-Varilla, *Panama: The Creation, Destruction, and Resurrection*, pp. 28–32.

his firm would undertake the construction at an estimate of 512,000,000 francs ($102,400,000). This was a figure still further reducing the inadequate estimates, which he explained was possible because of improvements made in excavating and boring machinery. Couvreux and Hersent wanted eight years to complete the work—two for organization, surveys, and assembly of material and six for the main work on the line of the canal. More than twenty years later it required about three years' preparatory work and seven years' construction for the United States to complete the canal with machinery vastly superior to that of 1880.

In that summer De Lesseps toured the cities of France. Speaking in the interest of the approaching subscription, he informed the public that the International Technical Commission had investigated the canal line on the Isthmus and declared it practicable; also that the work would be undertaken by Couvreux and Hersent, the contractors who had proved their ability at Suez, who estimated that eight years were required for completion.[23] The annual traffic, he prophesied, would be 6,000,000 tons and produce a revenue of 90,000,000 francs. His prophecy of tonnage was justified.

Late in the summer of 1880 came reports from the United States that financial obstacles were being resolved. The difficulties of winning American capitalists and public confidence were overcome by securing three bankers to form a committee in New York: J. and W. Seligman & Co.; Drexel, Morgan & Company; and Winslow, Lanier & Company. Secretary of the Navy Richard W. Thompson resigned his Cabinet post to accept a position at the head of this committee at the attractive salary of $25,000 and to become a promoter for the Panama Canal Company.

However, in the United States it still looked as if the subscription were being unduly delayed, but this delay was explained as a desire of the Panama Canal Company to await the

[23] I.C.C., *Report, 1899–1901*, II, 12 (U.S.).

opening of the United States Congress. It was reported that De Lesseps expected no opposition from the United States Government and was not apprehensive of any interference with his plans.

At last came the announcement. The Panama stock would be offered in December. The promotion was undertaken vigorously. The movement became so universal as to insure success. All countries in Europe were reported as taking part. Offices were opened in Germany, Austria, Italy, and England. In the *Bulletin du Canal* of November 15 the definite announcement was made that the subscription would take place on December 6, 7, and 8, 1880.

The capital structure was described as 600,000 shares at 500 francs each, totaling 300,000,000 francs, with 590,000 shares available for the public and only 10,000 shares reserved for founders—the result of De Lesseps' desire to encourage the small investors. Suez shareholders were to have a preference, with one share of Panama stock allowed for each share of Suez held. The subscription was announced as covering only half the cost of the canal, of which the total cost was estimated to be 600,000,000 francs.

The *Bulletin* of November 15, 1880, quoted a letter from De Lesseps answering the arguments of his critics, which he placed in two classes. To those who presented false estimates to prove the enterprise could not pay, he stated that Couvreux and Hersent, the contractors of Suez, were going at the moment to Panamá to make new studies for undertaking the work. As for those who wished to inspire fear of the United States, he simply referred them to the successful trip from which he had just returned.[24]

In one of his many press conferences held a few days before the subscription, De Lesseps was highly elated at the favorable news coming in from all directions and at the subscriptions "flowing in" from the United States. He had a greater confi-

[24] *Panama Star and Herald*, Dec. 14, 1880.

dence in Panamá than he had had in Suez and enthusiastically classed the Isthmus as a "wonderful country," where "the Atlantic and Pacific breezes blowing over it will make it the healthiest region in the world. We were there for months—my wife, children, friends, and laborers—and we had not a single death."[25] Then, with a rare sense of unreality, he referred to the reservoir which he planned to receive the waters of the Chagres, thus providing water "to irrigate 500,000 hectares of waste land"—this in a land which has one of the greatest annual rainfalls in the world. Thereupon he invited his interviewer to attend the opening with him in 1887—words that were echoed over the world!

THE RESPONSE IN FRANCE

The lack of financial interest shown in the United States was more than compensated by the exceptional enthusiasm and support in France. When the subscriptions were closed on the ninth of December, the public had subscribed 600,000,000 francs—more than twice the offering. He had succeeded in interesting the small investors—the shopkeepers and peasants of France. De Lesseps was the idol of Suez. He had kept Suez in the hands of many stockholders instead of the financial hierarchy. Panamá would be another Suez.

Plans for organizing the company quickly evolved. To provide financial services a Panama Bank was founded in Paris; to supply food a Commercial Panama Company was organized; and a general meeting of the stockholders of the Canal Company was called for January 31.

This was followed by a second constitutive meeting on March 3, when De Lesseps read his report. It was definite. There were 102,230 shareholders, and the canal was to be completed in 1888. The total excavation was estimated to be between 73,000,-000 and 75,000,000 cubic meters. The total cost of construction was estimated at 512,000,000 francs.

Marine dredges would work at Colón on the Atlantic sea-level

[25] *Ibid.*, Dec. 28, 1880.

section and at La Boca on the Pacific. In the difficult Culebra Cut, work would start in October 1881. Between 8,000 and 10,000 men would be recruited quickly from Colombia and the West Indies to work on the canal, and the canal would be completed.

The picture presented was too simple. It was admitted that De Lesseps was an experienced man, that the railroad along the line of the canal was a tremendous advantage, and that De Lesseps and his project had the good will of the world. But there were some who had misgivings.

The tragic fact remained that De Lesseps was not fundamentally familiar with Panamá. He had not lived there long enough, not even through the cycle of one year. He did not realize that he could not apply all the lessons of Suez to the American Isthmus. Circumstances forced him to stay at home to raise money for the enterprise, while the work was to be carried on so far away that he could not observe closely enough to avoid or correct mistakes. He had underestimated the cost, and right from the first the company was destined to be hard pressed for funds. He would be victimized. Also, he was aging.

The climate which De Lesseps had tried so hard to prove salubrious was in a land endemic with tropical diseases and "notoriously more pestilential than any part of the Desert of Suez." The Government of Colombia, on the surface friendly, was not strong enough to be of any support. On the contrary, it was the cause of much delay and confusion, for the Bogotá politicians looked upon Panamá as the "milch-cow of Colombia."[26] The resources of the region were such that practically all materials and food would have to be imported. But of more importance, all labor would have to be imported, for "In Panama [De Lesseps] has no gangs of Fellaheen forced to work for scant wages, no enthusiastic Khedive willing to command the resources of the State for the benefit of the undertaking."[27]

[26] J. B. and F. Bishop, *Goethals, Genius of the Panama Canal: a Biography,* p. 113.   [27] *London Standard,* Dec. 8, 1880, p. 5.

Chapter IV

De LESSEPS STARTS A SEA-LEVEL CANAL

For [De Lesseps] the sea level canal he had proposed at the beginning was a question of honour.—ANDRÉ SIEGFRIED.[1]

Forced upon the first French Company by the commanding influence of M. de Lesseps, a diplomatist and not an engineer, it entailed financial ruin upon his associates.—HENRY L. ABBOT, Brigadier General, United States Army, Retired, Formerly Member Comité Technique.[2]

ORGANIZING FOR WORK ON THE ISTHMUS

The first French construction group arrived at Colón on January 29, 1881, on the "Lafayette," in a party of forty engineers and officials led by Armand Réclus, an Agent Général of the Panama Canal Company. Five of them brought their wives to the Isthmus—the land so widely advertised in France as the "healthiest region in the world." Luxuriant in vegetation stimulated by the heavy rainfall, it was also subject to a most oppressive humidity, monotony, insects, and diseases and was as inhospitable to the unacclimated as it had been in the days of the railroad construction.

Although the Isthmus was crossed by rail, the land could claim only two cities, Colón and Panamá, the terminals of the railroad. The only other settlements were small groups of native huts near the railroad stations. Otherwise, the whole countryside, according to Lieutenant Charles C. Rogers, who had crossed the Isthmus in 1881 before excavation had been started, was a mass of "thickly matted jungle"[3]—a growth which could be penetrated only by means of a machete. Even today the jungle of the Isthmus presents essentially the same primeval appearance, except in those few spots where the land is kept cleared.

[1] Siegfried, *Suez and Panama*, p. 256.
[2] Abbot, *Problems of the Panama Canal*, p. 249.
[3] C. C. Rogers, Intelligence Report, p. 40 (U.S.).

This party under Réclus was probably the first real construction organization of the Panama Canal. It consisted of a Superior Agency, a Real-Estate Department, a Sanitary Service, and a Work and Construction Division.[4] The tasks facing Réclus were: to mark the exact location of the canal line, to clear the line of timber and jungle, and to open the country for excavation—all essential preparatory work which he expected to complete in about a year, using a system of direct employment of labor which was continued until Jules Dingler took charge in 1883.

It was De Lesseps' plan to start work with the large contractors, Couvreux and Hersent, who had agreed on March 12, 1881, to undertake and complete the work for 512,000,000 francs. But that contract was conditional; it was not to become binding until after two years.

The contractors sent their director, Gaston Blanchet, to the Isthmus to make preliminary plans. Rumors indicated that relations among the high officials were not harmonious, and within a short time Blanchet returned to Europe. To end these rumors of discord and dissension, on April 5 Réclus addressed a circular to all chiefs of brigades, letting them know that Blanchet had left for a short visit to Paris to settle the "definite order and course"[5] of the canal works and to advise about the manner of sending machinery and material to Panamá.

Gradually work took shape. "Leveling and surveying" were finished, and the line of the canal was more accurately determined. Activity started in construction of buildings and of dwellings for the laborers. A large frame house imported from New York was erected near Gatun, a sawmill was built at Colón, twenty small houses received from New Orleans were erected and partly occupied at other places, and twenty more from France and fifty from New Orleans were under order. In Europe and North America machinery was being manufactured,

[4] *Panama Star and Herald,* Feb. 1, 1881.
[5] *Ibid.,* April 8, 1881.

and by October deliveries were expected for excavators, flatcars, rails, dredges, hoisting apparatus, steam launches, telegraph materials, and even telephones.[6]

Besides planning for construction, another real obstacle of governmental nature faced the Canal Company when it learned that the Government of Colombia in 1867 had modified the railroad concession so as to give the railroad company a monopoly of transportation—canal, road, or rail. But the Government had reserved the right to grant a canal concession, subject to an indemnity to be paid by the canal to the railroad and to be shared with the Government.

De Lesseps from the beginning realized the necessity of controlling the railroad as an adjunct to his work. But from the first there was difficulty with the railroad, characterized by repeated delays of shipments, until arrangements for obtaining control of the road got under way in June. Faced with this difficult situation, he had no choice but to buy a controlling interest in the railroad's capital stock of 70,000 shares of $100 par value, at whatever price was demanded.

Not until August 1881 did the French gain that control. But at what a price—$17,133,500 for 68,534 shares at $250 per share, $7,000,000 for the company's bonds, and a bonus of $1,102,000 to the directors![7] Totaling over $25,000,000, or about one-third the resources of the Canal Company, it represented what André Siegfried called a "real Stock Exchange holdup." This arrangement, however, gave the French the necessary influence over the railroad company, while permitting retention of its status as a New York corporation—an effective gesture to public feeling in the United States.

In Paris the canal work was of another kind. De Lesseps had to keep up promotion campaigns with all his skill and optimism and at the same time run the Suez Canal. In his enthusiasm he was quoted as saying that the Panama Canal would

---

[6] *Ibid.*, July 29, 1881.
[7] J. B. Bishop, *The Panama Gateway*, pp. 53, 79.

be completed in six years, at another time in four years, although the period planned for the contract was eight years. In Panamá the press was critical of this exuberance in Paris; it wanted bigger salaries and more power to local officials. Before long reports were received in Panamá that the stockholders were kept informed by "watchers" and were dissatisfied with the way things on the Isthmus were being handled. But De Lesseps always had Suez to fall back upon; he reported an increase of 40 per cent in traffic during the past year and a remarkable net profit of 12,979,000 francs, or 21 per cent, and that he was preparing to light the Suez Canal with electricity to permit night transits.[8]

EARLY OPERATIONS IN 1881 AND 1882

Working forces increased monthly, with activity; but arrival of the unacclimated was followed by mounting illnesses. The first death from yellow fever among the 1,039 employees occurred in June 1881.[9] Later, the deaths from malaria exceeded those from yellow fever.

By fall materials had arrived via steamer in such volume as to fill the Colón storehouses, which at the time covered an area of 1,400 square meters. These arrivals included such large material as locomotives, cars, cranes, barges, and dredges.

Men could not be obtained as fast as required for the equipment, and it was proposed to import French convicts from New Caledonia. But local resentment against forced labor caused the idea to be discarded.

At first the offices of the company were located in separate buildings in Panamá. Consolidation under one roof was decided upon, to enable better enforcement of hygienic laws. The Grand Hotel on Cathedral Plaza, built during the years 1874 and 1875, was purchased and in December 1881 became the headquarters of the company. Upon the front of the building was placed a large sign "Compagnie Universelle du Canal Interocéa-

---

[8] *Panama Star and Herald,* July 5, 1881.

[9] I.C.C., *Number of Employees and Deaths from Various Diseases among the Employees of the French Canal Companies,* pp. 19, 24–37 (U.S.).

nique." Today this same building is the Panamá Post Office; but few of its callers realize that this building was once the French headquarters, nor do they know that it was the scene of historic festivities at the inauguration of the Panama Canal.

The year 1882 witnessed a variety of activities. First was a strike of canal and railroad workers on the Pacific side. Agitated by "Friends of Labor," the men demanded $1.50 per day, which they probably got in that day of rising wages and rising prices.

Next came the start of real excavation in Culebra Cut, which began formally in the Empire section on January 20, 1882,[10] and was celebrated by a banquet and ball in Panamá. This beginning was followed by the starting of excavations in the same year at Culebra, Mindi, Monkey Hill, Bas Obispo, Gorgona, Cristóbal, and Paraiso. But the dry season of 1882 was allowed to pass with little accomplished. Although excavators were available for use, there were no tracks arranged to carry either the excavators or their spoil. These ominous delays were the cause of general disappointment. Couvreux and Hersent continued with their surveys and preliminary work, but people became skeptical of what their machines could do on the Panamá Isthmus, which was alleged to be a "different affair altogether from the sands of Suez."[11]

While people were so anxiously waiting for serious work to start, all available space in Colón was covered with machinery in "glorious confusion," together with rails and ties for excavator tracks. But a great boom was expected in March, when between 3,000 and 4,000 men were due to arrive.

There were also events of civic importance in 1882. The first was the importation by the Canal Company of the first steam fire engines. Another was the adoption by the *Panama Star and Herald* of editions in three languages. The first issue, containing French, Spanish, and English, appeared on March 10, 1882;

[10] *Canal Record*, July 14, 1909, II, 362 (U.S.).
[11] *Panama Star and Herald*, Feb. 23, 1882.

the practice continued for over twenty-two years, extending into the period of United States occupation.

Engineers continued investigations of the Gamboa Dam and the Pacific terminal, and reports were sent to Paris. At the stockholders' meeting there on July 1 it was announced that the exact canal course had been decided, that the canal was a "private and commercial" enterprise, and that the first announcement date of completion was a certainty.

In New York an office of the American Committee of the Panama Canal Company was opened for the sale of canal securities under the direction of ex-Secretary of the Navy Richard W. Thompson. But his venture was not successful enough to help the French, who continued to be dependent upon private subscriptions in France.

In San Francisco the two brothers, Moses A. and Henry B. Slaven, and Prosper Herne became interested in the French canal work at Panamá. The elder brother, M. A. Slaven, was a mechanical engineer; the younger, a druggist. Desiring to benefit from the large contracts which they knew would be awarded, they bid $2,000,000 on a 6,000,000–cubic-meter contract, which was accepted about January 1882. With only meager resources, they interested capital in their project, formed the American Contracting and Dredging Company with offices in New York under H. B. Slaven, constructed a dredging fleet, and moved it to Colón with expectations of starting work in November.[12]

Meanwhile the Canal Company established a medical corps. Sisters of St. Vincent de Paul arrived from France to nurse the ill, and plans were rushed for hospitals. At Colón a 200-bed hospital was completed in March 1882. It was located on brick pillars extending out into the sea on the northern shore line, where it received the full force of the cooling breezes from the Caribbean. At Panamá the elaborate Ancon Hospital was started

[12] Robinson, *Panama: A Personal Record of Forty-six Years, 1861–1907,* pp. 150–58.

on the northeastern slope of Ancon Hill. The plant included an admission building, ward buildings, canteen, dispensary, servants' hall, kitchen, and residence of the Sisters. For its privileges the Sisters were authorized to charge each patient five francs per day. Dedicated on September 17, 1882, the direction of the hospital was given to Bishop Paúl of Panamá. Both vegetable and flower gardens, with many varieties of flowers, were set out under the direction of Sœur Marie Rouleau, Mother Superior of the Sisters of St. Vincent de Paul.[13] To protect the flowers from ants, waterways were built around the beds, and these became efficient breeding places for mosquitoes close to the unscreened windows of the hospital. Many of the patients thus became victims of mosquito-borne diseases.[14]

The hospital system was not complete, however, until a place could be obtained for convalescents to recuperate. This was found on Taboga Island, where the climate is drier and more bracing than at Panamá. Here the Hotel Aspinwall was purchased by the French Company and converted into the Taboga Sanatorium about 1885.

On the Isthmus preparatory work continued, and near the end of 1882 all arrangements for cutting of the canal had been made. Many houses had been built for laborers, great numbers of borings completed, several sections of railroad constructed near the work, and soundings had been taken in the sea near the future canal terminals. More than half the canal route had been cleared of jungle growth and the canal axis marked by stakes.

A contract was awarded the American Contracting and Dredging Company of New York to dredge the channel on the Pacific side toward the cordillera. The difficult central zone through the highlands was divided into small sections so that the contractor on each section could become expert in the problems of his particular terrain.

[13] *Canal Record*, Aug. 3, 1910, III, 390 (U.S.).

[14] L. T. Hess, "Ancon Hospital," *Surgery, Gynecology, and Obstetrics* (October 1920), XXXI, 424–29.

Most important, however, was the greatly increased understanding of the problems gained by the engineers, in spite of the many loose statements that had continued to be issued since the early promotion days. These promotional statements had been so exaggerated and flippant that people in the United States, who had been waiting a year to see work start, began to look upon the canal project with "doubt and distrust." The early publicity campaigns were accepted as necessary in the formative stages of the promotion, but there was an increasing demand for reliable and definite information. It was hoped that with an increase of understanding by the engineers there would be better dissemination of information and a corresponding reduction of the political and financial opposition as the work proceeded, thus leaving the veteran De Lesseps free to carry on his great work unimpeded.

But this was not to be. Powerful interests in the United States continued working against the French Company. De Lesseps was compelled to stay in France to campaign for money in the December 1882 drive and had no opportunity to follow the project through personally on the Isthmus. This absence of the leader was perhaps one of the greatest causes of the many difficulties and mistakes which the French Company experienced.

Admiral George H. Cooper of the United States Navy on March 2, 1883, reported that the undertaking was so gigantic that it could not be finished quickly; that the French were in earnest; and that even if they should fail for want of funds, the work accomplished would be so well done as to give the Panamá route a great advantage over any other. Completing the canal he considered as only a "question of money, for the undertaking offers no insuperable engineering difficulties"; but the enormous cost would deter investors from sinking money in an enterprise from which any return would take so long. To its great promoter he paid the compliment of stating that, even if this attempt failed and another attempt should succeed at Panamá, credit for the "design of the enterprise and of its energetic commencement" would always be accorded to the French and especially to Ferdinand de Lesseps.[15]

With everyone thus expectantly waiting for work to start, a great blow came. The chief engineer of the contractors, Gaston Blanchet, died on the Isthmus. His company, Couvreux and Hersent, had rendered great service at Suez, but they did not know Panamá. They had not realized the debilitating influence of the climate upon Europeans, the prevalence of tropical diseases, the conditions of labor, the difficult terrain to be cut, and the great problems of supplying such extended activities in an undeveloped country so utterly lacking in productive enterprise. This large contracting company decided to withdraw from the undertaking, and on December 31, 1882, wrote to De Lesseps requesting cancellation of their contract. However, they offered to undertake the construction program on the basis of prices as determined by the preliminary work, but invited attention to the fact that these would be "onerous,"[16] as they would include the costs of mistakes, "groping in the dark," and the difficult conditions of labor and work in Panamá. Also they informed De Lesseps that they had found the system of awarding small contracts was the better. With the contractors off the Isthmus and with Blanchet dead, conditions went into a disheartening confusion. With no leader there was no program. De Lesseps had no other recourse than to accept the cancellation, and, with the assistance of his son, Charles A. de Lesseps, he proceeded to "rally the troops and to reorganize the army"[17] to carry on the struggle.

De Lesseps acted quickly by appointing Jules Dingler as Director General. He was an engineer of outstanding ability and splendid reputation and had served as Chief of Bridges and Roads in France. When his friends protested to him about going to work in the unwholesome climate of Panamá he scoffed at

[15] G. H. Cooper, *Progress of Work on Panama Ship-Canal*, p. 4 (U.S.).

[16] I.C.C., *Report, 1899–1901*, II, 12 (U.S.).

[17] Bunau-Varilla, *Panama: The Creation, Destruction, and Resurrection*, p. 32.

their words: "I am going to show them that only drunkards and the dissipated take the yellow fever and die there."[18]

Accompanied by his family and Charles de Lesseps, he sailed for Colón, arriving March 1, 1883. The first task was a round of Isthmian receptions. At the Grand Hotel, where the Company's offices were then located, there was a great arrival banquet with all the local celebrities present. Charles de Lesseps returned the courtesy with another at the same place. In his address he reflected the optimism of his father. He stated that there was much of which to boast—the different sections were installed, work was progressing on all sides, and within a year powerful machines would be competing. He assured them that his father would come again to watch the progress. The high light came when he told his guests they would be invited to witness the passage of the "world's commerce through the Canal"[19]—a view that was held by Ferdinand de Lesseps until 1885.

Dingler devoted himself to bringing order out of chaos. He restored discipline in the organization but in doing so incurred the dislike of those disciplined, who thereupon started rumors of extravagance. He organized work yards, studied the entire canal project, and submitted a voluminous report on the sea-level canal which was approved by the Superior Advisory Commission. He ordered machinery in quantity sufficient to undertake the work. Dingler's influence, as described by Bunau-Varilla, was "bold, loyal, scientific, and stimulating." He adopted the system of small contracts, of which nearly thirty were granted; for these the Canal Company rented the necessary equipment at low rates. The system had its difficulties—very frequent payments, many inspections to be made, and numerous suits before the Colombian courts.[20] But he got results, even in the early years when much of the excavation was done by

---

[18] W. C. Haskins, *Canal Zone Pilot*, p. 194.

[19] *Panama Star and Herald*, March 21, 1883.

[20] Abbot, *Problems of the Panama Canal*, p. 40.

hand and removed by Decauville handcars well suited to the low grade of labor available.

Dingler's plan of the canal is interesting for comparison with other plans. All the French plans used the metric system, the line of the canal from Colón to the Pacific terminal being 74 kilometers. Originating in Limon Bay, it followed the valley of the Chagres about 45 kilometers to its Obispo branch. There it turned away from the Chagres and followed the Obispo toward the summit, which it crossed in a saddle 333.5 feet high between what are now called Contractors Hill (410 feet) and Gold Hill (540 feet). It then followed the Rio Grande valley to the Pacific. The bottom width of the canal was to be 22 meters (72 feet) and depth 9 meters (29.5 feet). The floods of the Chagres were to be controlled by a dam at Gamboa and by lateral diversions. The total excavation on the canal was estimated at 120,-000,000 cubic meters (approximately 157,000,000 cubic yards) —or 45,000,000 more than estimated by the International Technical Commission in 1880.[21]

Dingler attacked the highest peaks of the central region in April with 3 excavators, 7 locomotives, 70 cars, and a force of 400 men in Culebra Cut. Work was prosecuted vigorously. Before long there was much apprehension about slides and what bank slope to adopt to prevent them. It was expected then to have Culebra Cut finished by May 1885.

In the high central portion the work consisted of dry excavation. At Colón and Panamá, dredging fleets were slowly starting their way toward the center. French, Belgian, and American machinery was working in friendly competition, while a great mass of discarded machinery in confused disarray presented an effective monument to the mistakes of the first two years. This was the picture at the beginning of construction, called the "engineers' period"—a period supposed to last six years, until scheduled completion of the canal in 1888. The key to the future rested chiefly upon the problem of Culebra Cut.

[21] I.C.C., *Report, 1899–1901*, II, 15 (U.S.).

In Paris, Ferdinand de Lesseps, carrying on his distant campaign, did not weaken, and at a meeting of the stockholders on July 17, 1883, he reaffirmed his belief in the 1888 completion date and announced that the prejudices in the United States against his plan had been dissipated. He said that the "sentiment of equity" which prevails among North Americans caused them to understand that the French builders of the canal had "no object in view but the removal of a material obstacle to beneficial intercourse."[22]

The working force increased rapidly by importation of labor, chiefly from the West Indies; in September there were about 10,000 men employed, mostly Jamaicans, with the work in "fullest swing." It is not surprising that the next issue of the *Canal Bulletin* announced that all the undecided projects recommended by Dingler had been approved by the Superior Advisory Commission. This included provision for tidal locks at the Pacific terminal.

Originally the promoters had in mind the idea of a single sea-level canal known as the "Strait of Panama." But Dingler observed that the tidal range on the Pacific was about twenty feet, but on the Atlantic only one foot. He concluded that the currents set up by the difference of levels of the two oceans during changes in tides would be too dangerous for safe navigation, and proposed a tidal lock at the Panamá end to preserve the level from Colón to Panamá, a plan he thought would save the excavating of 10,000,000 cubic meters. The locks were to be in three sections, one for exit, one for entrance, and one for repair, with dimensions 25 meters in width and 180 meters in length.

Another public subscription for 171,000,000 francs,[23] offered in October 1883, was successful. De Lesseps was overjoyed and in a circular expressed his gratification and thanks for the assistance in cutting the Isthmus of Panamá, which he thought would be an achievement destined "to realize all the promises

[22] *Panama Star and Herald*, Aug. 2, 1883.
[23] Wolfred Nelson, *Five Years at Panama*, p. 258.

of the Suez Canal." But with each new subscription, money was becoming more difficult to get.

Near the end of 1883 activity on the Isthmus was so much greater that transportation facilities at Colón were overtaxed. The harbor was described as full of steamers, ships, barks, brigs, and schooners. All were laden with every class of material for the canal—machinery, iron, wood, and coal. Dock space was insufficient in spite of the seven wharves at Colón, and ships had to wait in the crowded harbor for weeks before they could discharge. But this did not hinder progress. Contracts were signed for excavation and for laborers, the company providing materials for contractors and houses for labor. It was confidently expected that the canal would be completed in 1888. This prediction was based on the assumption that during the first four months of 1884, the dry months, excavation would exceed that of the previous two years.

TRAGEDIES AND DIFFICULTIES

The year 1884 started off with a succession of difficulties and tragedies. In January one of the Slaven dredges, the "Prosper Herne," was destroyed by fire only a few days after arriving on the Isthmus. This loss slowed down the dredging program, but H. B. Slaven telegraphed his builders in New York to send down the next dredge and ordered an additional dredge in replacement.

In the last of the same month death struck the family of the energetic Chief Engineer. His daughter, Louise Dingler, who had just entered Isthmian life under such brilliant circumstances, contracted yellow fever and after a brief illness died. The population of Panamá was profoundly touched by this untimely death of the young woman. The funeral ceremony in the Cathedral of Panamá, with Bishop José Telesforo Paúl officiating, and the cortege to the cemetery left a picture that was indelibly written upon the memories of the entire community.

But that was not all. One month later the twenty-year-old

son of Jules Dingler, a picture of health and strength, showed signs of yellow fever. Three days later he was dead.[24] The Cathedral of Panamá was the place of another pathetic scene.

Nor was that all. The young fiancé of the daughter, who had come over with the family from France, also was taken ill with yellow fever and died. Dingler did not falter, but kept the work going. Bunau-Varilla, who later worked under Dingler, wrote thus: "These trials which might have shaken the reason of any man did not drive this hero one step out of the path of his duty to the task in hand."[25] It was not until early June that Dingler, with his wife, left for France, not so much for rest as to take up the Canal program for 1885.

Unfortunately for the French, the part played by mosquitoes in causing yellow fever was not discovered until many years later. Because of that, even though the French Company had an excellent medical service and large hospital facilities, they did not take the steps which would have prevented yellow fever and malaria—that is, the eradication of the stegomyia and the anopheles and the screening of houses.

The French did not learn that breeding grounds for mosquitoes must be eliminated. Water troughs in the hospital grounds and water pans placed under bed posts to keep off insects served as fertile breeding places dangerously near unsuspecting victims, so that often after arrival in the hospital patients would contract yellow fever.

The disease obtained a reputation for mystery and elusiveness beyond description and struck fear into many hearts. But in spite of all that, Lieutenant Raymond P. Rodgers, writing on January 27, 1884, reported that the climate thus far had not proved so fatal in most of the canal sections as expected, that employees appeared in fair health, and that Europeans suffered more than the laborers who were natives of the tropics.[26] Such

[24] *Panama Star and Herald*, Feb. 25, 1884.

[25] Bunau-Varilla, *Panama: The Creation, Destruction, and Resurrection*, p. 33.

[26] R. P. Rodgers, *Progress of Work on Panama Ship-Canal*, p. 24 (U.S.).

flare-ups of yellow fever as occurred in the neighborhood of Panamá usually followed new importations of unacclimated and nonimmune northern labor.

Rumors began circulating regarding the financial condition of the company. A United States naval officer, Lieutenant Robert M. G. Brown, sent to the Secretary of the Navy a report dated June 2, 1884, stating that the company was in serious financial straits, with $60,000,000, representing about one-half the capital, already expended, exclusive of the $20,000,000 paid for the Panama Railroad stock, and with half the estimated time for completion already elapsed but only one-thirtieth of the work accomplished, and that largely theoretical rather than pracical. He concluded: "The completion of this Canal, according to present plans, is very doubtful. It certainly will require much more time and money than originally estimated."[27]

To this, De Lesseps replied that there was no ground for thinking the canal would not be completed in 1888. The excavation of 700,000 cubic meters[28] in June 1884 marked a new high of production, attributable to the work of Dingler. But even so, De Lesseps had to start another campaign for money in August and September, and it was successful. De Lesseps announced that he intended to visit the Isthmus again in 1885 and that the financial condition of the company was "so flourishing" it would enable excavation with "energetic impulse."

Later the generally pessimistic conclusions of Lieutenant Brown found another advocate in Captain Bedford Pim of the British Navy, who had visited the Isthmus in October 1884 "to set at rest conflicting reports . . . . as to the progress of the Canal." On November 8 he submitted his conclusions to the Secretary of the United States Navy as a "private and confidential" communication. Using De Lesseps' own estimates for Panama that had been based on the totally different Suez work,

[27] R. M. G. Brown, *Report Regarding Progress of Work on Panama Canal* (MS). J. E. Nourse, *Maritime Canal of Suez*, p. 148 (U.S.).

[28] *Panama Star and Herald,* July 24 and July 26, 1884.

Pim figured that excavations alone would require at least fifteen years because of the nature of the soil, ranging from slimy alluvium to strata of boulders and hardest rock and all subject to alarming slides, and also because of the difficulty of keeping the necessary 10,000 men employed during the annual long rainy season, with the certainty of sickness and death among them.

He said that the people of France were beginning to open their eyes "at the non-fulfillment of the promises of their idol," De Lesseps. There was "no perfidious Albion in the person of Lord Palmerston," who had opposed De Lesseps at Suez; and the absence of the United States flag from the Isthmus removed that country also from a position convenient for blame. He concluded: "It appears that the physical obstacles are insurmountable while the financial difficulties are scarcely less, although it is not yet too late to build a canal with locks. . . . . Every credit, not to say praise, has been given to the gallant employees who have struggled manfully to carry out the wishes of their . . . . chief, Mons. de Lesseps."[29]

The French people did not know what blackmail and coercion was going on in Paris. They only knew their aim to complete the canal, to win for France the double honor of opening the two great canals, and to immortalize the name of De Lesseps.

BUNAU-VARILLA BECOMES CHIEF ENGINEER

It was in this year of 1884 that a man destined to play an important part in the history of the Panama Canal and also in the formation of the Republic of Panamá entered the service of the company as a young engineer. His name was Philippe Bunau-Varilla. Able and ambitious, young and energetic, he possessed the qualities of character that admirably fitted him for his tasks on the Panama Canal, where he was to gain the actual experience that made him such a formidable protagonist for Panamá in later struggles.

Leaving France on October 6, 1884, he went to Panamá in

[29] Bedford Pim, *Remarks on the Panama Canal, October 1884.*

company with Chief Engineer Jules Dingler and wife on their return voyage to the Isthmus. Young Bunau-Varilla considered his
trip to the Isthmus and his association with the Panama Canal
as the realization of a childhood dream, and spent his twenty-one
days on the voyage under Dingler's careful and probably exacting instruction.

At this time the canal was divided into three major construction divisions. The first extended from Colón over the greater
part of the Chagres valley. A second included the remaining
part of the Chagres and the Obispo valleys up to the foot of the
Culebra slope. The third included Culebra and the Pacific slope.

Upon arrival, Bunau-Varilla was assigned as division engineer in charge of the Culebra and Pacific slope division, just in
time to step into the key problem of Culebra Cut and the dredging
of the channel from the Pacific up the Rio Grande valley. The
work at Culebra had not proceeded rapidly. During January
1884 only 60,000 cubic meters were excavated, with 25,000,000
remaining in a section of two kilometers. At this rate it would
have required a long time to complete, particularly with the
necessary slowing down during the wet season. But tracks had
been prepared and dumps were ready near by.

When the New Year's celebration arrived, another tragedy
struck. Mme Dingler died of yellow fever.[30] Dingler, though
crushed again, went to his office the next day as usual and kept
the work going. He remained at his post until June, when he returned to France for the last time, exhausted and alone, having
given up all his loved ones for Panama. He never lived in the
fine quarters erected for the Director General's residence on the
southern slope of Ancon Hill overlooking the islands on the
Pacific. These quarters were eventually called "La Folie Dingler" by detractors of the canal.

This left Maurice Hutin as Director General; but he also suffered attacks of fever and in September had to return to France
for his health. Young Bunau-Varilla at the age of twenty-six

---

[30] Bunau-Varilla, *Panama: The Creation, Destruction, and Resurrection*, p. 38.

then became acting Director General of the greatest engineering project of the world. He launched into his duties with the enthusiasm of youth, describing himself as "pitiless for all moral shortcomings, and the sincere friend of those who were valiant and devoted."[31] He restored morale among the workers and endeavored to establish cordial relations with the admirals of the two United States forces that were observing the progress of work on both sides of the Isthmus.

Shortly after Bunau-Varilla took charge, a new French Consul General, François Sébastian La Vieille, arrived, in August 1885. When introduced to the youthful chief engineer he expressed his astonishment at seeing so young a person in a position of such vast responsibility. In reply, Bunau-Varilla exhibited his astonishment at the Consul General's suggestion, saying that he thought it a republican principle to "judge men only according to their intrinsic value," and forthwith invited La Vieille to inspect the canal works and decide for himself as to his qualifications.

Later there was a welcoming party for the diplomat to meet the Company's employees. He had just come from home and brought words of hope to calm the minds of the workers disturbed by the incessant rear attacks on the Panama Canal—attacks that so unfortunately had kept De Lesseps promoting while he should have been at the helm on the Isthmus. Addressing the group, he gave a stirring appeal in support of Bunau-Varilla. Touching on the Frenchman's patriotic sentiment, he said: "The Canal work is French, and French it shall remain! France has begun it and France will complete it!" Then, referring to the work of De Lesseps and the many hindrances placed in his way, he said that "envy and evil prepossessions" would "sink conquered and impotent, like nature itself, before the will of the great Frenchman."[32]

Equipment continued to arrive from faraway places. "Dredge

[31] Bunau-Varilla, *op. cit.*, p. 48.
[32] *Panama Star and Herald*, Oct. 31, 1885.

No. 19," built by M. M. Loebnitz & Co. near Glasgow, completed in October its voyage of eighty-eight days through the Straits of Magellan. That was a long voyage for the crew of twenty men to make in such a clumsy craft, which the Captain described as behaving "remarkably well." The eighth Slaven dredge, "The City of New York," arrived at Colón after a twenty-day trip from New York.[33] Put to work in the jungle, these dredges presented an imposing sight as the powerful forces of science and the relentless forces of nature competed for mastery.

In his effort to promote good will, Bunau-Varilla made a formal call upon Admiral McCauley and upon Commander Lull of the U.S.S. "Hartford," taking along a map to show the exact line and the state of the work. On November 9 he conducted a party of visitors to the work at Bohío Soldado, among whom were Consul General La Vieille, United States Consul Thomas Adamson, Commander Lull, and Bishop Bernardo A. Thiel of Costa Rica. There he showed some of the most difficult work and explained that, contrary to rumors, the work was being carried on rapidly.

Later this same group went to Culebra to witness the work of digging the Cut. The mountain was decorated with Colombian, French, and Dutch flags and with flowers, presenting a sight unusual for the jungle of central Panamá. They visited the workshops, saw some dynamiting, examined the Cut, and watched the experimental loading of an excavator, of which forty more were on order. Bunau-Varilla explained that he had to extract 20,000,000 cubic meters in a distance of two kilometers and that the slowness of the preliminary work revealed the difficulties that were ignored by those who had not experienced them. The party left, convinced that the work not only was possible but would be finished soon.

Bunau-Varilla laid plans to increase excavation in a program to total 1,400,000 cubic yards a month by January 1886. Work progressed all along the line. At Culebra, work on the Panamá

[33] *Ibid.*, Oct. 1 and Nov. 2, 1885.

side was mostly by Decauville handcars, as only two hand-filled trains carried spoil to the dumps; on the Colón side, five excavators were taking 300 cubic meters each a day but were delayed by lack of spoil trains. Switching arrangements made it necessary for excavators to wait while trains went to the dumps and returned. At Paraiso rains caused slides of whole hills. In one slide the entire bank was carried "almost intact across the Cut with the top surface unbroken, and with vegetation undisturbed."[34]

This point cannot be left without paying a tribute to all the French engineers who directed this early period, particularly the unfortunate Dingler, whom André Siegfried has praised so highly for his "driving force and organizing ability" in getting the vast project under way.

CONDITIONS AT THE END OF 1885

Rumors of financial difficulties had spread widely. De Lesseps was having increasing trouble in raising funds. In May 1885 he wrote to the French Government, requesting authority to issue lottery bonds—a procedure he had followed at Suez when that project was about to fail for lack of money. But the Government hesitated. It desired to wait until the canal was investigated before acting upon the request. Armand Rousseau, an eminent engineer, was selected to conduct the inquiry on the Isthmus—an event to involve more delay and to have other serious repercussions. His function as understood in Panamá had nothing to do with the financial prospects of the company but was simply to determine whether the work could be completed with new efforts.

Apparently these rumors of financial difficulties had stimulated United States interest in securing later information than that contained in the reports of 1883–84 by Admiral Cooper and Lieutenant R. P. Rodgers. Another United States naval officer,

---

[34] W. W. Kimball, *Special Intelligence Report on the Progress of the Work on the Panama Canal during the Year 1885*, pp. 17–18 (U.S.).

Lieutenant W. W. Kimball, visited the Isthmus in 1885 and called upon Bunau-Varilla. Received with exceptional courtesy, he was given access to maps, tables, and descriptions of projects and was encouraged to make a complete inspection of the line of the canal.

His general observations as reported January 20, 1886, are of interest. Much housing, mostly barracks for laborers, was under construction; considerable construction plant was on hand, but not enough nor of the right type. Dredges were too few. French bucket-chain excavating machines were too light and were stopped by stones. Too much work was being done by small Decauville handcars—good for clearing ground but not for removing spoil on work that had been under way for two years. Kimball could not understand the necessity for constructing an artificial harbor in the east side of Limon Bay. With his background of experience on board ship in the bay, he naturally thought a better harbor could have been made by enclosing the bay with exterior breakwaters.

As to labor, largely Negroes from Jamaica and other islands of the Antilles, there was a large turnover, attributable to many causes—desire to return home to spend savings, poor food and high prices, inadequate medical care, fear of political disturbances, desire to leave the Isthmus before becoming ill, and probably simple fatigue from the Isthmian monotony.

In 1885 it was not possible to estimate a date of completion, as a normal excavation rate had not been determined. The company had made serious and costly mistakes; but these were not irreparable, and funds were being expended with economy. The company had the "necessary brains and energy" but needed more funds. Kimball concluded that if De Lesseps could raise the funds the work would be so far advanced as to make its completion necessary.

There had been much illness, and many French had died of yellow fever during the year; but malaria was an even greater destroyer. Deaths from diseases were not considered of great importance in relation to the completion of the canal, for there were always others to take the places of the fallen. While on the scene of operations, Kimball expressed the same idea differently: "As for human life, that is always cheap."[35] Later studies by Colonel Gorgas confirmed this view.

Adequate funds as the basic factor in assuring completion of the canal by the French Company is summed up by Lieutenant C. C. Rogers in his report of March 30, 1887, p. 57: "From all sources, whether friend or enemy, there comes the same admission concerning the great enterprise—that the canal presents no insuperable obstacles, and that its final completion is merely a question of time and money."

The time had come when De Lesseps would have to stage another spectacular act to attract attention. In Paris he publicly announced another voyage to the Isthmus to inaugurate the "period of final excavation of the Maritime Canal."[36] He stated that because the entire line was under construction with twenty-seven contractors under fixed-term contracts it was important that there should no longer exist any doubt concerning completion, so as not to discourage shipping interests from taking prompt advantage of the opening. He also said that, besides the French Chamber of Commerce, delegations from England, Holland, the United States, and Germany would accompany him on the visit.

The years 1883 to 1885 had been a period in which small contractors had operated under Dingler's aggressive leadership. Expenditures in the earlier years had been limited, but under Dingler's active schedule they mounted rapidly, making it necessary to seek funds continuously. But conditions in France in 1885 were not conducive to ordinary public financing because of heavy losses sustained by French investors in a stock-market crash. Small investors could not be interested. Furthermore, the delay of the Government in acting upon De Lesseps' request had made matters embarrassing.

[35] W. W. Kimball, *op. cit.*, p. 32.
[36] *Panama Star and Herald*, Feb. 13, 1886.

On the Isthmus, Culebra Cut had proved to be the almost insurmountable obstacle. In the dry season progress would be made, but when the rains came "the dumps began to slide, the tracks were cut, and general subsiding of the ground inside the Cut paralyzed any movement of trains, and often overthrew the excavating machines."[37] The large Anglo-Dutch contractors had worked for a year and a half and had failed. One Dutch contractor had let so many subcontracts in the western hill at the saddle that it became known as Contractors Hill. It looked as if the canal would be completed everywhere along the line but fail in Culebra Cut—a one-mile section through the main saddle which seemed to overpower all efforts. Bunau-Varilla considered it was "the life, the whole life, of the Canal which was to be staked on this one card: the successful excavation of Culebra."[38]

In the effort to obtain money, advantage was taken of every practical scheme. Gold was reported discovered in Cerro Culebra. The reputed discovery was publicized in the *Bulletin,* and Cerro Culebra became known as Gold Hill. Much gold was poured into that hill, but none was taken out. Indeed, the Culebra Cut became a "bottomless pit into which money could be poured forever."[39] This was reflected in the market price of the company's securities and forced consideration of less expensive plans for crossing the Isthmus.

The engineers knew the only solution was a high-level canal, to reduce the enormous quantity of excavation as well as to prevent slides. But Ferdinand de Lesseps, obsessed with his earlier canal lessons, had to be convinced. He tenaciously clung to the idea of another sea-level canal, as at Suez, and was unalterably opposed to the idea of a permanent lock canal, although as late as July 1885, after several years of work, only about one-tenth of the estimated total of 120,000,000 cubic meters had been excavated. However, work had advanced enough to permit use of

[37] Bunau-Varilla, *Panama: The Creation, Destruction, and Resurrection,* p. 67.
[38] *Ibid.,* p. 68.
[39] Siegfried, *Suez and Panama,* p. 261.

locomotives and excavators by the last of the year. Use of hand labor by small contractors then was definitely out of order, and contracts were awarded to large companies which could work rapidly. Something had to be done to reduce the excavation to limits within the capacity of the Canal Company to pay and permit its completion within a reasonable time.

It was necessary for De Lesseps to visit the Isthmus a second time to dramatize the great work and to offset any injurious report which the Government Commission might make. Averring that the Panama Canal was far easier to construct than Suez, he reiterated his plan to complete it at the end of 1888. But valuable time had passed without making progress proportional to the time and expenditures. Almost six years had elapsed since De Lesseps had formally inaugurated the Panama Canal on January 1, 1880. And he was aging—then in his eighty-first year.

CHAPTER V

FROM SEA-LEVEL TO LOCK CANAL

Construct a lock canal first and transform it later into a sea-level canal, by dredging.—PHILIPPE BUNAU-VARILLA, Acting Director General, Panama Canal Company, 1885–86.[1]

DE LESSEPS' SECOND VISIT TO PANAMA

Two hundred persons were waiting on a railroad platform in London on January 27, 1886, to bid Ferdinand de Lesseps and his party farewell on his second voyage to Panamá. Amiable as always, he was generous in his farewells to his many friends. Standing by the window of his railway carriage, he was smiling and confident. All present were profoundly impressed at the sight of this brave old man setting forth to effect the second union of the oceans. It was impossible to shake his hand without being awed by "so unfaltering a determination."

The locomotive blew the departure signal. He turned to the cheering crowd and said: "I shall be back in 60 days. I cannot die before opening my second canal."[2] Traveling with him to Panamá were representatives of the Chambers of Commerce from Marseilles, Rouen, Bordeaux, and Saint-Nazaire and also an eminent engineer, Peschech, from Germany, and another from Holland.

Arriving at Colón on February 17, he was received by the expectant crowd as a visiting monarch rather than as the president of a great corporation. To the engineers of the Panama Canal he had become a legendary figure whose decisions were sacred; to the Isthmians he was to be the creator of their age-long dream of a canal; to the French Nation he was the Great Frenchman; and to the world he was the great genius who was expected to effect a second union of the oceans.

---

[1] Bunau-Varilla, *Panama: The Creation, Destruction, and Resurrection*, p. 48.
[2] *Panama Star and Herald*, Feb. 27, 1886.

His son, Charles de Lesseps, was nominally vice-president of the company but actually its managing head. He had arrived on the Isthmus earlier in February and was the first to board the ship and greet his illustrious father. The party was joined by three representatives from the United States: John Bigelow, of the New York Chamber of Commerce; Nathan Appleton, of the Boston Chamber; and Admiral James E. Jouett, Commander of the United States naval forces in the Atlantic. Representing the British were the Duke of Sutherland and Admiral W. C. Carpenter of the British Navy.

Ferdinand de Lesseps looked well after his long voyage and moved around like a young man in spite of his eighty years. Nevertheless, six years of struggle had brought about its changes; he had aged perceptibly.

Two young ladies, one representing Colombia and the other France, presented him with flowers, initiating another elaborately planned program for entertainment as well as inspection.

His inspection covered the entire line of the canal, starting with a trip to Cristobal. There he was greeted by one of his pioneers, Alfred Tronchin, in an address indicative of the deeply loyal and intensely patriotic feelings of his employees. To De Lesseps he said: "You are for us the venerated chief around whom we are all grouped ready at all times to sacrifice even our very lives to assure your trimphant success in your present great and glorious work." Then, to stress the confidence retained by the canal personnel in spite of all opposition from its "detractors and calumniators," he declared emphatically, amidst shouts of approval and cheers, that the canal would be finished. The old man, moved by this stirring appeal and its enthusiastic responses, replied that he was proud of the "courage, energy, and abnegation" shown on the Isthmus and appreciative of the sentiments so clearly demonstrated. "With hearts and minds like yours everything is possible," were his concluding words.

A luncheon followed, attended by all the prominent Isthmian families. Admiral Jouett's band supplied music. De Lesseps

circulated through the group saying pleasant words to all, often
remarking that neither money nor hands would be lacking, for he
considered the canal "an accomplished fact."[3] Later in the day
he took a stroll about the city at a gait remarkable for a man of
his years.

At Panamá his reception was equally lavish. The city was decorated with flowers, arches, and placards acclaiming the Great
Frenchman; and crowning all were a triumphal procession, fireworks, and another banquet replete with speeches. The chief
speaker was the eloquent Pablo Arosemena, who prophesied to
De Lesseps that "the day will come when from the summit of
the overpowered Culebra, the flags of all nations will announce
to the world that you have crowned your glorious work; and the
two united oceans will proclaim your victory and your great-
ness."[4]

In his youth De Lesseps had been an accomplished rider, and
on his inspection tours of the canal he was usually at the head
of his party on horseback. A member of the party wrote: "I saw
him escalade at a gallop an escarpment of Culebra amid a roar
of enthusiastic hurrahs from blacks and whites, astounded by so
much ardor and youthfulness."[5] When he visited Empire, an
accident occurred to the locomotive of his special train and the
party had to walk to the foot of a hill where mules were waiting.
Mounting, he galloped away to address a group of workers.
Bishop records that there was a tradition on the Isthmus that
De Lesseps rode like an eastern monarch in a "flowing robe of
gorgeous colors."

At Colón, De Lesseps dedicated the statue of Columbus on
February 24, 1886, at the site he had selected on his first visit
to the Isthmus. Within a few days, when he was ready to leave,
Colón tendered him a farewell breakfast. This was followed by
his farewell address at the Columbus statue, in which he expressed his appreciation of the efforts of his collaborators. He

[3] *Panama Star and Herald*, Feb. 27, 1886.
[4] *Ibid.* [5] J. B. Bishop, *The Panama Gateway*, p. 83.

then departed, "bright, vigorous and genial,"[6] for France, to re-
sume the financial campaign that was necessary to keep the canal
work going. The engineers and workers left behind were inspired to greater efforts.

THE LOCK PLAN STARTS

The reports submitted by the French Chambers of Commerce
were favorable. That of Government Commissioner Rousseau
was more searching. His inspection report, distributed in June
1886, supported the canal project. He considered it possible to
cut the Isthmus and that the project had gone so far that abandonment would mean disaster to the investors and to French
prestige in all the Americas. He recommended that the French
Government use its "diplomatic and administrative powers" to
aid the enterprise. He stated that the names and records of the
men who were directing the work, its humanitarian character,
and the serious efforts already made and still being made to accomplish it were deserving of the "special good will"[7] of the
Government. He urged the Government to avoid placing obstacles in the way, but instead to extend all aid compatible with
its position. Apparently Rousseau questioned the possibility of
completing the approved program under private subscriptions.
He suggested simplifications designed to advance the probable
date of completion and asked if it would not be possible "to
modify and simplify"[8] the plan—a question which implied the
lock-canal idea.

Another report was made by Jacquet, who had been sent by
the Company. He recommended abandonment of the sea-level
project and the prosecution of a lock canal in spite of the well-
known views of De Lesseps. Still another report was submitted
by Léon Boyer, who had worked with Bunau-Varilla. He bluntly
declared a sea-level canal impossible within the limitations of
the estimates and time. If not a diplomat, he had been in-

[6] *Panama Star and Herald*, March 13, 1886.
[7] *Ibid.*, July 18, 1887.   [8] Bunau-Varilla, *op. cit.*, p. 84.

BOHÍO LOCK EXCAVATION, 1887

CULEBRA CUT OPPOSITE GOLD HILL, 1895
Showing house used by Bunau-Varilla

fluenced by a diplomat. Boyer, not wishing to oppose De Lesseps too strenuously, recommended the idea of Bunau-Varilla—construction of a temporary high-level canal, later gradually deepening to sea level by dredging.[9]

Even with these reports De Lesseps would not be moved at the time from his insistence on a sea-level canal, and the Government delayed consideration of his request for a lottery loan, the committee in charge adjourning until fall.

De Lesseps was disappointed but not defeated. "They have adjourned on me. I will not accept this postponement. True to my part, when they try to stop me, I go on." He had many thousands with him in that decision; but the result must have been uncertain, for he circularized his stockholders, stating that although six deputies were trying to prevent him from winning a "victory in this peaceful work undertaken by France in the Isthmus, we will overcome every obstacle yet. You will march with me to a second victory by providing the 600 million francs I need!"[10]

Acting quickly, De Lesseps withdrew his lottery request and went to the stockholders at their meeting of July 29, 1886, when he asked for authority to issue bonds. He reconsidered previous public statements and admitted that estimates would reach the cost predicted by the Paris Congress of 1879. On the basis of Suez data and the monthly excavation in Panamá in 1885 of 658,000 cubic meters, he optimistically predicted for 1886 a monthly average of 1,079,000 cubic meters, for 1887 of 2,000,000, and for 1888 of 3,000,000. Basing his estimates upon these figures, he declared the canal would be completed in June 1889. He said the heaviest expenses for the first years had been for organization, installation, and transportation, but that the necessary plant had now been obtained and that all expenditures henceforth would be merely for fuel and wages. He acknowledged, however, that the higher charges on loans "must

[9] I.C.C., *Report, 1899–1901*, II, 17–18 (U.S.).
[10] Siegfried, *Suez and Panama*, p. 265.

augment the cost of the canal." He added that an early meeting would be held by the Consulting Commission to consider "modifying the plan of construction."[11]

Unfortunately, a definite decision was not announced promptly, and investors were left in doubt and in ignorance of facts. Although he appealed for 600,000,000 francs, the 354,-000,000 francs ($70,000,000) actually subscribed was nevertheless a truly remarkable response by the investing public for an undertaking then under such violent attack and resting upon such a precarious foundation. The subscription represented a tremendous personal tribute to the man in whom the people had faith and who symbolized their desire to support the resurgence of a defeated France.

So large were the fees required by the officials and extortionists in France that the company received only 200,000,000 francs out of the issue—enough to provide only temporary relief. De Lesseps looked to the United States for assistance, crossing the Atlantic later in 1886 in a vain effort. As a result he had to prepare for another financial campaign the next year.

THE ISTHMUS IN 1886

While the campaign for funds was going on in France in 1886, activity on the Isthmus did not stop. Early in the year Léon Boyer arrived with Charles de Lesseps to assume the position of Director General, relieving Bunau-Varilla. Though still a young man, Boyer already had attained distinction by constructing a great bridge in France. Described as having a powerful mind, he was just the type needed to succeed Bunau-Varilla, and after a month's instruction under him, Boyer took charge.

Shortly afterward Bunau-Varilla, worn out by many months of hard work on the Isthmus, contracted the dreaded yellow fever. With careful nursing by his friends he recovered—an event commented upon editorially by the press, which considered him a valuable member of Panamá society, an invaluable offi-

[11] *Panama Star and Herald*, Aug. 12, 1886.

cial of the Canal Company, as well as a man possessing "elevated traits of character and sterling qualities."

Weakened by his severe illness, he was carried on board a steamer for New York. Boyer saw him off, with a farewell embrace so typical of the French; and his friend sailed away, leaving the new chief engineer fully on his own.

In a short time Boyer was in a controversy with M. Lillaz, a member of the firm of Baratoux, Letellier, et Lillaz then working on the canal and the only member willing to direct the company's work on the Isthmus. The firm had a contract for dredging in the Rio Grande and Pacific entrance. One of its dredges sank, and Lillaz claimed reimbursement. He had already suffered some misfortune and resented Boyer's insistence that the contract prices covered all such unexpected losses. While nervously upset, Lillaz was taken ill with yellow fever. In delirium he summoned Boyer for an appearance with him before the "Supreme Judge within eight days" and shortly after died. For some reason there was a delay in the church service. The funeral cortege did not reach the cemetery until after dark, and the mourners had to stumble over tombstones as they walked to the grave.

Boyer, who attended the funeral of this contractor he had respected so much, was overcome with distress. Chilled by the dampness of the evening, the next day he too showed signs of yellow fever. Boyer had studied the problem of building the canal in detail and knew that the great struggle of the French was of critical importance. As he lay dying, his thoughts were of the great enterprise of which he was the leader and of the fear that it would be discontinued. His last words were: "Do not give up Panama."[12] Jacquet succeeded him.

Work kept on, with excavation records exceeding the performance in the same month of previous years. On January 1, 1886, the total of excavation from the beginning was nearly 18,500,000 cubic meters. For the entire year 1886 the total was about 11,700,000 cubic meters—a quantity equal to about two-thirds

[12] Bunau-Varilla, *Panama: The Creation, Destruction, and Resurrection*, p. 66.

the entire previous canal excavation record and almost approaching the prediction of 12,000,000 cubic meters for 1886 that De Lesseps had made in 1885[13]—an omen of success.

However, life had its gay side as well as dark, its sense of art and music as well as of industry. In December word came of the early arrival of Sarah Bernhardt, the noted French actress, after a triumphal tour of South America. Panamá, having had for several years a French-language section in the *Star and Herald,* had become quite cosmopolitan and was in the right mood for her visit. Her ship arrived December 28, 1886, just in time to permit changing dresses for the inaugural performance in a new theater filled to capacity by her admirers.[14] In response to popular appeal the performance was repeated the next evening. Then she departed, and the Isthmus reverted to its normal routine of work.

The year 1886 was marked by a large increase in the plant of the Canal Company on the Isthmus. The place now afforded a contrast to the unpopulated and impassable jungle of 1881. A United States naval officer, Lieutenant C. C. Rogers, who visited the Isthmus about this time, wrote that the canal and railroad appeared to lie in a "populous and prosperous" area. From Matachin to Culebra—the district of heaviest excavation—the region appeared as "one continuous settlement" instead of several stations on the railroad.

Also, the French had evolved a well-ordered permanent organization on the Isthmus under a Director General. There were eleven administrative divisions: Secretariat; Technical Bureaus; Accounts and Money; Material and Supplies; Workshops; Transport and Water Operations; and five Construction Divisions located at Colón, Gorgona, Empire, Culebra, and Panamá. There were 926 officials and clerks and 10,640 workers, mostly Jamaicans—too many officials for that number of employees.

To house canal activities, an amazing number of dwellings,

[13] C. C. Rogers, *Intelligence Report* . . . . *March 30, 1887,* p. 24 (U.S.).
[14] *Panama Star and Herald,* Dec. 30, 1886.

shops, and various kinds of buildings had been constructed, 1,131 being erected in 1886. As a rule, dwellings were located on hills along the line of the canal or railroad, so as to benefit from cool breezes. Rogers described them as of wood, clean, well ventilated and well suited to the hot climate of the Isthmus. Houses were rented to contractors by the Canal Company at 10 per cent of their value, and where workmen were quartered free they had to pay their own board at canteens kept as a rule by Chinese, who had gained the confidence of the blacks. Whites and blacks had separate quarters, and the offices and houses of officials and employees of the canal were "especially capacious and comfortable."[15]

ATTACKING THE GREATEST OBSTACLE

By the summer of 1886 work in the one-mile Culebra Cut had been progressing slowly for about four years, the last two under a large Anglo-Dutch company. Rains, slides, climate, sickness, transportation difficulties, and small equipment all joined with the laziness of workers to retard progress. The high peaks had been removed, but little else. In the four years the average altitude of the lowest points had been reduced by only 12 feet from the original 307 feet—that is, to 295 feet above the bottom of the 30-foot sea-level channel—a rate of only 3 feet a year. At that rate it would have required about 99 years to complete the trench between the oceans.

The Panama Canal Company officials became greatly perturbed. Bunau-Varilla, then recuperating in Paris from his illness and work on the Isthmus, suggested to Charles de Lesseps as managing head of the Canal Company that a special section of the Company be allowed to take over the Culebra Cut project under De Lesseps' direction, with full powers and freedom to select a group of men from the "best products of Isthmian selection," that is, those who had been tested and found qualified by actual work on the canal. While acting as Director General he

[15] Rogers, *op. cit.*, pp. 39–40 (U.S.).

had brought the monthly total of excavation up from 720,000 cubic yards in January 1885 to 1,400,000 in January 1886 and felt confident of his ability to produce results. He was looking forward to resuming his position of leadership on the Isthmus and felt that, by remaining in the company's employ and solving the Culebra problem, he would be in a strong position to succeed as regular Director General. However, the Board of Directors did not approve of company operation for so important a task and desired to continue on the contract basis.

Thereupon, Charles de Lesseps proposed to Bunau-Varilla that he form a company to take over the work on the Culebra: "Why should you not put yourself at the head of a contracting company, the elements of which you would select according to your judgment? You would then be able to employ the full liberty of action which the strictness of the regulations of a great company like ours will never allow you. Act on the Panama Canal the part of Borel and Lavalley at Suez."[16]

Bunau-Varilla liked the idea of being a hero and accepted. His brother, Maurice Bunau-Varilla, took over the financial management. Two brilliant engineers, Artigue and Sonderegger, were the technical members, and Bunau-Varilla agreed to take over actual direction of the work at Culebra. The name "Artigue, Sonderegger et Cie." was adopted. The combination was certainly unique—technical knowledge, experience, youthful energy, and Bunau-Varilla's "passionate devotion to the Canal."

Resigning from the Panama Canal Company's service in September, he proceeded to Panamá. Within a short time he was living in a house on the side of Culebra Cut, watching the work proceed.

The Canal Company by then had succeeded in raising much of the money authorized in July, and the position of the contractors appeared more secure as work was rapidly resumed. The United States naval officer, Lieutenant W. W. Kimball, who inspected the Isthmus about the time Bunau-Varilla was starting

[16] Bunau-Varilla, *op. cit.*, p. 72.

his work at Culebra, stated that conditions on the canal were about the same as in January 1885, with one exception. That exception was Culebra Cut under Bunau-Varilla, of whom he wrote that since there was "plenty of capital behind him, great results may be expected from the efforts of a man of such marked and well-known ability, such energy, courage and perseverance."[17]

Work on Culebra Cut entered its most active stage during the French effort early in 1887, when 26 French excavators were digging and 42 locomotives were drawing 2,000 cars over a network of track, carrying the spoil to near-by dumps as it was excavated. Rogers wrote that the "Two thousand workmen engaged by hand, Decauville cars, excavators, and load-trains present a very animated scene."[18] But under the French regime the tracks of the Panama Railroad were not used for transporting excavated spoil to the dumps.[19]

With the "splendid plant" that the French then possessed, run by able contractors, Bunau-Varilla expected an increase in excavation despite the rainy season and the natural indolence of the laborers. There were, however, other great and unforeseen dangers in the path of progress.

When the rains came, the great mass of Cucuracha on the east bank south of Gold Hill began to creep slowly into the Cut at a rate of about 18 inches a year. The layers of clay, separated by mixtures of sand, alluvium, and conglomerate and made slippery by water saturation, moved as a result of the unbalancing of natural forces caused by the excavation. Bishop described the feeling of the French engineers as approaching consternation. They saw in the slides the end of the sea-level-canal dream. Excavation at Cucuracha was stopped, the slides came to rest, and the engineers undertook studies of the new problems which the advent of major slides presented.

Charles de Lesseps, with other company officials, arrived at

[17] Kimball, *Special Intelligence Report* . . . . *1885*, p. 32 (U.S.).
[18] Rogers, *op. cit.*, p. 33 (U.S.).
[19] Abbot, *Problems of the Panama Canal*, p. 41.

Colón from Paris in early March. He wanted to check the situation by a personal inspection and to arrange for future work with the contractors. Soon realizing the impossibility of completing the sea-level canal within the time limit, he admitted trouble in raising money for continuing the work and that its completion in time would require a revision of plans to a lock canal.

The solution of the Culebra problem then veered toward the lock-canal idea. Charles de Lesseps felt that two years of work would be saved by the reduction in excavation. The Director General, L. Jacquet, thought a lock might be placed at Culebra. But Ferdinand de Lesseps still had to be convinced, as he persisted in his views that locks were simply one of those "engineer's conceptions which had caused so much annoyance at Suez," where he had eliminated them by "letting nature and common sense take control."[20]

It was already too late. The company with its dwindling resources could not continue the sea-level plan, and only a high-level plan that would radically reduce excavation could save the day for the hard-pressed French Company.

Bunau-Varilla's earlier experience in dredging through the Mindi Hills provided the idea. He proposed to subdivide the central mass into a series of pools, place floating dredges in them, and then connect the pools by locks to make the waterway continuous. This would eliminate the problem of drainage caused by the tropical deluges and the resulting difficulties, such as detritus on rails and derailings, which had caused so much trouble to the French.[21] Also, by making the locks sufficiently large, it would be possible to conduct transits and to levy tolls while the work progressed. Such a lock canal was not to be considered permanent, but only as a transition period to permit the gradual digging of a sea-level canal. This concept of a "provisory lock canal" with a summit level of 170 feet met the objections of the old man, who reluctantly accepted. However, he

[20] Bunau-Varilla, *From Panama to Verdun*, p. 38.

[21] John Bigelow, *The Panama Canal and the Daughters of Danaus*, p. 16.

kept his ideal of a sea-level canal and still refused to accept the lock plan as the final solution, though announcing at a meeting of the stockholders in July 1887 that the company was seeking a new solution in opening a temporary canal without abandoning the sea-level plan.

Work at Culebra progressed rapidly while awaiting plans. During 1887 the average level was lowered 10 feet, instead of 3 feet as in the previous year. In 1888 it was lowered 20 feet, bringing the level to 235 feet when the works were stopped. On the basis of performance, Bunau-Varilla estimated that the level would be lowered 30 feet in 1889 and 50 feet in 1890, leaving 15 feet for lowering in 1891 to bring the level to the 140 feet required for a 30-foot depth with a summit level of 170 feet.[22] It appeared to him in 1888 as if this key problem were solved, that the excavation of Culebra Cut was within two and one-half years of completion, and that the canal would be open for traffic in 1891.

THE FINANCIAL CRISIS ARRIVES

What was happening in Paris during these critical months? Ferdinand de Lesseps realized the seriousness of the company's position. Pressure upon him came from all angles to alter the canal plans so that a waterway could be completed at reasonable cost and within the time limit. A meeting of his Superior Advisory Commission was called in January 1887 to consider the subject, and it promptly turned over the work of examining the several plans to a subcommission not due to meet until September. But no definite public announcement as to change of plans was made to prepare the public mind, in spite of the fact that all experts and even the commission headed by Charles de Lesseps recognized the impossibility of executing the company's program. Instead, the assertions of confidence in the sea-level canal continued, regardless of the ominous warnings of engineers. The public was kept propagandized to a view that was

[22] Bunau-Varilla, *Panama: The Creation, Destruction, and Resurrection*, pp. 73–74, 83.

without basis in fact. Perhaps a campaign of education as to real facts of the problem might have successfully maintained public confidence and prepared the way for raising additional funds certain to be requested.

The opposite was done. On January 18, 1887, De Lesseps wrote to the stockholders that he was convinced a sea-level canal was "realizable,"[23] as determined by the Paris Congress in 1879. He announced, however, that he had requested the Superior Advisory Commission to report on the lock plans already submitted and to examine other projects that would permit opening of the waterway with least delay but at the same time permit uninterrupted work toward the sea-level plan. In this last idea he probably referred to Bunau-Varilla's plan of a provisory lock canal as a logical step to permit construction of a sea-level canal later by dredging.

Canal circles in Paris were discouraged by the failure to raise funds in the United States. The directors vigorously opposed payment of the $25,000 annual bonus to ex–Secretary of the Navy R. W. Thompson for the use of his name. They wondered if it would not be better for the Canal Company to discontinue the American committee of bankers and depend upon France alone.[24]

There were other distractions, some humorous and some disconcerting. In Panamá a report on "Engineering Problems of the Isthmus" by a "teetotal liar" was reprinted. The report considered the difficulty of the Panama Canal as "two-fold, how to dam the water of the Chagres River and the flood of whisky at the same time."[25] He concluded that, had the cube of excavations "equalled the amount of liquor drunk along the line," the canal would have been half-finished.

The company had to face attacks not only from its natural critics but even from disloyal ex-employees. For example, on June 17, 1887, a cable from New York stated that J. Boulangé,

[23] *Panama Star and Herald,* Dec. 17, 1887.
[24] *Ibid.,* April 6, 1887.   [25] *Ibid.,* April 12, 1887.

an ex–chief of section at Bohío Soldado who had been discharged by Léon Boyer after a big fire in that section, had said in a speech before the American Society of Civil Engineers in New York that only 30,000,000 cubic meters out of a total of 140,000,000 had been excavated, that the company had only enough money to last four months, and that he doubted De Lesseps could raise any more in France.[26]

Rumors about financial difficulties intensified, and, even by July 1887, reports of impending bankruptcy of the company were frequently mentioned. The development of slides, the failure to control the floods of the Chagres, and the increasing difficulty of raising money gave the rumors credence. Such a disaster would involve French national pride, affect her prestige among the nations, and ruin thousands of small investors—a condition of affairs certainly expected to force any French Ministry to aid the company.

A meeting of the stockholders was called and a new issue of bonds planned. The stockholders met in Paris on July 21, with the Emperor of Brazil in attendance. De Lesseps' report indicated a reduction in his confidence that the canal would be completed in 1889, but expressed the hope for a speedy joining of the oceans that would permit navigation pending completion. De Lesseps had come out for new plans belatedly and reluctantly. A misunderstanding arose because one of the plans provided for the definite substitution of a lock canal for the sea-level plan. To this De Lesseps replied: "I shall never consent to such a substitution." He said he would never depart from the plan of the Paris Congress of 1879, the "*sine qua non* of our enterprise."[27]

Financing required greater inducements to attract new investors. The new subscription for $100,000,000 announced for July 26, which was at a discount of 57½ per cent, gave a net return of only $42,500,000. With only $20,000,000 reported as left in the treasury, this small amount would not last long at the rate funds were then required on the Isthmus.

26 *Ibid.*, June 18, 1887.   27 *Ibid.*, Dec. 17, 1887.

In faraway San Francisco the situation was being watched.
The *San Francisco Bulletin* commented that this bond issue
"probably marks a crisis in the affairs of the Company." It
further stated that, if the new loan were taken, it would indicate
that "well-informed financiers discredit [Isthmian] rumors of
. . . . insurmountable obstacles to the completion of the great
work; and that the enterprise will be pushed to a finish." If it
failed, the company was in danger. In any event the Panama
Canal would go down as the greatest business promotion in the
history of the world. To escape a real catastrophe, two solu-
tions then seemed possible: France might take over the work,
or a new company might be organized to take over at a small
fraction of the original investment.[28]

First dispatches from Paris announced that the loan was
subscribed in full, that there would be no delay or stopping of
work, and that there was "unbounded faith" in De Lesseps. But
that faith did not stop rumors, for in Panamá reports were rife
that the loan was not subscribed in full; but nothing could stop
the optimism for final success, despite the "idle rumor." When
the final result was announced it showed that only two-thirds
of the loan was subscribed, producing 114,000,000 francs,
which De Lesseps considered sufficient to meet needs to carry on
work for two more years.[29]

While the lock-canal project was being considered, De Lesseps on September 25 called another stockholders' meeting to
obtain their opinion about the change of plan forced by circumstances. He reported that "incessant and bitter assaults" of
adversaries, which did not frighten the shareholders, had succeeded in intimidating the financial world, making financing
increasingly costly by the mounting annual fixed charges. He
stated that everything to expedite work had been done and that
nothing had been neglected "which would encourage, support,
and assist"[30] those working with him. Some had measured up

[28] *San Francisco Bulletin*, July 16, 1887.
[29] *Panama Star and Herald*, Aug. 8, 1887.   [30] *Ibid.*, Dec. 17, 1887.

to expectations with "courage and devotion," residing on their sections of the work. Others produced inferior results by obtaining inferior laborers, causing what he hoped were only temporary delays. It would require another $150,000,000 to open the canal, with 60 kilometers of the total 74 completed on time. The 14 kilometers through the cordillera, already deeply cut, would have to be closed to form a lake with locks at each end, to permit dredging to sea level at the same time as the canal was being used for transiting vessels across the Isthmus.

The Superior Advisory Commission, consisting of the most eminent engineers of France, submitted its report in October, stating that it was possible to establish a high-level canal through the central mass on the Isthmus so as to permit later dredging to sea level and that it would be possible to transit ships during the process. De Lesseps was then ready for his next move.

On November 15 he sent out two letters. One was to the French Minister of Finance, again requesting authority to issue 600,000,000 francs of lottery bonds to cover expenses from January 1, 1888, to inauguration about 1890. He briefly outlined the conditions facing the company, stating that latest plans left about 40,000,000 cubic meters to be excavated—10,000,000 rock and 30,000,000 dredgable.[31] To the shareholders, De Lesseps "the untiring," in another dramatic move, announced arrangements with Alexandre Gustave Eiffel, the builder of the Eiffel Tower, for construction of locks to open navigation. He referred to the attacks made on the company—false letters, false telegrams, false circulars and pamphlets, designed to cause the fall of canal securities on the Bourse and "to dispossess you of your property and of your titles on the eve of your efforts being crowned with success." He appealed for unity among both bondholders and shareholders. "Let them remain deaf to the advances of their intended defenders" and to the "menaces of their foes," for he would be the first to warn of danger to their great enterprise.[32] The French Government de-

[31] *Ibid.*, Dec. 14, 1887.   [32] *Ibid.*, Dec. 17, 1887.

layed, but De Lesseps displayed confidence with his business associates. When H. B. Slaven, who was with De Lesseps during this period, returned to New York he reflected the views of his chief, based upon six years' working on the Isthmus and not upon "observations made from car windows."[33] He reported the canal as more than half completed, that the Culebra was still the greatest problem, and that De Lesseps and Eiffel expected to visit Panamá in January. He expected the canal to be opened in January 1891, because machinery was available, the organization had been perfected, and men were becoming acclimated.

But De Lesseps could not make his trip to Panamá. He had to stay in Paris to raise more money when the French Parliament refused his request. Irked by this refusal, he announced he would appeal directly to the people. He declined to accept the Government's decision as to the lottery bonds, urged the shareholders to put pressure on representatives for a public inquiry, and called a meeting of the shareholders for March, while the shares on the Bourse continued their downward spiral.

In spite of these preoccupations he had time enough to travel, always in the interest of Panamá, and time to be interested in people. One day two salesmen found themselves in the same compartment with an old man whom they supposed to be of the same profession, and one of them started conversing with him:

"Beg your pardon, sir. What is your line?"

"Isthmuses."

"Wh-wh-what?" was the puzzled reply.

"I am introducing ship-canals."[34]

The old man was Ferdinand de Lesseps. He was certainly trying to sell canals, for while heading the great effort at Panamá he was still running Suez. But he also had another great vision which he was interested in promoting—the Kra Canal across the Malay Peninsula as the natural supplement of the Suez route to China—thus completing the canal route around the world.

---

[33] *Panama Star and Herald*, Dec. 13, 1887.   [34] *Ibid.*, Feb. 27, 1888.

Chapter VI

FRENCH MONEY RUNS OUT

He [Ferdinand de Lesseps] offered . . . . the magnificent spectacle of an old age retaining to the full the energy and buoyancy of youth. No difficulties deter him, no obstacles, natural or financial, present themselves to his mind as too vast to be overcome.—LONDON TIMES, September 7, 1888.[1]

WORK ON THE ISTHMUS IN 1887 AND 1888

When it became evident late in 1886 that the French plans would have to be changed, many contractors, fearing to risk expending too much effort on uncertain plans, slowed down their works and thereby delayed prospective completion until 1889. At Culebra Cut, however, all excavation was usable regardless of the type of canal, and work continued unabated.

How was the canal work organized to enable completion by 1889? Laid off in sections measured in kilometers, beginning at Colón, the canal was 74 kilometers long. For construction it was divided into five major construction divisions, each assigned to a large contractor. The first 25 kilometers from Limon Bay, following the valley of the Chagres to Bohío Soldado, were being excavated by the American Contracting and Dredging Company, controlled by the Slavens. The section from kilometer 26 to 44, which extended as far as Gamboa, was assigned to Vignaud, Barbaud, Blanleuil et Cie. The Public Works and Construction Company operated from kilometer 44 to 53.6, up the valley of the Obispo to the high Culebra Cut, and also worked on the dam for the Chagres at Gamboa. The highest part of the central mass then called Culebra Cut, between kilometers 53.6 and 56, was under Artigue, Sonderegger et Cie., the firm organized by Bunau-Varilla. Baratoux, Letellier et Cie. worked from Culebra Cut to the Pacific Ocean.[2]

[1] *London Times*, Sept. 7, 1888, p. 7.
[2] I.C.C., *Report, 1899–1901*, II, 16 (U.S.).

Although there was much uncertainty as to definite plans, work progressed in spite of periodic rumors of many discharges on the Isthmus, which always spread alarm. Excavations in April 1887 and again in August were over a million cubic meters each month. By the beginning of 1888 Bunau-Varilla estimated remaining excavation at 56,000,000 cubic yards, which an average annual quantity of 16,000,000 would complete in less than four years, permitting opening the waterway in December 1891.

Work continued on diversions as well as on the main canal, so as to keep the Cut free of water. Everyone was looking forward to diverting that turbulent river, known as "Father Chagres," into new channels to eliminate its recurrent ravages, which from the first had constituted a major problem for the French.

It was heartening to De Lesseps in Paris to receive word late in November 1887 from the engineer Nouailhac-Pioch[3] that he had steamed from kilometer 17.4 (near Lion Hill) to Limon Bay on the Atlantic, and that on the Pacific the mud scows were towed at low tide as far as kilometer 67.8, a point where today the Balboa inner harbor is located.

Work on the canal was not without its amusing incidents. The engineer of the Pacific division, Norge, after an inspection of the work at La Boca, had returned to Panamá City. There his mules became frightened and made a wild rush toward the Canal Office Building. In the dash through the gateway one of the wheels struck a post and was wrenched off, but the mules kept on going and would have run into the sea in a short time. Unfortunately for one of the mules, a sailor was waiting for a boat with an oar in hand. With a wide swing he struck the head of one mule with such force that the animal was felled forever. For this act he received the plaudits of the crowd, who in their exultant relief from Isthmian boredom took up a subscription for the valiant mariner.[4]

[3] *Panama Star and Herald*, Jan. 4, 1888.   [4] *Ibid.*, Nov. 1, 1887.

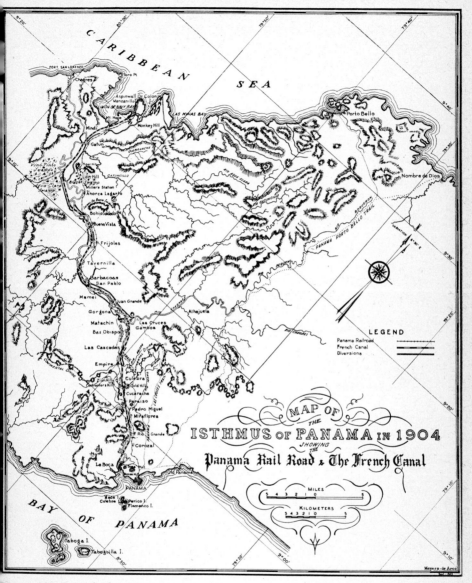

MAP OF THE PANAMA RAILROAD AND THE FRENCH CANAL, 1904
Drawn from records of The Panama Canal

From New York came more rumors about canal difficulties—
there was no work in progress, two leading contractors were embarrassed, judgments had been filed against the French Canal
Company with seizures and sales, and there was a too obvious
effort to "keep up the appearance of life."[5] Offsetting these attacks, the *Canal Bulletin* in December announced that ships were
landing cargoes directly to trains at the Pacific terminal, thus
avoiding the double handling previously necessary. On the
Atlantic end the canal was used to deliver supplies for work on
the Chagres.[6]

Work on the lock canal finally started at Pedro Miguel on
January 15, 1888, and at San Pablo in February. The same
general canal route was followed, with a summit level of 49
meters (170 feet). This placed the summit level above the flood
waters of the Chagres so high that it was necessary to feed the
summit level by machinery. There were to be ten locks, five on
each slope. On the Atlantic slope were Bohío Soldado, San
Pablo, Matachin, Bas Obispo, and Empire. On the Pacific side
were Cucuracha, Pedro Miguel, Miraflores, and a double flight
at La Boca. This was a small canal with a bottom width only a
fraction over 61 feet. All locks were to be located over compact
rock near railroad stations, and lock gates were to be manufactured in Europe by Eiffel, using a modified form of his plans for
a Nicaragua Canal.[7]

Meanwhile, Panamá witnessed another celebration. On
Washington's birthday in 1888 the stone barrier at Mindi Hill
was removed after five years of hard work. This meant that
the canal was open from Colón past Gatun to Bohío Soldado,
with sufficient depth for vessels of 1,000 tons. It was the occasion for a celebration, with a visit from celebrities who went by
steamer past Gatun.[8]

In May 5,000 men were working on ten lock sites. The

[5] *Ibid.*, Nov. 23, 1887.
[6] *Ibid.*, Feb. 4, 1888.   [7] *Ibid.*, May 18, 1888.
[8] *Ibid.*, Feb. 23 and Feb. 24, 1888.

Pedro Miguel site was reported as one-third completed, and five locks were expected to be ready in several months. Dredging continued with increased momentum. With ten new dredges due to arrive before the end of the year, excavation was expected to reach a monthly total of 1,500,000 cubic meters, with prediction of completion dates varying from 1890 to 1891.

One writer has left a vivid record of work at the San Pablo lock. Viewed from one end, he saw about 600 men working in the 270-by-18-meter lock space. "Here, boring the holes for the next blasting, are the 120 miners; here are men loading the large buckets which as soon as filled are lifted by the cranes up to the level of the top cut, some fifty or sixty feet, and emptied upon railroad tracks; and here on a higher cut are men who load the cars from the ground; at the ends of the locks are still other gangs with wheelbarrows wheeling the earth away to the dumps as fast as the barrows can be loaded."[9] Many kinds of machinery and labor-saving devices were near by—rock crushers to prepare rock for concrete, machine shops with lathes, bolt-cutters, punches, and saws, all steam-power operated, and a blacksmith shop with flaming forges. Work was pushed night and day.

At Paraiso and Miraflores were the same pictures of action. There winches were hauling "large and heavy trains of the Decauville dumping cars out of the work, up steep inclines," pumps were draining water from the sites, and the appearance presented was that of a "gigantic undertaking well-handled,"[10] with workers in good health.

Another tragedy struck the engineering staff when the new Director General, Antoine Vanneau, died on June 27, 1888. He had symbolized the speed and the energy of the French in trying to accomplish their belated plans and to protect the interests of the company and of France. Buried near his work, his own words were used for his epitaph: "However sad may be the mis-

[9] *Panama Star and Herald*, July 17, 1888.
[10] *Ibid.*, May 12, 1888.

fortunes which have befallen us in this climate, we must not lose confidence. Let us remember that we have given ourselves to a work which is very important and has become national, and, proud of engaging in it, I had almost said of fighting with it, for the glory of France; let us close our ranks and push on to the completion of the Canal in three years."[11] The death of another leader did not affect the work. There were always three more to replace each one who fell.

Sections of the canal were nearing completion; Culebra was advancing, and preliminary work on the Chagres Dam commenced. Relocation of the Panama Railroad was started so as to get it clear of Culebra Cut, the new location requiring a large bridge across the canal at Paraiso. At Matachin the head of the lock was almost ready to receive fittings. All lock sites were being excavated.

As the year 1888 closed, Culebra Cut work under Artigue, Sonderegger et Cie. showed remarkable progress. In July about 5,000,000 cubic meters remained to be excavated in that short but difficult section. Between 2,500 and 3,000 men were employed day and night in a cut lighted by electricity. With 800 dirt cars and 54 locomotives operating on 37 kilometers of track at a rate of 100 trains a day, these scenes of feverish activity were intensified by the 23 steam excavators that kept the trains supplied.[12]

At first the critics claimed the Cut structure was "too hard to be pierced." When the work appeared successful the form of attacks changed—it was "too soft." Then the theory of "sliding mountains" that would defy all efforts arose to cast its pall upon men's minds. But the work continued at Culebra and was vividly described as late as December 1888 by one who said that even to see the machinery in operation would take one's breath. "Enormously powerful dredges tear up the earth from the bed of the Cut and force it through seemingly impossible

---

[11] *Ibid.*, June 28 and June 29, 1888.
[12] *Ibid.*, July 26, 1888.

lengths of pipe to its destined resting place, whilst all along the sides of the Cut mighty excavators, moving slowly along the railroad tracks, tear away the bowels of the mountains with incredible rapidity, and deposit the debris in cars that bear it away . . . ."[13] It was expected that the Paraiso bridge would be ready in January and that the dredging of the actual channel in Culebra Cut would begin in March.

But in the midst of such promising activity there was a suppressed sense of danger. Disconcerting messages that had arrived from Paris were whispered around but not published. Only a few realized the gravity of the rumors, as the work was pushed onward with completion expected in 1891.

LAST EFFORTS OF DE LESSEPS TO KEEP GOING

While such great effort was being made in Panamá, what was happening in Paris? The shareholders' meeting, called by De Lesseps when the Government refused to authorize lottery bonds, met on February 29, 1888. More than a thousand attended, and Ferdinand de Lesseps presided. With excellent precision he read his report for forty minutes. The audience consisted chiefly of middle-class small investors to whom a collapse of Panama would be a personal disaster. De Lesseps, interrupted by frequent applause, gave a résumé of the situation— the necessity for more money, how the ill will of the opposition forced higher interest rates upon the company, and how the directors had been induced to adopt a temporary lock canal so that it could be opened in 1890 and completed later.

Charles de Lesseps followed with an appeal for confidence and advised the investors to hold their shares as the only way to safeguard their great enterprise. The shareholders then authorized a loan of 340,000,000 francs. It was estimated that the cost to complete would be 654,000,000 francs: 254,000,000 for excavating, 125,000,000 for locks and masonry, 15,000,000 for reservoirs and summit-level supply, 50,000,000 for mate-

[13] *Panama Star and Herald*, Dec. 4, 1888.

rials, and 210,000,000 for general purposes. With the loan of 340,000,000 francs and the 260,000,000 already authorized, plus 110,000,000 on hand, there would be a margin of 56,000,-000 francs.[14]

At the same time the French Parliament reconsidered its previous action, and a bill authorizing issue of lottery bonds was introduced. It met determined hostility. Some opposed because they considered the company's estimates unreliable, others because they did not believe it a government function to guarantee a private company. Friends of the company in Parliament appealed for members not to abandon this national enterprise, and the lottery law was passed by the Chamber of Deputies on April 28 and by the Senate early in June 1888, after long debates in both Houses. On the ninth of June De Lesseps announced the terms of the issue, scheduled to take place on June 26.[15]

De Lesseps continued with his campaign, on one occasion speaking before the Topographical Society of France (Société de Topographie de France, Paris). Wearing the large ribbon of the Legion of Honor, he read an illustrated paper, renewing his assurance that the Panama Canal would be open in 1890. As proof he pointed to his photographs, saying, "The sun is our best collaborator, for he furnishes to photography the means of refuting the calumnies of our adversaries."[16] He then reverted to the familiar refrain that he would triumph at Panama as at Suez.

In Panamá the *Star and Herald* advertised the offering of 720,000,000 francs in bonds of a normal value of 400 francs, offered at 360 francs.

The Canal enemies did not wait till the day of issue. Three days before that date they dumped shares of the company on the market to depress the prices. Then, knowing how much the

---

[14] *Ibid.*, April 20, 1888.
[15] I.C.C., *Report, 1899–1901*, II, 20 (U.S.).
[16] *Panama Star and Herald*, June 27, 1888.

public pinned their hopes on De Lesseps himself, on the day of issue they telegraphed throughout France the false news of De Lesseps' death. Notwithstanding these insidious attacks, out of 2,000,000 bonds issued, 800,000 were subscribed by 350,000 persons. But this failure of the offering represented a great break in the company's credit and was quickly reflected in depressed security values. Bunau-Varilla thought De Lesseps should have been permitted to limit the issue to 660,000 bonds, as advised by Baron Jacques de Reinach; but this was not permitted by the bank, which insisted that all the 2,000,000 bonds be offered at one time. Bunau-Varilla considered this failure in financing the fundamental error that precipitated the collapse of the Old Panama Canal Company.[17]

In their desire to economize, the company did not cable the news to Panamá. Other lottery drawings were scheduled for October and November. To stimulate interest, De Lesseps and his son visited many industrial and commercial areas in a frantic and "laborious work of propagandism."[18] In their appeals they referred to the Loire factories in Nantes, where the lock parts were being constructed by Eiffel and where they had seen sizable parts 24 meters long, 3 meters thick, and 10 meters high, weighing 230 tons. They continued to speak in November but did not meet with their expected success, and hope was abandoned of disposing of all the remaining 1,200,000 unsold bonds.

In Panamá security prices trembled. The propaganda of De Lesseps' enemies was bearing fruits. On November 24 word came from London of the alarm felt by De Lesseps. He threatened "to publish an account of every step he had been forced to take in the Panama Crusade"[19]—steps that were supposed to involve several members of the Cabinet.

The November issue was not to be irrevocable unless 400,000 bonds were subscribed, but less than 200,000 had been sub-

[17] Bunau-Varilla, *Panama: The Creation, Destruction, and Resurrection*, pp. 87–88.

[18] *Panama Star and Herald*, Nov. 13, 1888.

[19] *Ibid.*, Nov. 26, 1888.

scribed. The French Government showed intense anxiety at the possible public reaction. Conferences were held between De Lesseps, the Directors of Credit, the Minister of Finance, leading jurists, financiers, and Senators. De Lesseps informed the Government of the facts. He wanted to promote a new company to continue the work. On December 14 a bill providing for a three-month moratorium on bills and for interest and securities was introduced in the Chamber of Deputies. The same day De Lesseps petitioned the Civil Court of the Seine to appoint temporary managers to take over, so as to prevent stoppage of work on the canal. Senator Denormandie, former Director of the Bank of France, Baudelot, ex-president of the Chamber of Commerce, and M. Hué were appointed. With them secured, De Lesseps cabled to Panamá his hopes of realizing such a combination[20] as to insure continued progress, and Denormandie sent authority to continue until February 15.

THE CULMINATION OF THE CRISIS

Another blow came just as De Lesseps had completed plans leading to the formation of a new company. The bill of the Government providing for three months' postponement by the company of payments on its bills and interest came up for a vote on December 15 and was rejected, 256 to 181, in the Chamber.[21] Ten minutes after the vote a reporter called on Ferdinand de Lesseps and told him about the rejection. Pale and speechless, his hand fell like a stone. Placing a handkerchief to his lips to stifle a cry, he said:

"*C'est impossible. C'est indigne!* I did not believe the French Chamber would sacrifice the interests of the Nation. They forget the milliard and a half of the savings of the French people that are compromised by this vote, and they could have saved all this by a firm decision. This will be a triumph for our enemies, and a disaster to our flag."[22]

[20] *Ibid.*, Dec. 17, 1888.   [21] Bunau-Varilla, *op. cit.*, p. 93.
[22] *Panama Star and Herald*, Dec. 19, 1888.

At the office of the company there were scenes of wildest confusion. The hall was crowded with subscribers. Women were weeping excitedly at the loss of their small savings, and men were facing ruin. All waited for Ferdinand de Lesseps to appear. Mounting a platform, he addressed them in an effort to restore confidence: "My friends! Your subscriptions are safe. Our adversaries are confounded, and we now have no need of financiers. You have saved yourself by your own exertions. The canal will be made!"[23] Cheers! Cheers! Cheers! De Lesseps wept at this powerful demonstration, as all hands closed in to shake his hand and women in tears tried to kiss his clothing.

The next day many came with more money. Some even brought their children's savings, but were disillusioned when they found that only by government aid could the canal be completed and that De Lesseps had withdrawn, leaving control to the temporary managers.

The Paris paper *Le Figaro* commented that the Chamber of Deputies had played into the hands of the North Americans. Friends of De Lesseps blamed the hostility of the United States and the lottery scheme for the debacle. But De Lesseps had asked successive public subscriptions of great sums, and probably the last was too much. He had been attacked at home.

From Washington came still another blow to those who hoped for assistance from the French Government. Senator Edmunds of Vermont introduced a Joint Resolution (Sen. Res. 122) on December 19, 1888, expressing "serious concern and disapproval" of any European government's connection with "the construction or control of any ship-canal across the Isthmus of Darien or across Central America." Declaring such connection or control as "injurious to the just rights and interests of the United States and as a menace to their welfare," the President was requested to "communicate this expression of the views of Congress to the governments of Europe."[24] In spite of all this

---

[23] *Panama Star and Herald*, Dec. 19, 1888.

[24] G. F. Edmunds, "Joint Resolution (Sen. Res. 122)," *Congressional Record*, Vol. XX, Pt. 1, p. 338 (U.S.).

opposition, a meeting of 4,000 bondholders passed a resolution of confidence in De Lesseps and expressed willingness to forego interest payments until the canal could be opened for traffic.

These combined events created profound depression in France. In Panamá the message of De Lesseps to Director General Jacquet on December 15, about the appointment of provisional managers, had restored calm but not confidence. Isthmian shareholders, instead of throwing over their "Grand Old Man," sent him messages of trust and promises of support. The canal became the principal topic of conversation. The Panamá public concluded that the crisis had become a collapse. But contractors continued work to show their faith, and all were asked to withhold judgment. France rushed a warship toward the Isthmus in anticipation of disorders, and two were expected from the United States—a precaution laughed at by the Isthmians, who pointed to their tatterdemalion army of 600 ready to handle anything. Word came to Artigue and Sonderegger on January 7 to suspend work.[25] Twenty-five hundred men stopped work in Culebra Cut, but order prevailed amid a state of general alarm.

Meanwhile strenuous efforts to reorganize were being made in Paris. President Slaven of the American Contracting and Dredging Company was having daily conferences with De Lesseps. Denormandie cabled to the Isthmus that new contracts to assure continuance would be signed.

France assumed a state of "political animation." Meetings of security holders were called throughout the country. At one 5,000 strong, held in a skating rink in Paris, the president of the committee addressed the crowd:

"Shall we leave this glorious work to be completed by foreign powers?"

"*Non, non, non!*" they thundered.

"Shall we agree to forego any return on our investments until the canal is completed?"

"*Oui, oui!*" they replied emphatically.

[25] *Panama Star and Herald*, Jan. 8, 1889.

"Shall we pledge ourselves, each according to his means, to aid this great enterprise by purchasing new shares of Panama stock?"[26]

Again they thundered approval and adopted a resolution covering all points.

In spite of the strongest efforts of De Lesseps and the temporary managers, the movement to organize a new company was frustrated. A last shareholders' meeting was held late in January 1889, when it was decided to request a judicial receiver, and on February 4 the Old Panama Canal Company was dissolved and Joseph Brunet was appointed as liquidator.[27]

The great French effort had expended its force. The savings of French peasants were gone. The company and its officials became the object of attack by both the opposition and the Government. Weakened by age, adversity, and criticisms, the veteran leader of the enterprise had been struck down.

When De Lesseps' directing hand relaxed its hold, there was no one big enough to rally the disillusioned investors and to mobilize another major effort to complete the waterway.

THE LIQUIDATION

The liquidation was painful. In February the last issue of the *Bulletin du Canal Interocéanique* appeared. Brunet made determined efforts to keep work going, but by May 15, 1889, all activity on the Isthmus was suspended after a series of gradual discharges.

Shops were closed, and machinery was slushed with preservative. Dredges were left where they had been working, whether in the low sea-level reaches or in pools near the summit. Excavators, locomotives, and all kinds of rolling equipment were placed on sidings, exposed to rain, sun, and the jungle. Villages along the line lost their population as the unemployed drifted away. The new Colón Hospital became an almshouse

[26] *Panama Star and Herald*, Jan. 12, 1889.
[27] I.C.C., *op. cit.*, II, 21 (U.S.). Paul Bressolles, *Liquidation de la Compagnie de Panama*, p. 20.

operated by Catholic Sisters. Ancon Hospital continued to function, but with the jungle gradually obscuring its statues and crowding out the flowers from its gardens. The areas along the line that had been the scene of so much activity reverted to the jungle, and each year that passed made it more difficult to determine if there had been any effort at all.

Brunet immediately organized a commission to conduct a searching investigation on the ground, by questioning engineers and examining records. Arriving on the Isthmus in the pleasant month of December, the Commission was soon engrossed in activities which did not lack social aspects. At a banquet given by the Director General, the President of the Commission, Aquiles Bergès, was frankly critical. He said that "many questions which should have been previously studied were not examined sufficiently." He considered the fixing of a definite completion eight years previously most unfortunate. He attributed that act of De Lesseps to "complete ignorance" of the conditions on the Isthmus, and his "desire to animate the labors of all."[28]

In the midst of the investigation another casualty occurred to the unfortunate organization. Brunet was taken ill and had to call Achille Monchicourt as coreceiver to assist. Because of failing health he resigned, and he died soon afterward.

The Commission reported on May 5, 1890, that the lock canal could be completed in eight years, that the plant on the Isthmus was in satisfactory condition and sufficient to complete the work, and that the cost to complete would be 580,000,000 francs. It recommended the most careful investigation before starting work and submitted a lock plan.

The liquidation dragged along during the period from 1891 to 1894, the only important work accomplished in Panamá being the collection of hydraulic data on the Chagres. The process was accompanied by great tragedies in the lives of the leaders. The Panama affair precipitated a political crisis in France. The Government, in response to popular pressure, decided to prose-

[28] *Panama Star and Herald*, Jan. 6, 1890.

cute those held as responsible, among them officials and directors of the company. Some fled the country. Baron de Reinach committed suicide. Ferdinand de Lesseps and his son,
along with Eiffel, were indicted for alleged corruption.
Charles de Lesseps was arrested to await trial, but Ferdinand
escaped that fate. At the trial, Charles fought valiantly to save
the company and to maintain the integrity of his name. He told
the story of how M. Baïhaut had extorted 375,000 francs from
the company. The President of the Court replied: "You could
have called the police." To this Charles de Lesseps asked: "But
what happens if the gendarme himself is the person holding you
up to ransom?"[29]

Ferdinand, sitting at home, surrounded by his family, was in
a state of mind "from which there is no recovery" and was not
molested. He had only momentary glimpses of passing events.[30]

The struggle was in vain. Both were sentenced to five years,
but the sentences were not executed. Charles lived on until 1923,
but Ferdinand lived only a short time; he died on December 7,
1894, at the age of eighty-nine.

THE NEW PANAMA CANAL COMPANY

The original Wyse Concession was to expire in 1893, and
there was danger of the French losing their franchise. Impressed
by the favorable report of the liquidators' investigation, Monchicourt called upon L. N. B. Wyse to serve Panamá. Again he
was sent to Bogotá, where on December 10, 1890, he obtained
a two-year extension to the concession.[31]

The strenuous work of liquidation wore out Monchicourt,
who died March 14, 1894. He was succeeded by Jean Pierre
Gautron, and the New Panama Canal Company was organized
October 21, 1894, under the name of "Compagnie Nouvelle du
Canal de Panama." One of the conditions imposed by the Old

[29] Siegfried, *Suez and Panama*, p. 279. D. W. Brogan, *France under the Republic*, pp. 268–85, contains description of French political conditions at the time.

[30] H. J. Schonfield, *Ferdinand de Lesseps*, pp. 209–30.

[31] I.C.C., *Report, 1899–1901*, II, 26, 247–50 (U.S.).

Company was the appointment of a Comité Technique to formulate a definite plan for a canal.

The frugality of the French in these years brought about an innovation by the Panama Railroad. With prices of food too high in Panamá, the company in 1894 formed a co-operative grocery store for railroad officials only. The experiment was successful, and two years later its privilege was extended to all employees of the railroad, steamer lines, visiting warships, diplomats, and Canal Company officials. This was the beginning of the tremendous Commissary Division of the Panama Railroad of today.[32]

Relatively, the New Panama Canal Company was a small organization with a capital stock of 650,000 shares of 100 francs each, of which 50,000 paid-up shares were assigned to Colombia. This left a capital of only 60,000,000 francs ($12,000,-000), a sum too small to launch any large-scale work.

When organized, the New Company wanted to retain the French character of the canal and "had no intention or wish to sell their rights on the Isthmus."[33] They wished to establish the value of the Panama Canal as an investment and hoped to reimburse the old investors for their losses. They aimed to realize the dreams of De Lesseps.

On December 9, 1894, the first expedition of employees for the New Company sailed from France; they consisted of a new Director General, Vautard, and twenty employees. Work was resumed in Culebra Cut, as this was excavation that would contribute toward any type of canal which might be adopted. The force grew from about 700 men to a maximum of over 4,000 in 1897.

The New Company quickly appointed an international investigating commission, the Comité Technique, composed of men of the highest professional attainment. One of its members was General Henry L. Abbot, the great student of the Chagres.

---

[32] *Canal Record*, Aug. 5, 1908, I, 387 (U.S.).
[33] Abbot, *Problems of the Panama Canal*, p. 8.

The Comité Technique arrived on the Isthmus in February 1896. Assisted by an able staff, it made studies to determine the best possible plan. Confident that Nicaragua could not compete with Panamá, they ignored the agitation for Nicaragua then being carried on so vigorously in the United States. Work on the Isthmus was limited to that which would contribute to the final plan and to the collection of data. In contrast to the previous days, "there was no blowing of trumpets,"[34] but instead a meticulous search for facts.

Near the close of the century there occurred the Spanish-American War—which Bemis has called the great aberration in United States history—the Asiatic incursion by the United States, and the spectacular cruise of the "Oregon" around the Horn.

The canal idea was thus dramatized, and the United States demanded complete control of the Isthmian Canal. The logical French realized that these events made their position hopeless. They could not compete with the United States.

The Comité Technique completed its plans on November 16, 1898, exactly three years before the Isthmian Canal Commission was destined to recommend a Nicaragua Canal. The report was the result of three years of study and an extensive examination on the Isthmus. It is interesting because of the evident simplifications which greater knowledge produced.

The canal route remained essentially the same. There were to be two levels, one an artificial Lake Bohío about 61.5 feet above sea level, to be created by a dam at Bohío and reached from the Atlantic level by a double-flight lock. In addition there was to be a summit level 97.5 feet high, also reached by a double flight of locks from Lake Bohío at Obispo. The descent into the Pacific was to be by three locks—a single-stage lock at Paraiso, a double-flight lock at Pedro Miguel, and a single-chamber lock at Miraflores. The canal was to have a bottom width of 98 feet and a depth of 29.5 feet. In dimensions the locks were to be

[34] Abbot, *op. cit.*, p. 6.

738 feet long, 82 feet wide, and about 32 feet deep in the clear. Cost was estimated at $101,850,000. The summit level was to be supplied by a feeder from a lake to be created at Alhajuela (now Madden Lake). A second plan, with Lake Bohío as the summit level and fed directly by the Chagres, was submitted as an alternate.[35]

These plans were designed to meet the problems of controlling the Chagres and the excavation of Culebra Cut. They were the result of a gradual evolution through a series of lock plans.

What would have happened had the Spanish War not attracted the attention of the people of the United States to the Canal idea one can only conjecture. General Abbot, who was familiar with the French documents and was a profound student, stated it as his belief that the Canal would have been completed by the French as just outlined.[36] In that case, there would have been a smaller and perhaps an earlier canal operated along the style of Suez, instead of the great Canal organization we have today.

The company, knowing that its only chance of assuring any return on its investment was to hold on until the United States should take control of the Isthmus, sent a copy of the Comité Technique report to President McKinley, which he received December 2, 1898. During its last years the company limited its excavation to that necessary for holding its concession.

THE FRENCH EFFORT IN PERSPECTIVE

With no other information than that contained in popular books on the Panama Canal, it is easy to minimize the value and extent of French contributions. Many have ignored them altogether, not realizing that the bitter lessons learned by the French supplied the foundation of success by the United States. Nor is it generally known that it was the French effort which determined the location of the first waterway across the Isthmus. The French as the explorers and investigators of the canal route

[35] I.C.C., *op. cit.*, I, 85–86 (U.S.).   [36] Abbot, *op. cit.*, p. 8.

deserve a place at least with other pioneers and builders of the
Panama Canal.

The Old Panama Canal Company, under the powerful influence of the great promoter, had launched the plan for a sea-
level canal without careful investigation and preparation. When
the error was realized, it was too late. Precious time had passed,
funds had been expended, and unfortunately the company failed
to understand the full magnitude of its task until too late to
readjust its plans.

Many reasons have been advanced for the failure of the
French—corruption, incapacity, malaria, and yellow fever.
There was corruption in certain high places in France, but
nothing involving the personal integrity of Ferdinand de Lesseps or his son. There were cases of incapacity, but the French
had men of sufficient ability and experience to accomplish the
task. There was suffering from malaria and yellow fever, but
disease was not the primary cause of failure. In fact disease
was almost ignored by the engineers. Yellow fever was never
so serious as malaria, a fact well shown by the researches of
Dr. Gorgas.

The real reasons for the collapse of the French were their
failure to accept the only feasible plan for constructing the
Panama Canal, submitted by Godin de Lépinay at the Paris
Congress in 1879, and the tragic decision to build a sea-level
canal at Panamá without sufficient knowledge of the vastness
of the sea-level project. When at last the French Company was
forced to change the plan of the canal to a more feasible lock
canal, it was too late to avoid a crash. The money of the company had run out, and there was no source to which it could
appeal for more funds once it became the object of political
attack in France.

At the time when failure became imminent in September
1888, the engineering problems had been largely solved. There
were over 14,000 men on the pay roll, and excavation was proceeding at the rate of about 1,000,000 cubic meters a month,

From *Scientific Monthly*, January 1942. Courtesy of Dr. Gorgas' daughter, Mrs. W. D. Wrightson

GENERAL WILLIAM CRAWFORD GORGAS, 1854–1920
Chief Sanitary Officer, Panama Canal Zone, 1904–1914

with a remaining estimated excavation of only 23,700,000 cubic meters to complete the canal. This would have enabled a completion date in 1891. It should be stated, however, that the canal as planned in 1888 was so small that, if it had been completed, it would have been outmoded even before its completion date.

The new company benefited by the experiences of the old and accomplished its task in a most thorough and scientific manner. It made elaborate studies of canal plans and of Isthmian topography, geology, and hydrology that later proved to be of greatest value to United States engineers. The Isthmian Canal Commission regarded the information as "much more complete than is usual before the inauguraton of an engineering enterprise in a new country."[37] Colonel Goethals later often stated that when he wanted accurate information he went to the French plans.[38]

The total excavation by the two French companies amounted to 78,146,960 cubic yards, of which 11,403,409 was by the new company—a greater volume than the excavation at Suez. Of this total, 18,646,000 cubic yards were taken from Culebra, where the Cut was lowered 333.5 feet to a high point 193 feet above sea level near Gold Hill.[39] The peaks and ridges were removed.

The French left a legacy of tropical buildings and machinery used for many years by the United States. They gained control of the Panama Railroad and developed it as an adjunct to the canal. They developed a splendid hospital service but did not discover the part played by the mosquito in disease and hence suffered by that ignorance. They made fundamental errors in financing and planning. Their equipment was light as compared with later machines, but it is doubtful if North Americans could have done better during the same years. The old Canal Company could have completed its canal had not a combination of circumstances in France destroyed the company and its leaders.

[37] I.C.C., *op. cit.*, I, 86–87 (U.S.).
[38] Dr. J. E. Lefevre, Conversation with the author, Sept. 21, 1941.
[39] Goethals, *The Panama Canal*, I, 336–37.

It was Ferdinand de Lesseps who paid most heavily for the collapse. Instead of coming to his assistance, the Government "abandoned him in a cowardly way, and then shamefully trampled on him."[40] Four years after his death the French nation erected at Port Said a massive statue of the Canal Builder, with his hand pointing toward the East. The United States later named one of its forts guarding the Atlantic entrance in his honor.

It is impossible to read the detailed history of the French effort without feeling the power of De Lesseps' influence, without understanding how he was acclaimed "The Great Frenchman," without knowing that as "The Great Frenchman" he will remain.

[40] Siegfried, *Suez and Panama*, p. 283.

CHAPTER VII

THE UNITED STATES TAKES OVER THE TASK

We have not the slightest intention of establishing an independent colony in the middle of the State of Panama, or of exercising any greater governmental functions than are necessary to enable us conveniently and safely to construct, maintain and operate the canal, under the rights given us by the treaty.—THEODORE ROOSEVELT.[1]

THE FIRST COMMISSION ORGANIZES FOR WORK
UNDER ADMIRAL WALKER

For almost fifteen years the Isthmian jungle grew thicker over rusting French machinery, but the hopes of the enthusiasts for resumption of the Panama Canal never faltered. The dramatic cruise of the "Oregon" around the Horn in 1898 centered public attention on the Isthmian Canal idea, and negotiations for a canal treaty were started between Colombia and the United States. After prolonged diplomatic discussion, the Hay-Herrán Treaty was signed with general acclaim and ratified by the United States Senate. In Colombia it was rejected, to the great dismay of all friends of Colombia and the Canal.

Then, suddenly, came the Panamá Revolution of November 3, 1903, and the declaration of independence from Colombia by that young republic, the diplomatic intervention of Theodore Roosevelt, and the negotiation of another treaty by Philippe Bunau-Varilla with an audacity and adroitness that startled Panamá and aroused enthusiastic interest in the United States.[2]

Roosevelt's impulsive diplomatic intervention, done under the impetus of the westward expansion of the United States into the Pacific, was an event of far-reaching consequences. It had wide repercussions in Latin America and did not escape notice

[1] Roosevelt to Secretary of War, Oct. 18, 1904. (The Panama Canal Record Bureau, File 28-I-62; hereafter designated as P.C. Rec. Bur.) (MS).

[2] M. P. DuVal, *Cadiz to Cathay* (chapters x to xii, pp. 255–316) contains a detailed account of these complicated negotiations.

by Japan. But by it Roosevelt undertook to build the Panama
Canal and became the leader for this great enterprise in the
United States. Thus, upon his shoulders fell the mantle of De
Lesseps.

After the ratification of the Hay–Bunau-Varilla Treaty, Roosevelt looked over the list of available men to build the canal
and appointed the seven-man Isthmian Canal Commission as required by the Spooner Act of 1902.[3] He selected a group of
high-grade men—men of strong personalities. Admiral John G.
Walker, who had headed the earlier exploring commission, was
chairman. General George W. Davis, a retired Army officer,
was designated as Governor of the Canal Zone. The engineer
members were William B. Parsons, Benjamin M. Harrod, William H. Burr, and Carl E. Grunsky. Frank J. Hecker was a business man. It was an Army, Navy, and civilian commission, with
the civilians in control of engineering. Unfortunately, the dominant members were not experienced in construction or business.
They could not be expected to handle the pressing problems
of employment, planning, and equipment for so large an effort.

The Commission in a body called on the President at the
White House on March 8, 1904. He told them that they had been
selected from the "best fitted" but warned that he expected resignations from anyone who should find the work "too exhausting
and engrossing." He expected them to be equally exacting with
regard to the selection of their own subordinates and not to pay
the slightest attention to political influence in making their appointments.

He singled out "sanitation and hygiene" for special emphasis and urged the use of the best medical and sanitation experts.
He wanted a rigorous supervision of expenditures but desired
the employment of the best talent for every need. Finally, he
warned, "What this nation will insist upon is that the results be
achieved."[4]

---

[3] DuVal, *op. cit.*, Appendix G, pp. 503–7.

[4] Roosevelt, "Instructions to Isthmian Canal Commission, March 8, 1904,"
I.C.C., *Proceedings*, first meeting, March 22, 1904, pp. 3–4 (U.S.).

The first meeting of the Commission was held in Washington on March 22, 1904. This was followed by daily meetings for a while. The members handled the many details that always fill the organizing days of any new enterprise.

They made a most thorough search among engineers for a chief engineer. A trip to Panamá was arranged, and, after considering the appointment while on the voyage, they decided to offer the position to one of the leading railroad engineers in the United States, John F. Wallace. Thus it was possible for Commissioner Parsons, while still at sea, to write Mr. Wallace on April 3—the first intimation that he was being considered for appointment as chief engineer of the Isthmian Canal Commission.

Accompanied by Colonel William C. Gorgas, the distinguished Army doctor of Cuban fame who had been selected as chief sanitary officer for the Canal Zone, the Commission arrived at Colón on April 5, 1904. They were welcomed by a committee headed by Tracy Robinson, who had welcomed De Lesseps before them.

These men, however, were not the first group from the United States to reach the Isthmus. Already there were Major William M. Black, Lieutenant Mark Brooke, and Civil Engineer A. C. Harper, who with their secretary, Harry D. Reed, had arrived on April 16, 1903, and also Dr. Claude C. Pierce as the first sanitary representative, who arrived December 31, 1903,[5] and had been studying French methods and Isthmian conditions for months.

The Commission set up headquarters at Colón in a building erected for De Lesseps. Major Black and Lieutenant Brooke showed them points along the line. At Culebra the Commission found about 500 employees of the New Canal Company excavating with a few old French steam excavators, loading cars and hauling spoil to near-by dumps. Fresh from the United States, the Commission could see at a glance how the tremendous

[5] Haskins, *Canal Zone Pilot*, pp. 282–83.

advances in engineering efficiency within a few years had rendered the French equipment woefully outmoded.

Although the Spooner Act contemplated a lock canal, they were encouraged to investigate further the practicability of the sea-level canal, as well as to determine the summit level and lock data for a lock canal. After a visit of two weeks they returned to the United States to organize engineering parties, while Dr. Gorgas and his associates made plans for sanitation. It would not be long before the dirt would fly.

ACQUISITION DAY, MAY 4, 1904

In Paris, final arrangements for the purchase of the New Panama Canal Company's rights by the United States had been completed. On the Isthmus, Major Black, not realizing the advanced state of the purchase negotiations, obtained leave of absence and returned to the United States with the Commission. He was naturally ambitious to become chief engineer and to build the Panama Canal.

Apparently without the knowledge of Major Black, Secretary of War Taft, anticipating an early exchange of the properties, authorized Lieutenant Brooke late in April to act in conformity with the instructions he would receive from the United States representative in Paris. On May 3 the instructions came. They directed him to receive all the Canal properties on the Isthmus from the New Panama Canal Company, except the Panama Railroad, and he prepared to take over the following day.

Early the next morning Lieutenant Brooke and Director General Renaudin; W. W. Russell, United States Chargé d'Affaires; Mr. J. W. Lee, Secretary of the United States Legation; Consul-General H. A. Gudger; and Dr. Claude C. Pierce, of the United States Public Health and Marine Hospital Service, were all assembled at the old Grand Hotel, which housed the French offices. Brooke read a declaration he had drafted, signed a $40,000,000 receipt to Renaudin for the French Canal holdings on the Isthmus at 7:30 A.M.,[6] and hoisted "Old Glory" over the building—an event that caused May 4, 1904, to become known as Acquisition Day.

This young second lieutenant, just two years out of West Point, cabled his action to the Commission then sitting at Washington and took charge. To the old employees he sent a circular announcing that he had taken possession for the United States and requesting them to continue in their positions.

The new organization comprised 746 employees at a monthly pay roll of $15,000 gold; they were organized into a Director General's Office, Disbursing Office, Sanitary Service, Supply and Material Department, Land and Building Department, and Engineering Department, all reporting to the Director General. Equipment included 2,148 French buildings, numerous files and records, and a tremendous quantity of machinery and rolling stock. The buildings included the magnificent Ancon Hospital, the Administration Building in Panamá City, the Taboga Sanatorium, the Dingler residence (Casa Dingler) on La Boca Road, and the residence of the Director General, used later for many years as the home of the United States Legation in Panamá.

GOVERNOR DAVIS FORMS THE CANAL ZONE GOVERNMENT

In Washington organization matters continued. At the eighth meeting of the Commission on May 6, John F. Wallace was definitely offered the position of chief engineer at a salary of $25,000. He not only accepted the position, effective June 1, 1904, but agreed to maintain a "residence on the Isthmus."[7] Captain George R. Shanton, who had served with Roosevelt as a Rough Rider during the Spanish-American War, was appointed chief of police. He proceeded to recruit a force, largely from ex-service men, and dressed them in the khaki uniform of the Rough Riders—a uniform worn by the Canal Zone Police until 1941.

[6] Governor Davis' Statement, April 2, 1906 (Hearings No. 18, III, 2423-24, 2492-93) (U.S.).

[7] I.C.C., *Proceedings*, eighth meeting, May 5, 1904, p. 40 (U.S.).

Under what department of the United States Government should the Commission be placed? Roosevelt was in favor of placing it directly under the War Department. Admiral Walker and General Davis preferred it to remain as an independent agency under the President. Following the advice of the Commission's counsel, Charles E. Magoon, and based on the precedent of the Philippines, President Roosevelt in an Executive Order of May 9, 1904, placed the Commission under the supervision of the Secretary of War and defined its jurisdiction and functions. He did this because the War Department was the Government agency which had charge of civil works on rivers and harbors.

This order was a powerful document. Not only was it the basis for forming the civil government of the Canal Zone, but it authorized the Commission to legislate for "military, civil, and judicial affairs"[8] until the close of the Fifty-eighth Congress. It vested the Commission with powers necessary to construct the canal, directed that members of the Commission be appointed directors of the Panama Railroad, outlined a Bill of Rights, emphasized sanitation as a matter of prime importance in preparatory work, and apponted Major General George W. Davis as the first Governor of the Isthmian Canal Zone. On the Isthmus the immediate reaction was that it meant "almost autocratic powers"[9] for the Commission.

What were the qualifications of Governor Davis? He had had a distinguished record in the Army, had landed the first regiment in Cuba during the Spanish War, and had organized the military government of the Cuban Province of Pinar del Rio. He had been Military Governor of Puerto Rico and had organized its civil government. He had been civil and military governor in the Philippines. There was no hesitation in selecting a man of his positive attainments or investing him with the authority of

[8] Roosevelt, "Letter to Taft, May 9, 1904." *Executive Orders Relating to the Isthmian Canal Commission, March 1904 to June 12, 1911*, pp. 4–11 (U.S.).
[9] *Engineering Record*, May 14, 1904, XLIX, 623.

managing representative for the Commission until the arrival of a chief engineer.

On the day after the Executive Order was issued, Governor Davis, with the first permanent party consisting of Major Black, Ernest Lagarde, Jr., Paymaster E. C. Tobey, Dr. R. L. Sutton, Captain Shanton, and M. E. Mitchell, sailed for the Isthmus.

Arriving at Colón on May 17, 1904, they were greeted by a boarding committee, with Tracy Robinson among the welcomers. M. G. de Paredes, reflecting the rising hopes and joy of the Isthmians, addressed General Davis and declared that the time had come to transfer the struggle "from the forum to the field; from the Capitol to the jungle," for a contest with the forces of Nature. Confidently he declared the "clang of the dredge, the boom of the blast, the clatter of the work trains, multitudinous steam whistles, and the glare of thousands of electric lights at night shall be as bugle and drum"[10] for the determined attack. The General replied that he had always been a man of action and that he hoped to measure up to expectations—as was to be found out very quickly.

General Davis did not go to Panamá City until two days later. As Governor, he issued a proclamation of occupation for the Canal Zone and appointed civil officers in the Canal Zone Government. As managing representative of the Commission, he outlined the work of the Canal departments: Engineering under Major Black; Secretariat under the First Executive Secretary, Harry D. Reed; Accounts and Material under Paymaster E. C. Tobey; and Buildings and Grounds under an old French employee, C. F. Bertoncini. Operations were to continue under the same general system already in effect, but with United States methods of accountability.

The one permanent activity of the United States that General Davis found on the Isthmus was the Quarantine Service. It dated back to 1893, when officers of the Public Health and Marine Hospital Service were detailed to serve in consular of-

[10] *Panama Star and Herald*, May 20, 1904.

fices in Panamá and Colón to inspect vessels bound for the United States and sign bills of health. When it was observed that Panamá authorities did not enforce quarantine regulations on vessels arriving from infected ports in South America, arrangements were made for these United States doctors to take over the quarantine duties at both terminal cities. Thus the oldest of the construction organizations was placed under the Isthmian Canal Commission.[11]

Rather tardily, Governor Davis made a formal call on President Manuel Amador of Panamá and announced that the United States had taken possession of the Canal Zone and was continuing the great work which had been under way for so long.

Panamá did not like this precipitate and direct action. It loved formality and wanted a celebration. The result was that Governor Davis found himself in his first controversy. Very shortly he received orders to participate in any ceremonies desired by Panamá, but not to invalidate any action he had taken.[12]

The Governor had more troubles. There was a controversy about La Boca, the Panamá Government claiming that port as the port of Panamá City. This was an impossible situation. Davis would not tolerate its exclusive jurisdiction under Panamá and refused to admit that La Boca was a part of the harbor of Panamá. On that basis he negotiated an agreement with the infant republic and prevented what otherwise would have become in later years a source of friction between Panamá and the United States.

He had been directed to carry on as the French before him had done. When time came for the first payday he had no local (Colombia) silver. The paymaster came to him in despair, but nothing daunted this doughty Governor. He ordered: "Post up an advertisement asking for bids"[13] for the required amount, as if the local silver were merchandise, payments to be by checks

[11] Sen. Doc. 286, 59th Cong., 1st sess. (U.S.).

[12] Davis, First Annual Report of Governor of Canal Zone, Nov. 1, 1904 (Hearings No. 18, III, 2466) (U.S.).

[13] Davis' Statement, March 30, 1906 (ibid., III, 2273).

on the Assistant United States Treasurer in New York. The money came rolling in.

Panamá bankers, however, did not like this procedure. They did not like public financing and wanted Davis to follow the French in getting a quotation, obtaining the required amount, and then paying by draft in Paris, with the public in ignorance. They protested and criticized. Their feelings were hurt. One banker promised to supply all money required, but said, "we are not going to bid for it in competition with every Chinaman."[14] Even so, they decided to comply with the Governor's wishes.

Because silver was the money of the Isthmus, native employees continued to be paid in silver. North Americans were paid in gold. Thus gold and silver became the bases for indicating race—gold for white employees and silver for colored. In exchange, one gold dollar equaled two silver dollars.

From the day he arrived until he left the Canal Zone, General Davis was a prodigious worker and probably was the largest single influence in determining the form of the Canal Zone Government.

WALLACE BECOMES CHIEF ENGINEER

Admiral Walker's first major task was to form an engineering organization. Early in May 1904, he appointed as assistant engineers: Boyd Ehle, H. F. Dose, A. B. Nichols, A. C. Harper, and Charles A. List, to lead several engineering survey groups on the Isthmus. These men in turn recommended other engineers, but it was to Boyd Ehle, who had served as assistant chief engineer on surveys in Nicaragua, that Walker turned to recruit the main body.

By the end of the month every steamer from the United States brought engineers. Nichols, with two transitmen, arrived at Colón on June 5, 1904, to make preparations. The main body under Boyd Ehle, with diamond drillers, arrived on June 8 as the first organized contingent of engineers after the

14 *Ibid.*, III, 2273-74.

acquisition. As the parties arrived the engineers were assigned to surveys: List and his party to Colón Harbor, Nichols at Gatun to investigate the practicability of that location for a dam site, Dose at Bohío, Harper at Culebra, and Ehle at Obispo.[15]

But engineers did not come in sufficient numbers. Many young engineers, under the influence of rumors and propaganda, hesitated to leave the security of the United States and before risking the trip wrote to engineering magazines for advice on health conditions.

To answer these pointed criticisms, Colonel Gorgas, upon return from his first visit to the Isthmus, came to the aid of the Commission by publishing an article on "Health Conditions on the Isthmus of Panama."[16] He was not particularly an alarmist, but he feared malaria as the disease on which the "sanitary measures" would depend. He thought that anyone who slept under a mosquito net, drank boiled water, and slept away from the native malaria carriers would be fairly safe. Certain engineering magazines that followed the Canal question closely also assisted the Commission by disabusing timid minds of their fears. The editors knew that the Canal would prove to be a "great training school" from which they might expect "many graduates of distinction." They wrote highly of the Chief Engineer as a man under whom it was a "great fortune to serve."[17]

Indeed, Wallace had a record of which to be proud. By efficient service on the railroads he had risen from rodman to chief engineer. He had handled the transportation of the crowds at the Chicago World's Fair. As chief engineer he had rebuilt the Illinois Central and become its general manager. He had been president of the American Society of Civil Engineers.

When he accepted the position as chief engineer of the

[15] G. M. Wells, Letter to author, Nov. 8, 1944.
[16] *Engineering Record*, June 4, 1904, XLIX, 704.
[17] *Ibid.*, p. 697.

Panama Canal, he conferred with Admiral Walker, who warned him that his tenure of office was as stated in the President's letter of March 8, 1904. But Wallace emphasized that he could not be expected to take orders in such a large work from any and every individual member of the Commission and that he could not give good service unless granted an "absolutely free hand."[18] He feared ideas of the Commission as individuals more than anything else and did not want to have seven superiors instead of one. It was with those reservations that he accepted.

Most of Wallace's background of experience had been in developed territory where the temporary dislocation of large construction projects could be absorbed. He had had no experience on the frontiers where the unfamiliar problems of the mountains and forests, labor and supplies, and climate would have given some insight into the difficulties of conducting a great enterprise in the primeval jungle. He felt, however, that he could obtain the experience that later would make him a valuable member of the Commission, should any changes occur. Admiral Walker was an old man and could not last long. Wallace was looking for higher things.

The first month of United States control was one of rapid transition. The urgent needs of the hour were sanitation, water supply for Panamá and Colón, and a sewer system. Many streets of the cities were quagmires of indescribable filth. But these problems were not all. Temperance organizations in the States descended upon the President in a drive to make the Canal Zone dry. "Friends of Labor" in Washington became interested in the welfare of their fellow workers and started agitation. The American Boycott Association pressed Admiral Walker for an eight-hour day in a land where a ten-hour day had been in use for many years. A controversy developed between Bohío and Colón as to which should be the Atlantic terminal.

As fast as carpenters arrived they were placed at work re-

[18] I. E. Bennett, *History of the Panama Canal*, p. 188.

pairing old canal buildings and railroad stations. Railroad shops started repairing cars. The private car and locomotive formerly used by De Lesseps were renovated and used on daily inspection trips by officers of the Commission. Ancon was selected as headquarters for the offices of the civil government.

Two old excavators continued the excavation in Culebra Cut near Gold Hill, where the high point was 193 feet. That was the only place where digging was actually going on and where all who wanted work could obtain it. But hard work was not popular. All wanted to be "watchmen, timekeepers, and foremen,"[19] positions which presented no difficulties in filling at first.

Resumption of work on the Canal aroused keen interest. Sunday excursions became popular, and curious employees and Isthmians explored along the line of the Canal.

The needs of the growing population increased. Food became scarce and expensive. Butter, cheese, and milk could not be obtained. No one stepped up to meet the demands for feeding the new canal diggers, and the demands continued to increase.

As the number of North Americans grew, the canal rapidly lost its cosmopolitan French atmosphere. It was becoming "Americanized" with a rapid crescendo. On June 12, 1904, the *Star and Herald* issued its last three-language edition, only one month and eight days after acquisition of the Canal Zone by the United States.

The hectic speed of the new occupants had a stunning influence on the Isthmus. When Chief Engineer Wallace, with Colonel Gorgas and sixteen nurses for the Ancon Hospital, arrived, there was no celebration. It was a quiet arrival; but Wallace must have been quite apprehensive about his health, for he brought along "fine metallic caskets"[20] to the Isthmus for use if he or his wife died.

19 *Panama Star and Herald,* June 9, 1904.

20 Stevens to Secretary of War, March 22, 1906 (P.C. Rec. Bur., File D-5-25) (MS).

Wallace called upon Governor Davis, brought up the question of his responsibility for all engineering work, and informed Davis that he understood the Governor would be responsible only until his own arrival. Davis showed him his commission as managing representative and agreed to turn over the engineering construction work but would hold on to the powers granted him which, he said, "practically leaves me in charge of the work, as I hold the purse strings."[21] They smoothed matters temporarily, and the Governor issued a circular relieving Major Black and announcing Wallace's assumption of duties on July 1, 1904. Major Black returned to the United States.

Wallace lost no time in inspecting the Canal, looking over French machinery and meeting engineers. The conditions he found were jungle and chaos from "one end of the Isthmus to the other" with much unrest among employees. The only excavation he saw was a "small amount of work on which four or five hundred men were employed at Culebra, and they were doing all their work there by hand."[22] They had worked for the French only enough to hold the concession and were kept on by the United States. So insignificant was their effort that even the drilling was by hand. Wallace stated it would have required 200 to 300 years to complete at the rate then in progress.

The machinery that was housed was in excellent condition, but that which had been issued to French contractors was still resting where it had been left the day French work stopped. Jungle had grown around dredges in the sea-level reaches and in the pools of Culebra Cut. Many dredges were sunk along the banks where they had been secured fifteen years before. Trees were growing through the fireboxes of locomotives. Jungle had so covered the tracks that United States engineers continued to discover sections of track in it for many months. The scene he saw was eloquent with the power of the jungle!

The inauguration of the work by Wallace was celebrated in

[21] Wallace's Statement, Feb. 5, 1906 (Hearings No. 18, I, 557) (U.S.).
[22] Wallace's Statement, March 20, 1906 (*ibid.*, III, 2013).

a really North American way on the first Fourth of July under United States control. Excursions were run from both Panamá and Colón to Empire for picnics, with bands playing. At Empire, in the midst of wind and rain interspersed with sunshine, there were athletic contests—events strange to Isthmians, but significant of the changes wrought by the North American successors of the French.

THE COMMISSION IN ACTION

Wallace gave his first attention to Ancon Hospital. The grounds were still beautiful but sadly neglected. As the brush was cleared from the gardens, statuary was uncovered; but much of the gardening work of the French Sisters was lost in the indiscriminate process. Buildings were renovated and quarters prepared for the staff. The hospital had to be ready for the sick that were always expected with the arrival on the Isthmus of large numbers of unacclimated. Along the line, where doctors were stationed, dispensaries were established and converted into line hospitals.

The Isthmus was practically without roads at that time, except the most primitive trails. The Old Spanish Trail had disappeared long before under heavy tropical vegetation. Even La Boca Road along the ridge to La Folie Dingler was half overgrown with jungle. Houses were without the essential conveniences, and many had to use candles[23] in the absence of electric power in the Canal Zone.

Wallace desired to create comfortable living conditions for employees and started two hotels, one at Corozal and one at Culebra. Unfortunately, he lacked building material so badly that he could not keep his carpenters busy nor use all his forces. He had to go into the open market for material brought in by schooners.

When requisitions were sent to Washington they were considered by the Commission with all formality, regardless of their

[23] Jessie Murdoch, "Ancon Hospital in 1904 and 1905." Society of the Chagres, *Yearbook 1913*, pp. 43–58.

AFTERMATH IN THE JUNGLE, NEAR TAVERNILLA:

French land excavator, abandoned 1888. The man sitting on top of the crane was First Lieutenant James G. Steese, Corps of Engineers, United States Army

AFTERMATH IN THE JUNGLE, NEAR TAVERNILLA:
French bridge conveyor, span 156 feet

urgency or cost, thus introducing great delays in delivery and adding to the difficulties of the Chief Engineer. But he kept on and employed a supervising architect to plan new buildings and repair the old; also a sanitary engineer to make plans for the Panamá water supply, which were ready by mid-August.

In the United States the press kept up an insistent demand to "make the dirt fly." The public wanted immediate action. Unfortunately, under this clamor Mr. Wallace and the Commission weakened in their original stand for thorough preparation before construction. Wallace started experimental excavations in July to determine the unit costs, and these were carried along for many months, with insignificant yardage. The French Comité Technique had experimented at Culebra Cut and had obtained excavation cost estimates there of 52 to 81 cents per cubic yard, depending on material encountered in the Cut. Abbot felt that Wallace wasted much time and energy because he did nothing except confirm available information.[24] However, he did place orders for some steam shovels, locomotives, unloaders, spreaders, and other new railroad and construction equipment.

From the beginning, Wallace had his troubles with government routine business procedure, better known as "red tape," which he described as a "system gone to seed"[25]—the tendency to consider the way of doing things as more important than the results. One time he wanted to advance money to labor agents. He called in Paymaster Tobey, a man whom he had recommended for that position on the Isthmus, and asked for money. The Commission organization had made Tobey, as chief of materials and supplies, independent of the chief engineer, and he had to comply with certain of its regulations. Wallace pleaded for funds, but Tobey had to ask embarrassing questions before issuing. Wallace did not like to be questioned by a young man of thirty-five years; that was intolerable to a man who was accustomed to issue transportation for thousands without question.

[24] Abbot, *Problems of the Panama Canal*, pp. 22–24.
[25] Wallace's Statement, Feb. 7, 1906 (Hearings No. 18, I, 669) (U.S.).

On August 3, 1904, Admiral Walker and Commissioners Grunsky, Burr, and Harrod arrived for the second visit of the Commission, accompanied by their general counsel, Judge Charles E. Magoon. That same evening, at Ancon, they held the twenty-first meeting of the Commission and began a series of sessions as the Canal Zone legislature. Governor Davis left the same day to go to the bedside of his invalid wife in the United States, and Admiral Walker took over the duties of Governor in addition to his position as chairman of the Commission.

The energy which marked the beginning of United States work had not produced the rapid results expected by the Isthmians. Gorgas had expected to complete sanitation within fourteen months, but both he and Wallace met many obstacles. The demand on the Isthmus was for greater powers for both the chief engineer and the chief sanitary officer. Results could not be obtained when they had to depend upon actions by a commission sitting 2,000 miles away!

As the number of employees increased, rents and food prices rose until it became increasingly difficult to live within income. Eating places were few, and no effort was made to provide more. Shortly a partial solution was found when an employee died and left a destitute widow. The division engineer suggested that she run a mess, assigned her a French building, and built tables and benches. Soon there was a "widow mess," then other messes were formed to help tide over the feeding crisis until the hotels could be completed.

The messes had their troubles. There was no cold storage for meat on the Isthmus. All meat was bought fresh from horse-riding peddlers on the streets. There was no ice, no fresh milk, and nothing but tinned butter. Local bread was dirty, and fresh vegetables decayed so rapidly that employees had to depend on canned foods.[26]

Water was the greatest problem of life in the early days. In

[26] J. J. Meehan, "The Early Days." Society of the Chagres, *Yearbook 1913*, pp. 137–47.

the dry season it was peddled along the streets, and a daily bath was a privilege only of the wealthy. W. C. Haskins describes how the same water served a succession of uses—first, washing the children's faces, then laundering articles of wear, then scrubbing stone floors, and finally cleaning the sidewalk. In the wet season water fell in copious volume and was no problem.

It was this atmosphere that confronted any new arrival as he alighted from the train at old Culebra Station near a swamp and received orders to report to the Division Engineer's Office on the hill. He would trudge along a "narrow trail, dense jungle, on a path so muddy" that he seemed to be stepping backwards. At the office he was supposed to receive "six chairs, a bed, three tables, washstand and tin pitcher, and a clothes rack." What he actually received was a cot and a box.

Employees had to find quarters of their own. Rooms that in the United States would rent for $5 a month, in Panamá cost $20—a rate too high for $100-a-month clerks.

The greatest of all complaints was about food. The young canal pioneers, with their appetites sharpened by work in the jungle, were not satisfied with the usual light tropical diet of fruit, bread, and coffee that was served with monotonous regularity by the Isthmians. They tired of crackers, sardines, and salmon at the Chino shops. They wanted a variety of real food, and they wanted more of it. They wanted ice. They wanted better quarters. They wanted excitement.

In every way the Isthmus was an undeveloped country, with few women and children and few diversions. Men wanted to read, but reading at night was almost impossible because of the poor oil or candle lights and the myriads of insects attracted through the unscreened windows. There was nothing for the canal builders to do except go to bed, pull the sheets over their heads for protection, and wait for the next day to come. It was under these conditions that "letters from home had a special meaning," and each mail was awaited with much impatience. It was too early to bring families to the Isthmus.

Many could not or would not stand the monotony, the privations, the climate, and the loneliness. Almost every vessel returning to the United States carried many back—the tired and the disillusioned. The frontier on the Panama Canal was no place for the weak or fainthearted!

Meanwhile, on August 3, 1904, at its twenty-first meeting, the Commission started daily sessions on the Isthmus at Ancon with a comprehensive program. It enacted the Canal Zone Code; and Commissioner Grunsky, an engineer, prepared the Health Department organization. After Governor Davis returned, the Commission at its forty-third meeting on August 31 revoked the instructions to him as managing representative of the Commission and placed Wallace in sole charge of all construction[27] on the Isthmus.

Governor Davis foresaw the difficulties ahead and tried to secure appointment of one responsible head on the Isthmus, as in the French organization, in which the director general had been supreme. He explained that the French organization was admirably suited for adoption by the United States. The position of Washington as seat of the United States organization was not similar to Paris as headquarters for the French Company, for in the United States there was only one stockholder, with the Commission as trustee. There were "no securities to place, nor a hostile press to placate with subsidies."[28] But the Commission would not accept the Governor's views.

After twenty-nine sessions, the Commission completed its program on September 7, 1904, and departed for New York, leaving Governor Davis as executive officer of the Commission and as President Roosevelt's personal representative.

The Commission was extremely conservative in its actions. It reflected the attitude of Admiral Walker, who, by long years of study, had become familiar with the history of the Canal and wanted to avoid pitfalls at all costs. He was an able man but

---

[27] I.C.C. *Proceedings*, 43d meeting, Aug. 31, 1904, p. 179 (U.S.).
[28] *Ibid.*, p. 185.

had many set ideas about small matters, particularly the necessity for economy. For example, Colonel Gorgas would take requisitions to him to sign. They would discuss matters and conversation would center on economy. Then the old Admiral would say: "Gorgas, there is one thing certain; whether we build the canal or not we will leave things so fixed that those fellows up on the hill can't find anything in the shape of graft after us." The Admiral then would place the requisition in his drawer and let it rest. It may have been this philosophy that formed the basis for the official inertia which caused so much trouble and took so much to overcome.

TROUBLES GATHER

When Admiral Walker arrived in the United States, he was optimistic. He announced that everything on the Canal was ready for real work, health excellent, and sanitary measures taken. Others had different views. Mr. Wallace pointed out, as he left the Isthmus for New York a week after the Commission, that it would be eight months before Panamá even had its water supply.

When Wallace arrived in Washington he checked on requisitions and found the most disheartening conditions. A typical case was that of pipes he had ordered in August. The Commission members could not agree as to details of specifications; but when he said he wanted pipe regardless of specifications, the order was placed with a firm not familiar with the expediting of shipments, and the pipes did not arrive until January 1905. The trenches dug on the Isthmus in the meantime had caved in because of rains. When Wallace tried sending cables to check on filling of requisitions, he was told politely not to cable so much. The Commission presumed that since he had had free cables on the Illinois Central he did not know that cables cost money.[29]

The Commission wanted Wallace to hurry back to the Isth-

[29] Wallace's Statement, Feb. 6, 1906 (Hearings No. 18, I, 589) (U.S.).

mus, but he wanted to go on leave. They acquiesced, and he went to his home in Illinois. In an interview there he said that the work would be mapped out and that digging the "big ditch" would be in full progress by April 1 of the next year. He lectured at the Chicago Press Club, where he commended Boyd Ehle and his young engineers of the survey parties for the high quality of their work.

But Wallace did not have well-defined plans for constructing the canal. He was interested in a sea-level canal, and for that Culebra was the key. Cutting Culebra, he said, was a railroad proposition similar to "relocating the Panama Railroad and reducing its grades, making a big, heavy cut along its line, using that line as one of the instruments to do your work."[30] It made little difference, he explained, whether a railroad was laid in the Cut to carry trains or whether water was run in the Cut to float steamships. His plan was not written. As he stated: "I had a regular system outlined in my mind. . . . . Of course, my subordinates did not know what that plan was."[31] He wanted a full year of experience before putting his plan into writing.

On the Isthmus congestion mounted with every passing week. There were not enough men to unload ships. Even if there had been, the railroad did not have enough cars to handle the traffic. Work along the line continued slowly. Acting Chief Engineer W. J. Karner made weekly reports to Wallace by personal letters during October and November 1904. Usually they were typewritten, but at times he had to write at his home in longhand by lamplight and amid the insects. But Wallace did not like to read longhand reports. In one of his replies he complimented Karner on his penmanship but added that his life was "too short to read long-hand."[32] Karner acknowledged the compliment and explained the reason, but fired back: "You did not have to read them unless you wanted to."[33] While the corre-

[30] Wallace's Statement, March 20, 1906 (Hearings No. 18, III, 1991) (US).

[31] Wallace's Statement, Feb. 6, 1906 (ibid., I, 600–601).

[32] Wallace to Karner, Oct. 16, 1904 (P.C. Rec. Bur., File D-5-25 [1]) (MS).

[33] Karner to Wallace, Nov. 1, 1904 (ibid.).

spondence was going on, so was the work. In spite of the rain, the mud, and the slides, on November 11, 1904, the first United States steam shovel was installed in Culebra Cut.

The first break in the Commission came on November 16, 1904, when Commissioner Hecker resigned because the Panamá "climate" was injurious to his health. Hecker was a businessman who had done good work on the Isthmus and demanded direct business methods. He saw the futility of remaining any longer and decided to leave.

Mr. Wallace returned with his wife from the United States just in time to prepare for receiving Secretary of War Taft, who was then arranging for his first visit to the Canal Zone. The Wallaces made their residence in Casa Dingler, formerly the home of the French Director General, and their house became the social center of the Isthmus.

In the meantime relations with Panamá under Governor Davis' energetic hand had not improved. Secretary Taft arrived at Colón on November 27, 1904, accompanied by Admiral Walker and William Nelson Cromwell, the clever general counsel of the Panama Railroad and formerly of the New Panama Canal Company. Arriving amidst the oratory and receptions of another Isthmian welcome, he found a full program for a distinguished visitor waiting.

Taft was entertained at the Wallace home. The visit gave him his first close observation of the Chief Engineer. He was impressed by Wallace's "earnestness and interest in the work, his ability, his facility of expression, his power of planning ahead, and his experience . . . . on the Illinois Central."[34]

Most of Taft's time was taken up with conferences. Wallace wanted to see Taft alone, but Cromwell was at his front door when they got up in the morning and was with the Secretary until late at night. At last, when Wallace happened to get Mr. Taft alone, Taft interrupted to let him know that he had promised Cromwell to have him present. Wallace stated that he did not

[34] Taft's Statement, April 19, 1906 (Hearings No. 18, III, 2557) (U.S.).

get a satisfactory interview at any time, even though the Secretary was living in his own home. Mr. Taft, however, obtained firsthand information of conditions on the Zone; and he gained the gratitude of Panamá by quickly presenting a "happy solution" to their problem through an Executive Order, issued by direction of the President on December 3, 1904, while Taft was still on the Isthmus. When he left he was given a great send-off. He had corrected all the "wrongs suffered by this young republic through the misrepresentation of certain treaty rights."[35]

After Taft left, Wallace sent him copies of many documents on Isthmian matters and on relations between himself and Governor Davis. He also wrote about the Panama Railroad, of which he thought the chief engineer should be in complete control, recommending that all its stock be obtained for the Government by either purchase or condemnation.[36] He was critical about the seven-man Commission, 2,000 miles away, exercising executive functions. He wanted the Commission reduced to three men—the chief engineer and the Governor on the Isthmus, and the chairman in Washington, all working on purchases, shipping, and labor. The engineers, he thought, should be engineering consultants rather than members of the Commission with executive functions.

In the meantime the Commission continued to hold meetings and to debate and vote on the most trivial expenditures, with each member considering himself individually responsible for each item. Today when one examines the records of those early years, it is difficult to see how anything at all was accomplished in such an atmosphere, and one wonders why that condition was permitted to last so long.

It had become apparent to Secretary Taft that the Commission had not measured up for large-scale construction work and was "clumsy and ineffective." Something radical had to be done. The Commission had been blamed, but Mr. Wallace had

---

[35] *Panama Star and Herald*, Dec. 8, 1904.
[36] Wallace to Taft, Dec. 5, 1904 (P.C. Rec. Bur., File D-5-25 [1]) (MS).

escaped censure. What did the Secretary of War have in mind? Governor Davis wrote the Secretary that he regarded Mr. Wallace as a "very superior man, and he ought to be retained."[37] He also suggested combining the offices of minister to Panamá and Governor into one office. The purpose of this suggestion was to remove the friction that had developed between him and the United States Minister to Panamá.

A most curious episode of this period was an attack by the medical profession on the Commission. Dr. C. A. L. Reed had served as a real-estate arbiter on the Isthmus in December 1904. Upon his return to the United States, Secretary Taft requested him to study the Isthmus and report on hygienic conditions.[38] Dr. Reed went down again, looked around, saw the conditions and the people, and wrote a report that was most extreme.

Colonel Gorgas was rightfully praised, but the Commission was condemned indiscriminately for every conceivable kind of failure. Dr. Reed resented placing the sanitary department under the Governor, the requirement that medical requisitions be reviewed by others, and having interns at Ancon Hospital. He accused the Commissioners of having petty antagonisms toward the medical service and of placing Canal doctors in cheapening competition with doctors of Panamá. For the yellow-fever cases he placed full responsibility upon the Commission, "more especially upon Mr. Grunsky," and for many other items responsibility was likewise placed "more especially upon Mr. Grunsky." The report read like the emanations of a radical agitator rather than a judicial document expected from a president of the American Medical Association.

Secretary Taft sized up the value of its contents accurately. He forwarded the report confidentially to Admiral Walker for a statement, noting its biased tone. The Commission's reply was a judicial and careful analysis of the points and made Dr. Reed's report appear ludicrous, especially since he had published the

[37] Davis to Taft, Jan. 6, 1905 (*ibid.*).
[38] I.C.C., *Proceedings: Circular No. 10*, Jan. 10, 1905, p. 473 (U.S.).

article in the *Journal of the American Medical Association* without official authority.[39]

EVENTS FORCE RESIGNATION OF FIRST COMMISSION

Early in 1905 work improved at Culebra. Two French excavators and two United States steam shovels were working, with spoil being sent to near-by dumps. The force had increased from 500 men in July to 1,200 in January. The "battle of the levels" was starting. The relative merits of the sea-level and lock canals were being discussed, but Wallace refused to state his views publicly. He appealed, however, for patience and careful preparation of a plan for an undertaking which had required over four centuries "to conceive in the womb of civilization."[40]

While Wallace was writing to the Secretary of War his letters so critical of the Commission's methods, the Canal employees wrote letters critical of conditions in the Canal Zone. They claimed to have been lured to the Isthmus with glamorous promises, but upon arrival found so many inconveniences that they became "homesick and disgusted," particularly when required to live six in a room. They wanted an occasional pleasant evening.

On January 24, 1905, two members of the Committee on Engineering, Parsons and Burr, arrived on the Isthmus. Because of his office, Governor Davis automatically became a member. The Committee examined the Canal and held daily hearings in the Governor's Office, always attended by Wallace, who supplied reports from field parties. While the Committee was inspecting Cristóbal Harbor on January 27, it encountered a severe norther that had begun on the preceding afternoon. Ships at anchor had to go to sea for three days while great waves rolled into the harbor, breaking over the entire water front in

[39] C. A. L. Reed, "Report to the Secretary of War *Showing How the Commission Makes Efficient Sanitation Impossible*," March 2, 1905. I.C.C. *Sanitary Conditions on the Isthmus*, pp. 38–63 (U.S.). Text of Reed's Report and the Commission's Reply.

[40] *Panama Star and Herald*, March 12, 1905.

deluges of water and coral that blocked the streets. The seas endangered the piers. Vessels which could not get under way and go to sea had to secure themselves far enough from the docks to roll and pitch alongside without danger. The Committee had no choice except to recommend a breakwater from Toro Point to the Colón light, as stated in its Report of February 14 to Admiral Walker.[41]

Yellow fever first became a subject of discussion among employees about November 1, 1904; but it was not until the following February that the Panamá press became alarmed at conditions on the Canal and in turn did its best to alarm employees. "Discontent reigns supreme"[42] from one end of the Canal to the other, was the lead in an editorial which announced that President Roosevelt was displeased and that changes were probable. A few cases of yellow fever were given wide publicity in the United States. Exaggerated reports served to keep men from coming to the Isthmus for work.

Mr. and Mrs. Wallace drove about the streets of Panamá to quiet the rumors, but to no avail. The press continued its campaign: "Resignation; transportation; humiliation and consternation. But what can we do? Such is life in the tropics."[43]

Governor Davis cabled Secretary Taft that press reports were "cruelly exaggerated." He deplored the fact that the Commission had not spent most of its time on the Isthmus so the members could realize that the canal was being built on the Isthmus. "Every day, every week and every month the conditions here are improving, little by little."[44] He blamed the agitation on the sensational journals. He knew there was no factual basis for the attacks by the press. He also knew that the end of the first Commission was approaching rapidly.

Wallace later reported that housing conditions had shown marked improvement. In his thirty-five years of experience he

[41] I.C.C., *Proceedings*, 80th meeting, Feb. 9, 1905, p. 375 (U.S.).
[42] *Panama Star and Herald*, Feb. 9, 1905.
[43] *Ibid.*, Feb. 14, 1905.
[44] Davis to Taft, Feb. 14, 1905 (P.C. Rec. Bur., File D-5-25 [1]) (MS).

had never seen any construction men "better housed or any better fed." He said that the ones who complained the most were those who had obtained their ideas of Panamá from the theater prior to arrival and that "they expected to swing in a hammock and sip mint juleps and smoke cigarettes and be fanned"[45] all day. Nor did employees enjoy the "semi-military rule" of Governor Davis. They wanted civilian control.

Without question, there had been great difficulty in getting competent men from the States. The United States Civil Service was no help, but rather a hindrance. In one instance twenty-five track foremen were requested; but when they arrived, Wallace estimated that not over two could drive a railroad spike. The only transportation experience of one had been on pack trains. Gradually the ranks of subforemen were filled with inefficient men who could not accomplish results, but who were retained simply because there was no other recourse.

One of Wallace's largest problems was the Panama Railroad. He knew from the start that the road would never be able to meet expected demands with its locomotives, cars and equipment, and leaders. He had a controversy with the old superintendent, J. R. Shaler, who was relieved by another old employee, H. G. Prescott. Warehouses were filled. With the arrival of steadily increasing quantities of freight the railroad proved incapable of handling the traffic, and severe congestion resulted. Would the new superintendent prove competent to handle the crisis? Wallace said it would take time to determine whether he was "broad enough, and has the ability to grasp the situation and give results."[46]

There was nothing to do except to secure complete control of the Panama Railroad. In January 1905 there were still 1,013 shares of stock outstanding in a total of 70,000 shares, the United States Government having obtained 68,987 shares from

---

[45] Wallace's Statement, Feb. 6, 1906 (Hearings No. 18, I, 611) (U.S.).

[46] Bristow, *Report of Special Panama Railroad Commissioner to the Secretary of War, June 24, 1905*, p. 238 (U.S.).

the New Panama Canal Company. Acting on Wallace's suggestion, Secretary Taft directed the Company's counsel, Mr. Cromwell, to buy the stock at par plus 5. Cromwell circularized the
holders in the United States, England, France, Italy, and elsewhere. He urged them to take advantage of the generous offer,
but made an implied threat of legal proceedings if they did not.[47]

The threat had the desired effect. Late in March, Cromwell
reported that he had obtained all the stock, whereupon he received Taft's commendation for the "patriotism and unselfish-
ness"[48] prompting his action in securing the stock and his refusal
to be compensated. With ownership by the United States complete, the Panama Railroad, financially, had become an adjunct
of the Canal.

Then, suddenly, Wallace was notified that he was appointed
general superintendent of the Panama Railroad. What he
wanted was to be general manager, with Prescott continuing as
superintendent because of his long service. Wallace did not
want to report to the vice-president of the railroad in New York.
That, he said, "would be beneath my dignity,"[49] having held
more responsible positions on railroads in the United States.
He protested strongly to Secretary Taft and Admiral Walker,
asserting his desire to give the "most perfect and loyal service."[50]

The old Admiral was generous and frank. The first he knew
about the appointment was Wallace's cable from the Isthmus.
He considered the action irregular and held matters in abeyance. The entire affair had been engineered by Cromwell.[51]

The Isthmus began to wear on Wallace. He heard rumors
of employing a $100,000-a-year man, much his junior in age
and achievements, to take charge and build the Canal. This was

[47] Cromwell to Stockholders of Panama Railroad, Jan. 17, 1905; quoted in his
Statement, May 11, 1906 (Hearings No. 18, IV, 3136, 3140–41) (U.S.).

[48] Taft to Cromwell, March 29, 1905; quoted in Cromwell's Statement, May 10,
1906 (ibid., IV, 3128).

[49] Wallace to Taft, March 21, 1905 (P.C. Rec. Bur., File Personnel, Wallace)
(MS).

[50] Wallace to J. G. Walker, March 21, 1905 (ibid.).

[51] Walker to Wallace, March 25, 1905 (ibid.).

no idle rumor, for President Roosevelt wanted Elihu Root to head the canal work. He had even written to Taft, indicating his willingness to employ Mr. Root at a salary of $50,000 or $100,000 a year which, he stated, he would "cheerfully give him to take complete charge and run this whole business."[52]

Anxiously, Wallace wrote to Secretary Taft that there could be no harmony in such an eventuality and that he had given up a fine home and civilization for that "God-forsaken country" to help him and Roosevelt "in carrying out this great work." As to his own personal desires for such a position he stated, "I do not ask it, am not after it, and prefer to be on the firing line."[53] To Admiral Walker he confided that he had worked too hard and that he wanted to go on leave in May or June, as he would have to recuperate before starting a second year.

In the preceding January President Roosevelt had decided that the Commission should be changed. The seven-man board was "inelastic and clumsy."[54] On January 13, 1905, he sent a special message to Congress, recommending more power to the President and a reduction of the Commission to five or preferably three members, but asking Congress not to restrict them to Army or Navy engineers, as he then had an "excellent engineer." Roosevelt discerned the future clearly. He doubted that Congress would act upon his recommendations and planned to secure his aims by changing the personnel on the Commission. In early February of 1905 the first Commission was on its way out of office, for the President wrote to Mr. Taft, "I am afraid Walker will have to go."[55]

As recommended by the President, the House of Representatives passed a bill embodying his plan, but the Senate refused, and Congress adjourned with no action. This failure to act left the Canal Zone with no government, for the authority of the

---

[52] Roosevelt to Taft, Feb. 4, 1905 (Taft Papers: Taft-Roosevelt, Box II) (MS).

[53] Wallace to Taft, March 15, 1905; quoted in Taft's Statement, April 19, 1906 (Hearings No. 18, III, 2706–7) (U.S.).

[54] *Messages and Papers of the Presidents*, XVI, 6938 (U.S.).

[55] Roosevelt to Taft, Feb. 4, 1905 (Taft Papers: Taft-Roosevelt, Box II) (MS).

Commission as a legislature under the Act of April 28, 1904, terminated when the Congress which enacted the law expired on March 4, 1905.

Thwarted in their plans by the inaction of Congress, Roosevelt and Taft cabled Governor Davis to continue the Canal Zone Government on the same basis as before Congress failed to act. To Mr. Wallace, on March 24, 1905, he cabled his plans for the reorganization, adopting practically all of the Chief Engineer's ideas. Wallace was elated. He pictured an organization with the real power embodied in an Executive Committee, each member being in supreme charge of a department, the chief engineer and the Governor residing in the Canal Zone and the chairman, as purchasing agent, staying in Washington. On the following day he cabled the Secretary: "Plan excellent. Satisfactory. *Gracias.*"[56] This was strange, coming from a man afraid of yellow fever, who already had intimated his intention to resign.

Now it was only a question of time when the reorganization would occur. It had been generally expected that the Commission members would resign. However, they did not, but worked assiduously, ignoring the attacks. Yet their fate was sealed. Secretary Taft and the President had decided, and Mr. Taft ordered Wallace to come to Washington. He wanted him there to assist in the reorganization.

In Washington, the Walker Commission of Construction carried on as if nothing had happened and held its ninetieth and last meeting on March 29, 1905.

It had performed an enormous volume of preparatory work. It had studied sanitation. It had organized a government. It had recruited the nucleus of a construction force. But as an executive body it had not proved equal to the demands of preparing for a great construction enterprise. It could not supply materials with promptness. The members had been the victims of bad advice and of misrepresentation by the press. Their methods

[56] I.C.C., *Minutes*, 98th meeting, July 1, 1905, p. 31 (U.S.).

were not "businesslike, expeditious, or systematic." At the request of the Secretary of War, the Commission resigned.

Wallace's reputation had been built up tremendously by the press. John Barrett, the United States Minister to Panamá, joined the chorus of approval with an article which appealed for confidence in Wallace and opposed placing the work under Army engineers. He contended that "few if any Army engineers have ever had such broad experience and training"[57] as Mr. Wallace. The bulk of resentment was solely against the Commission for its "red tape" and its delays.

As Mr. Wallace left the Isthmus on March 30 for Washington the purpose of his visit was understood by all and much was expected from him. He was acclaimed as the "man behind the gun."

[57] *Panama Star and Herald*, Feb. 22, 1906.

CULEBRA CUT NEAR GOLD HILL, DECEMBER 1904
Steam shovel excavating and loading spoil into French dumpcars

Chapter VIII

REORGANIZATION, RESIGNATION, AND CHAOS

Mr. Wallace was not an aggressive man, and there are times and conditions when fighting becomes a righteous duty. The situation which had developed at the date of his resignation was such as demanded a one-man control, control by a man who was heedless of his technical reputation; and one only bent upon smashing a way through all obstacles, a kind of politic "roughneck," who did not possess too deep a veneration for the vagaries of constituted authority.—JOHN F. STEVENS, Chief Engineer of the Isthmian Canal Commission, 1905–1907.[1]

ROOSEVELT APPOINTS A SECOND COMMISSION

Wallace had attained a wide reputation as the first chief engineer of the Panama Canal and had passed through the ordeals of the first Commission unscathed. He had the support of such men as Governor Davis, who wrote directly to Secretary Taft in his behalf, and his retention was decided upon. As Wallace was a railroad man, Roosevelt looked to the railroads—the great constructing agencies in the United States—for a chairman of the reorganized Commission. A man with proper qualifications was found in Theodore P. Shonts, President of the Clover Leaf Railroad. He had been engaged in construction and operation of railroads for many years and was considered a hard-hitting businessman. He was endorsed by many leaders in the railroad world, and was selected because he was thought to be on friendly terms with Wallace.[2] The two men had been schoolmates in their early years.

But Mr. Shonts could not be attracted for less than $30,000 a year. That appeared a high salary, and other men with proper abilities were available, but they demanded large pay. Later, Secretary Taft explained, "They did not have the reputation, the skill, and experience, unless you paid them a salary."[3] Shonts,

[1] J. F. Stevens, "The Panama Canal," A.S.C.E., *Transactions*, XCI, 949.
[2] Taft's Statement, April 19, 1906 (Hearings No. 18, III, 2557) (U.S.).
[3] *Ibid.*, April 21, 1906 (III, 2773).

however, was the type to do his utmost on a task when once he had accepted. As he said, "I am going to put the best I've got in me into it—and I think right now I'm better than I ever was before in my life."[4]

When plans for the reorganization were ready, Secretary Taft forwarded the resignations of the first Commission to the President, with recommendations embodying many of Wallace's ideas. He wished the executive work of the succeeding Commission to be divided into departments, with sanitation retained under the Governor. He wished the seat of power to be on the Isthmus with meetings of the Commission there, and an executive committee resident on the Isthmus with power to act for the Commission in its absence.[5]

Roosevelt covered the appointment and duties of the second Commission in an Executive Order of April 1, 1905. Shonts was designated as chairman, Charles E. Magoon as Governor of the Canal Zone, and Wallace as member and chief engineer. Other members were Rear Admiral Mordecai T. Endicott, Brigadier General Peter C. Hains, Colonel Oswald H. Ernst, and Benjamin M. Harrod. The work was divided into three departments: first, Fiscal Affairs, Purchasing, and General Supervision under the chairman in Washington; second, Government and Sanitation under the Governor; and third, Engineering and Construction under the chief engineer.

All of these men were well known in their fields. Magoon had been in intimate association with Secretary Taft and had been former Secretary Root's chief adviser on island government; he was also well versed in Canal organization. It is no wonder that when announcements of these appointments, with a successful businessman as executive head of the Canal, were made in Panamá they were hailed as marking a new beginning.

The second Commission of Construction held its first meeting in Washington on April 3, 1905, accepted resignations of

[4] *Panama Star and Herald*, May 7, 1905.
[5] Taft to the President, March 30, 1905 (I.C.C. *Minutes*, 91st meeting, April 3, 1905, pp. 7–10) (U.S.).

the retiring Commission, organized the work into three departments, and formed an executive committee of Shonts, Magoon,
and Wallace, as required by the President's order. Meanwhile,
Governor Davis remained at his post on the Isthmus.

Roosevelt had promised Shonts a "free hand in carrying out
his policies."[6] Shonts looked over the old personnel and found
there was much he did not like. For example, the requisition
clerk in Washington was so overwhelmed that many requisitions
had not been opened; some had not been acted upon in four
months; some had been divided into parts and spread over the
country for political expediency. It is not surprising that Mr.
Wallace had complained so bitterly that he could not get materials promptly. Shonts sized up the purchasing officer in Washington as "an earnest and honest and ambitious man." The chief
of material and supplies on the Isthmus was also classed as another of those "splendid, hard-working, honest, well-meaning
men."[7] Unfortunately, they were not trained for the large volume of business required to build the Canal. Shonts proceeded
to line up many experienced railroad officials for key positions—
men with experience who had the ability to push things through
the labyrinth of manufacturing and of transportation difficulties,
from the factory to the Isthmus.

While the new Commission was holding its first meetings,
Wallace was on his way north. When he arrived at New York
he was met at the dock by Cromwell's secretary, who told him
that it was necessary for him to be sworn in as a commissioner
at once and escorted him to Cromwell's office.

Wallace did not understand the reasons for such haste. Why
could he not wait until he reached Washington? The suave
Cromwell overcame his reluctance, suggesting that he might meet
the new chairman and be required to do business. Wallace soon
discovered that the new Executive Order had been written with
conditions different from those which he had expected. It pro-

---

[6] Shonts's Statement, March 6, 1906 (Hearings No. 18, II, 1405) (U.S.).

[7] *Ibid.*, Jan. 26, 1906 (I, 336–37).

vided for a distribution of authority rather than the dictatorship he wanted on the Isthmus. It also required Chairman Shonts to spend some time on the Isthmus.

Wallace's first session with the new Commission was at its fifth meeting on April 10, when he explained conditions on the Isthmus. The next day he was appointed chairman of the Engineering Committee, the other members of which were Commissioners Endicott, Hains, Ernst, and Harrod, who were given specific assignments in a study to determine the best type of canal for submission to the Board of Consulting Engineers, as required by the President's order.

Right from the start the second Commission did not work smoothly. The members who were not on the Executive Committee did not like their subordinate status. Their salary was $7,500, as compared with $17,500 for the Governor, $25,000 for the chief engineer, and $30,000 for the chairman. They did not expect to perform any of the executive work, but they did not want to serve in subordinate capacities and wrote Mr. Taft demanding that their status be clarified.

Taft was patient. He replied, explaining that the President desired construction to be placed under the chief engineer and that they were not subordinated to the chief engineer in any way. Copies of this reply were sent to Wallace and Shonts. Thus the embarrassment of these members was removed.

In the meantime the Executive Committee, composed of Shonts, Magoon, and Wallace, started to function with its first meeting on April 21 at Washington. Two members were a quorum. The Committee took charge in a businesslike manner and kept formal records like those of the Commission, which ceased its sessions for that quarter after the meeting of May 3. The result of having experienced businessmen in key places was shown in quick decisions and quicker action.

Besides assisting in reorganization, Wallace had gone to the United States to procure needed men and materials. Acting Chief Engineer W. E. Dauchy kept him informed in weekly reports, in which he appealed for more help on the railroad, as none of the thirty-one foremen had had any railroad experience. He demanded that Wallace stop sending down inexperienced men, as he did not have time to run a "kindergarten in track work"[8] in the Culebra Cut. Also, delays in paydays on the Isthmus had produced serious situations. Pitiable cases were found of men trying to work without food and accomplishing nothing.

Wallace never had liked his appointment as superintendent of the Panama Railroad and continued to protest vigorously. His chagrin was not eased until he was elected vice-president and general manager in charge on the Isthmus of all affairs of the railroad and its steamship line.[9] With Wallace in that position the Commission hoped there would be better co-ordination of traffic, which was expanding rapidly as the large construction program got under way.

When the reorganization was complete, it appeared to be a powerful one. A strong businessman of wide experience was at its head in Washington. That was what Secretary Taft called the "one thing of all others" that was needed. The Governor of the Canal Zone was thoroughly familiar with the War Department and acquainted with the leaders of the United States Government. The nonexecutive members were able engineers— men with proper connections to secure competent employees for key positions and with the experience required for pushing things through. Chief Engineer Wallace, as a member of the Commission and vice-president and general manager of the Panama Railroad, had been acclaimed by the press. He was definitely the man of the hour—the man toward whom all looked to be the builder of the Panama Canal.

In contrast to the fine pictures presented in the press, Secretary Taft began receiving alarming reports of conditions on the Isthmus and of the dreaded yellow fever. He urged Wallace to

[8] Dauchy to Wallace, April 18, 1905 (P.C. Rec. Bur., File D-5-25) (MS).

[9] Panama Railroad, *General Order No. 8*, April 17, 1905 (P.C. Rec. Bur., File Personnel, Wallace) (MS).

return without delay; but Wallace took two weeks' leave to visit his home in Chicago.

In the meantime Governor Davis, who had been continued at his post pending arrival of the new governor, wrote the absent Chief Engineer, imploring him to return, stating that his absence at that time was a very great misfortune, for the Canal was in a transition period. "The old Commission is discredited and dismissed, and not one of the new Commission has as yet arrived, while you have been absent for reasons that you could not control. . . . . There is no head here to command the necessary confidence and respect, and there is a great deal of bickering and fault-finding and scolding among the employees all along the line."

Davis had had to pitch tents for men at Culebra. The yellow-fever panic was just starting, and in spite of all efforts to prevent the hysteria it was spreading with demoralizing effect all over the line of the Canal. Men were discontented and faultfinding, and the acting chief engineer had proved unequal to the task. The tired Governor appealed for Wallace to return and put an end to the chaos, stating that he had never known of an instance in which the "strong directing hand of a man in power was more necessary than it is here now."[10] On May 4 the Governor even cabled Taft, urging the return of the Chief Engineer and stating that his absence was very detrimental to the Canal.[11]

Worn out by a year of hard work, Governor Davis was taken ill with malaria and ordered to the United States. He protested his orders; he did not wish to run away. But as Secretary Taft insisted, he left the Isthmus on May 9, 1905, respected by all and recognized as an able executive, although considered to have been the victim of an inefficient and incapable Commission. The highest appreciation of his services came from Secretary Taft, who stated that Governor Davis was an "admirable man for the organization of the government of the Zone—painstak-

[10] Davis to Wallace, May 2, 1905; quoted in Taft's Statement, April 19, 1906 (Hearings No. 18, III, 2658–59) (U.S.).

[11] *Ibid.*, p. 2559.

ing, hard-working, clear-headed, economical, courageous, and loyal."[12]

Colonel Gorgas, as Acting Governor, relieved General Davis and carried on the fight to hold down panic, pending inauguration of Governor Magoon. The acting chief engineer did his best but was not equal to the task, and the wave of hysteria continued unabated.

WALLACE RETURNS TO THE ISTHMUS FOR A SHORT STAY

Before leaving Washington for the Isthmus, Wallace had a final conference with the Secretary of War, in which he expressed his gratitude to the Secretary and to the President for their reorganization of April 1. As he departed he told Mr. Taft he could return to the Isthmus "with happiness in his heart and with confidence that the canal would be built and that he would build it"[13] and requested Mr. Taft to convey that message to the President with the assurance that he could have every confidence in him. Taft implored Wallace to place the care of the employees first.

Wallace also saw Shonts, who confided in his "easy, smiling way" that the President had given him absolute power as chairman of the new Commission. Wallace did not know how to take that, except as Shonts's intention to "run the job."

At New York he was entertained at the home of Cromwell, who tried to impress his importance and his views in a way that Wallace took to mean an interference with his own prerogatives as chief engineer. Infuriated, he replied heatedly. It must have been rather irritating to hear Cromwell speak of "my canal" too frequently, even though he had been connected with the work since about 1896. Wallace would have to smooth the affair after his return to Panamá!

Wallace was not to be alone on his return voyage. He had as a fellow passenger Governor Magoon, who was going to Panamá on the same ship. While waiting to depart, Magoon re-

[12] *Ibid.*, p. 2539.   [13] *Ibid.*, p. 2558.

ceived letters from Secretary Taft expressing appreciation of his seven years of work in the War Department and relating the flattering report that the Attorney General considered Magoon knew more law governing relations between the United States and its dependencies than any other lawyer in the nation. He predicted that Magoon would win his way to a position of "great prominence" and was sure that he would discharge his duties in a way to make certain his return to Washington in a higher capacity. He acknowledged that service on the Isthmus was not free from danger, but that the "courage, persistence and tenacity" required in the task would enhance Magoon's reputation in the country and among those "whose functions it is to distribute the rewards of public life." Affectionately, Taft concluded: "May God bless you and bring you home to enjoy a well-earned reward after you have well discharged the task to which you have now set your hand."[14] Taft followed this the next day with a pleasant-voyage telegram, stressing the importance of the work on the Isthmus. "Make it your first duty. Remember, we stand behind you and our thoughts are always with you; the country and the President have the utmost confidence in your ability to work out problems before you."[15]

Although Wallace and Magoon appeared in fine spirits when leaving New York, there was an undercurrent of feeling. Wallace was oppressed by a problem. He had discussed the matter with family and friends, but it was only after six days' deliberation[16] on the trip that he came to his decision. When he arrived in Colón on May 24 he knew what to do, but his thoughts had not been discerned by Magoon.

Although there was little formality about the arrival, the party was met by United States Chargé d'Affaires William Franklin Sands, for Governor Magoon was coming to the Isthmus not only as Governor but also as Minister to Panamá. Wal-

14 Taft to Magoon, May 16, 1905 (P.C. Rec. Bur., File Personnel, Magoon) (MS).

15 Taft to Magoon, telegram, May 17, 1905 (ibid.).

16 Wallace's Statement, Feb. 5, 1906 (Hearngs No. 18, I, 552) (U.S.).

lace was ready to reorganize the Engineering and Construction Department with general approval of all in the Canal Zone, who expected much from it.

A small crowd gathered around the Civil Administration Building at Ancon on May 25. President Amador and his Cabinet were there to witness the inauguration of the new Governor, whose praises had been publicized so widely. The oath was administered by Judge Gudger of the Canal Zone Supreme Court. Magoon, in his inaugural address, explained the plan of reorganization for the Commission and the intention of Roosevelt to transfer authority to the Isthmus. He paid high tribute to Wallace for his engineering work and to Governor Davis. For the work accomplished in sanitation he said the name of the Chief Sanitary Officer would be placed "as high upon the roll of fame as that of the Chief Engineer."[17] He outlined plans for the Government to place a Panamanian jurist on the Supreme Court of the Canal Zone and to organize a school system. He praised the contributions of Spain to the civilization of the world.

Wallace cabled to Secretary Taft a report of the enthusiastic reception given the new Governor, and Magoon cabled Shonts. Both these officials were impressed by their "auspicious beginning."[18]

Within two days after arrival Wallace had time to write Cromwell to placate his ruffled feelings. He was grateful for Cromwell's "word of advice and counsel" during the visit in New York. Fresh from his voyage, he was impressed by the wisdom of the President's "privy counsel" and the way Canal matters had been guided through "the troubled waters of the sea of complication." Admitting his own manners were "blunt and direct," they served to enhance his evaluation of the "skilled and polished diplomat who has made this great work a possi-

[17] *Panama Star and Herald*, May 26, 1905.

[18] Magoon to Shonts, cable, May 30, 1905 (P.C. Rec. Bur., File Personnel, Magoon) (MS).

bility and whose thoughtful care and guiding hand will be the most important factors"[19] in its final success.

Later, when his own conduct became the subject of investigation, Cromwell placed this letter in the Senate records to show how highly he was regarded by Wallace.

The same day that Wallace arrived on the Isthmus, Mr. Shonts started a speaking campaign in the United States, beginning at the Bankers' Club of Chicago. There he explained the work in progress for maintaining better health conditions on the Isthmus and expressed his faith that, if Mr. Wallace could keep in good health, he would be able to solve the problems of excavating Culebra Cut and of controlling the Chagres.[20]

Wallace continued working toward his new organization, but apparently there were differences of opinion among his assistants. They thought preparation was of "paramount importance, and the output of shovels of secondary importance."[21] But Wallace wanted to press actual construction without any "let up in care or energy."[22] He would not listen to any change of policy. He wanted preparation and construction to go along "hand in hand." This was impossible under prevailing conditions.

The rainy season had begun, delaying further both organization and preparatory work. Sanitation kept on, but the number of fever cases continued to rise. Enthusiastic Magoon reported that there was nothing among employees "approximating panic" and that the Executive Committee had decided to "pave, gutter and curb" the streets of Panamá as a sanitary measure. He infused new life and confidence into government and into sanitation.

Wallace decided to act on the problem that had oppressed him during his trip south. On June 4 he wrote a vague note to

[19] Wallace to Cromwell, May 26, 1905; quoted in Cromwell's Statement, Feb. 26, 1906 (Hearings No. 18, II, 1048) (U.S.).

[20] Shonts, *Address before Bankers' Club, Chicago, 1905*, pp. 5–6.

[21] Dauchy to Wallace, May 22, 1905 (P.C. Rec. Bur., File D-5-25) (MS).

[22] Wallace to Dauchy, May 25, 1905 (*ibid.*).

the Secretary of War that "certain complications"[23] in his personal affairs would make it necessary to return to the United States upon receipt of a telegram. He did not wait for the Secretary to receive the letter, but followed it with a cable the next day that "important complicated business matters," which could not be handled by correspondence and might affect his position as chief engineer, required his immediate return to the United States. He requested the Secretary to order him to return for consultation to "prevent apprehension on part of employees."[24]

Taft was greatly alarmed and conferred with Roosevelt and Shonts. He could not understand why Wallace should want to return so soon after resuming his work, since all his suggestions had been adopted in the reorganization and his power increased. Taft did not order him back. Instead, he cabled approval "without knowledge of circumstances that justify."[25]

Wallace, however, innocently confided to Magoon, and the Governor promptly cabled the Secretary of War, following with letters explaining that Wallace had been offered a position with a salary between $50,000 and $60,000, that he considered himself essential to the Canal and was trying to obtain a bigger salary.[26] Wallace later stated that he wanted to leave at the time, but did not want to resign until he had discussed the matter with Taft. He later said that his relations with Shonts and Cromwell were near the breaking point and that Shonts wanted to dominate the work of building the Canal.

In the meantime Wallace worked feverishly on his reorganization of the Department of Construction and Engineering. He put the eight-hour day in effect, replacing the ten-hour, with hours from 7 to 11 A.M. and 1 to 5 P.M. He planned to re-

[23] Wallace to Taft, June 4, 1905 (P.C. Rec. Bur., File Personnel, Wallace) (MS).

[24] Wallace to Taft, cable, June 5, 1905; quoted in Taft's Statement, April 19, 1906 (Hearings No. 18, III, 2560) (U.S.).

[25] Edwards to Wallace, June 6, 1905 (P.C. Rec. Bur., File Personnel, Wallace) (MS).

[26] W. L. Pepperman, *Who Built the Panama Canal?* pp. 111–15.

ward the "efficient and faithful."[27] At the sixteenth meeting of
the Executive Committee of the Commission on June 14 to 16,
1905, attended by Wallace and Magoon, the new organization
was outlined. It was largely a skeleton, with "vacancy" written
opposite many key positions having resounding titles. It divided
the Canal into construction divisions, much after the French
system.[28] When the Executive Committee adjourned, there were
to be no more meetings until August.

Wallace made a final inspection along the Canal. At Corozal
he saw the new Commission Hotel. At Culebra, eight steam
shovels and three French excavators were digging spoil and
carrying it to near-by dumps. Main shops for locomotive repair
were to be at Matachin and a machine shop at Culebra, at Empire, and at Cristóbal. Dock facilities at Cristóbal and La Boca
were being enlarged. Double-tracking of the Panama Railroad
was barely started. Hotels had been completed at Cristobal
and Culebra, and ten more were planned along the line. The
need of the hour was for more and more laborers.

The press announced that Mr. Wallace would leave on June
16 for the States to obtain a large quantity of machinery. The
public did not know what had gone on behind the scenes and
were expecting great things from his efforts. "Mr. Wallace is
a man we cannot do without here"[29] was the public talk as he
sailed away.

TAFT, CROMWELL, AND WALLACE

When Secretary Taft received Wallace's strange message, he
was preparing to leave for the Philippines, and it upset him. He
went to New York, however, to be on hand when Wallace should
arrive. Shonts also came up to meet Wallace. The day before
the Chief Engineer's arrival, Cromwell called upon Chairman
Shonts at his hotel and asked, "Has Roosevelt or Taft told you

[27] *Panama Star and Herald*, June 11, 1905.

[28] I.C.C., Executive Committee, *Minutes*, 16th meeting, June 14–16, 1905, pp.
203–5 (U.S.).

[29] *Panama Star and Herald*, June 16, 1905.

what Wallace is coming up here for?" Shonts did not know. Then the smooth Cromwell suggested, "They don't want you to know that he is coming up here to get your job, until after they've disposed of him."[30]

Wallace arrived at New York on June 22, 1905. Hardly had he reached his hotel when Cromwell called and greeted him with all the "suavity and courtesy"[31] for which he was noted, explaining that he had been instructed by Taft to find out the reasons for his return and discuss them. Wallace refused to discuss matters with the lawyer and insisted upon a personal interview with Taft in strict privacy. Cromwell suggested the Manhattan, where Secretary Taft was stopping, but kindly offered his own home if that were not private enough. Wallace did not want to go to Cromwell's home. He wanted to see Mr. Taft, and he wanted to see him alone.

The next day Jacob E. Markel, whom Wallace had interested in getting a contract for feeding employees on the Canal, called on Wallace at his hotel. He had heard rumors of Wallace's separation and, having made all arrangements to go to the Isthmus, was anxious about losing what appeared as a good business opportunity.

"Well, now, Mr. Wallace, if you are going to quit, do you think I had better go to the Isthmus?" asked Markel.[32]

Wallace advised him to go to the Isthmus for the trip anyhow, if he was not afraid of yellow fever, and bring back a letter of introduction from Magoon to Shonts.

It was not until Sunday, the twenty-fifth, that Cromwell arranged an interview for Wallace with Secretary Taft at the Manhattan. Wallace called with his son, and they were ushered into the Taft apartment by Cromwell. The son withdrew, expecting Cromwell to do likewise. Cromwell made a start to leave, but Taft motioned him to remain, saying, "I want you to hear all

---

[30] Pepperman, *op. cit.*, p. 116.

[31] Wallace's Statement, Feb. 5, 1906 (Hearings No. 18, I, 552–53) (U.S.).

[32] Markel's Statement, March 2, 1906 (*ibid.*, II, 1287).

this." Then, turning to the chief engineer, Taft said, "Now, Wallace, go ahead and tell what you came up for."[33] This unusual procedure irritated Wallace and made him apprehensive, as he observed that Taft was angered. Being Taft's subordinate, he did not protest against the lawyer's presence and accepted the intrusion without calling in his own witnesses.

Wallace told the Secretary he had two matters to discuss, one personal and the other general. The personal matter was his office as chief engineer, and the other was the state of the work on the Canal. He explained why he wanted to resign to accept a new position that had been offered. He acknowledged his apprehension about living on the Isthmus and that he found life there "lonely and accompanied with risk"—to himself and his wife. Taft waited patiently as Wallace explained that his separation from the Canal Service could be effected without embarrassment and harm to the Canal. When finished with the first part, Taft said, "Now, go ahead and tell us the general matters that you want to talk about."

During this latter explanation Wallace was cross-examined by Cromwell, who wanted yes-or-no answers on whether certain work could proceed regardless of the type of canal adopted. Taft disagreed with some of Wallace's statements, and Wallace felt as if he were being goaded into losing his temper, which he tried hard to control. He was willing to remain with the Commission as an adviser and to assist in preparing reports of his work. Taft spurned this offer, stating that he did not want his reports, nor did he have any use for Wallace or any of his "counsel or advice."[34] Wallace was crushed.

He explained that he had a right to resign but wanted to make some arrangement to continue serving the Government in a way that could be of most benefit as long as it was necessary. Taft was adamant. Turning around he said, "Well, I will not stoop to dicker with you. That would be to dicker."[35] What Taft

[33] Wallace's Statement, Feb. 5, 1906 (Hearings No. 18, I, 570) (U.S.).
[34] Ibid., Feb. 6, 1906 (I, 606).
[35] Ibid., Feb. 5, 1906 (I, 573).

wanted was a construction engineer to build the Canal and nothing else.

Taft told Wallace that he held a position to which great fame was attached and that he would have become famous the world over. Then he added, with brutal frankness: "For mere lucre you change your position overnight without thought of the embarrassing position in which you place your government,"[36] at a time of crisis on the Isthmus when the working forces were without a leader and before the engineering organization had been completed.

There were some heated exchanges between the two men, Taft taking the position that Wallace could not resign and Wallace refusing to be dictated to in the matter by Taft or the President. Although at a distinct disadvantage, he asked: "You and Mr. Cromwell are supposed to be the two smartest, shrewdest lawyers in the United States; and do you mean to sit there and tell me that there can be an implied contract that would bind me to give my service to the United States Government forever, regardless of changed conditions . . . . ?"[37] To this Taft stated that he expected at least a year's notice.

Finally, Wallace explained that he did not want to return to the Isthmus at all, whereupon Taft said: "If you are going to resign at all you might as well resign now," and this was agreed upon then. Wallace felt that there would be reconsideration after the parties cooled. But Taft and Roosevelt felt differently.

Wallace tried to ease the situation. The next day he wrote Shonts a confidential note, explaining the character of the offer he had received and that his family and friends were united in advising him to accept, but that he felt he should discuss matters with the Secretary before resigning, that he wanted to avoid embarrassing the Administration, and that he feared that Shonts would be replaced by a man with whom he could not work harmoniously. He also mentioned he had heard rumors that the

[36] Pepperman, *op. cit.*, p. 121.
[37] Wallace's Statement, Feb. 5, 1906 (Hearings No. 18, I, 573) (U.S.).

interview was to be published, which he thought would be deplorable, and stated "you will certainly be doing a wise act and a kind deed if you can head it off."[38] He intimated it would not go unchallenged. Shonts was not moved and did not intervene. In response to a nonofficial request for an interview, Wallace replied that for some time he had considered severing his connection with the Commission and was very busy with his "arrangements for a new connection."[39]

Thus it is clearly shown that Wallace's resignation was not a spontaneous decision, but deliberate. However, perhaps still thinking the affair would be smoothed over, when he wrote his resignation to the President on June 26, 1905, he phrased it as effective at his "pleasure and convenience." Roosevelt accepted it on June 28, effective "immediately."[40]

Taft returned to Washington. With the assistance of Cromwell and Shonts he prepared a detailed statement covering Wallace's relations with the Commission, his suggestions for reorganization and their adoption, the events leading to his resignation, and a detailed account of his interview with Taft. He telephoned Roosevelt for approval, and the statement was given to the press in a public castigation seldom encountered in official public life.[41]

Wallace, of course, was profoundly hurt and considered the statement an "unjust denunciation." Taft was not thinking about justice. He was thinking about the Canal and had castigated Wallace to encourage the future engineers to remain at their posts in times of crisis. He later expressed himself as regretful if he had done Mr. Wallace an injustice but said he thought himself justified.[42]

[38] Wallace to Shonts, June 26, 1905; quoted in Markel's Statement, March 5, 1906 (Hearings No. 18, II, 1362–64) (U.S.).

[39] Wallace to E. L. Zalinski, June 26, 1905 (P.C. Rec. Bur., File Personnel, Wallace) (MS).

[40] I.C.C., *Minutes*, 98th meeting, July 1, 1905, p. 36 (U.S.).

[41] "Secretary Taft's Statement Regarding Mr. John F. Wallace," copied from *Washington Post* (Hearings No. 18, II, 1364–69) (U.S.).

[42] Taft, *Speech at St. Louis Commercial Club*, Nov. 18, 1905, p. 12 (U.S.).

JOHN FRANK STEVENS, 1853–1943
Chief Engineer, Panama Canal, 1905–1907

Wallace had accomplished something during his short term of office. He had continued investigations he had found under way, had started the repair of old buildings and the construction of new ones, had commenced working on sewer and water problems, and had requisitioned some steam shovels and other important supplies.[43] But he had also delayed work on the Canal by reviving interest in the sea-level plan. After his resignation he lost much of the reputation that had been created by his work on the Canal, gained many detractors, and suffered greatly from his public castigation.

After he passed from power, few came to his assistance. It was his successor, John F. Stevens, who came to his support most strongly. Wallace was Stevens' esteemed friend, whom Stevens knew to be an engineer of great ability. Stevens felt his resignation was justified, considering the methods of the first Commission. Wallace had been ambitious for work, but his zeal had been dulled, and he had no more hope from the new Commission than from the old. His character could not be impugned, nor his ability. He was not an aggressive man. Stevens' most telling comment was that a "more strenuous attitude toward his superior officers would have been more efficacious and would have tended toward a more active state of affairs."[44]

CHAOS AND CONFUSION

Yellow fever had broken out in the Canal Zone in December 1904, when the wife of the chief engineer's private secretary died. This spread alarm, and cases continued to develop during the dry season of 1905, but without reaching epidemic proportions. Wallace's return to the United States for the reorganization of the Commission in April had not helped matters psychologically. Instead, it served as an example for hysteria and desertion and helped to create panic.

Strangely, the Administration Building in Panamá became

[43] Abbot, *Problems of the Panama Canal*, p. 22.
[44] Stevens, "The Panama Canal," A.S.C.E., *Transactions*, XCI, 949.

a focus of yellow-fever infection. Deputy Auditor R. R. West was taken ill and died. Supervising Architect M. O. Johnson likewise was struck down, dying on April 25, 1905. Governor Davis was touched by these tragedies, particularly by the death of the chief architect. It was, he wrote, like the "ending of many a bright young man I have seen on the battlefield."[45] As the chief engineer was away, Johnson was buried in Wallace's coffin.[46] This use of the chief engineer's coffin did not serve to create confidence.

The Governor took all possible steps to allay panic, but the epidemic had started. In May there were thirty-three cases of yellow fever with seven deaths. Fear among employees increased. All things suggestive of death assumed an exaggerated importance in the minds of men. Funeral processions appeared to come too frequently. Coffins piled up at the railroad stations became so depressing that they were ordered out of sight. The daily funeral train to the Mount Hope Cemetery had a detrimental effect on the new arrivals. Employees generally attributed to yellow fever many deaths not caused by it and overlooked the other causes of death.

Absenteeism and desertion became so rampant that at Canal Offices it was almost impossible to accomplish any work. Ships returned to the United States with increasing crowds of deserters, 500 men returning during April, May, and June.

New arrivals were timid, and old employees delighted in playing upon their fears. The hardened veterans of one year frightened them with lurid stories of yellow fever. At times new men overheard so many tales of horror in their visits to the Washington House dining room that they wanted to leave the Isthmus at once. Frequently they would arrive, report for work one day, and resign and leave the next day by the same ship, explaining that they would come back to see the inauguration

---

[45] Davis to Wallace, May 2, 1905; quoted in Taft's Statement, April 19, 1906 (Hearings No. 18, III, 2659) (U.S.).

[46] Stevens to Taft, cable, April 10, 1906 (P.C. Rec. Bur., File D-5-25) (MS).

of the Canal. Among those left behind there was much bickering.

To this tense situation Wallace had returned in May. Unfortunately he did not act so as to instill confidence. He did not
occupy the house that had been prepared for him in Colón, and
his name was associated with coffins. He had a "thorough case
of fright, and instead of endeavoring by his example and pre-
cept to calm the minds of his subordinates, took steps almost exactly the opposite."[47] However, he gave no indication of his intended early separation from the Canal Service. And in spite
of the "wave of fear," most other engineers remained calm and
tried to carry on their work.

When Mr. Wallace left in mid-June he received a farewell by
a large crowd of lonely employees. They did not know what
was ahead. The epidemic was then at its height, with sixty-two
cases in June, but had not reached hysterical proportions. The
overt act to start panic had not then occurred.

In the United States, papers published sensational reports.
Friends and relatives of men on the Isthmus wrote imploring
them to come home. The influence that restrained them was the
example of those on the Isthmus who had gone through the
Spanish-American War in the West Indies and the Philippines.
These veterans fought for sanity and calm and urged the men
to stay at their posts until the new chairman and chief engineer
could arrive.

After Wallace left to consult the Secretary, rumors began to
circulate about the reasons for his departure. People could not
understand leaving a work at that stage and at first refused to
believe rumors of impending resignation, so strong was their
confidence in Wallace. When he left, they had no leader to
whom to look, and his return was awaited anxiously. They
expected him to come back with new equipment and restored to
full vigor. It was Wallace's resignation that precipitated the
real panic.

[47] Stevens to Secretary of War, March 22, 1906 (*ibid.*).

MAGOON TIDES OVER THE CRISIS

Magoon had arrived at a critical time. There was a great difference between the tenor of his public utterances of confidence and his descriptions sent to Chairman Shonts. He found a group of North Americans "ill-paid, over-worked, ill-housed, ill-fed, and subjected to the hazards of yellow fever, malarial fever,"[48] and other diseases—all engaged in an effort involving the prestige of the United States and under deplorable conditions bordering on complete demoralization.

He found great "unrest and insecurity," with all departments of the Canal disorganized except the Sanitary Department, in which the veterans of the Cuban yellow-fever work were battling against yellow fever, malaria, and hysteria.

As Governor, he was in charge of both government and sanitation. He had several conferences with Dr. Gorgas, who told how his requisitions had been cut by the old Commission. Magoon cabled Washington for everything Gorgas wanted for fumigation, and in twenty-four hours it was under way for the Isthmus.[49]

As soon as Magoon had time he wrote to Taft, appreciating the confidence shown him. He told about his welcome, the ceremonies at his inauguration, and that Secretary Taft's name was one "to conjure with in Panama."[50] Magoon already had published statements that he had no more fear of yellow fever than of typhoid, and to the Secretary he wrote that there was "no sacrifice too great" to justify Taft's good opinion of him.

Up to Magoon's time, Gorgas had made little headway on fumigation in Panamá. The number of cases in June was double those in May, in spite of all efforts. Magoon thought fumigation should be extended to all houses in Panamá and directed Gorgas to have daily "house-to-house" inspections.[51] He employed com-

---

[48] Magoon to Shonts, June 3, 1905 (P.C. Rec. Bur., File D-5-25) (MS).

[49] Magoon's Statement, Feb. 9, 1906 (Hearings No. 18, I, 697–99) (U.S.).

[50] Magoon to Taft, May 29, 1905 (P.C. Rec. Bur., File Personnel, Magoon) (MS).

[51] Magoon's Statement, Feb. 9, 1906 (op. cit., I, 704).

petent Panamanian doctors as inspectors, offering $50 reward for discovery of unreported cases of yellow fever. Panamá was divided into districts and every house fumigated again and again in a systematic campaign. All crevices of houses were sealed with paper. Fumes of sulphur and pyrethrum were always in the air. Householders did not like this thoroughness, which was repeated almost before they had recovered from the previous disinfection. So thorough was the sanitation that even the holy water in the Cathedral was disinfected.

The work pushed by Magoon was successful. During the next month, July 1905, the number of cases dropped to forty-two and continued to drop until the epidemic was over—a work which drew highest praise from Secretary Taft for Governor Magoon and Colonel Gorgas.

What were the actual facts about yellow fever during all this commotion and hysteria? Among canal employees, from July 1, 1904, to January 31, 1906, there were 134 cases with 34 deaths. Among nonemployees during the same period there were 112 cases with 50 deaths. The grand total thus numbered 246 cases with 84 deaths. The last case was reported December 11, 1905.[52]

When it is considered that the yellow-fever epidemic extended over a period of eighteen months with only 34 deaths among employees, it would appear that the situation was one to be ignored rather than magnified out of all proportions. Losses from malaria were more serious. The yellow-fever epidemic in itself was not serious. It was the hysteria and panic that proved serious.

Another result of this era was the inauguration of the hospital car on the Panama Railroad, requested by Governor Magoon on June 16, 1905, at Colonel Gorgas' suggestion. The car was to make one trip each way daily, collecting patients along the line on the way to base hospitals or returning them to their homes.[53]

[52] I.C.C., *Report, Dept. of Health for January 1906*, pp. 3, 5 (U.S.).
[53] I.C.C., Executive Committee, *Minutes*, 17th meeting, Aug. 2, 1905, p. 244 (U.S.).

In the midst of this epidemic the news of Wallace's resignation came like a thunderbolt and caused panic. Wallace was considered a deserter who had abandoned a great effort, and it was feared that others would do likewise. Had there been means of leaving the Isthmus, the project probably would have been abandoned in hysterical alarm.

Then came word of Taft's bitter castigation of Wallace. The effect was "immediate, far-reaching, and beneficial"[54] and did much to restore calm. On all sides was heard the expression, "Well, that ought to stop the cold-footed brigade."

One of the results of the yellow-fever crisis was a sensational journalistic campaign in the United States. Men who deserted and fled, as well as incompetents who were discharged and returned to the States, vented their resentment and feelings in wild rumors to the press, which did not fail to exploit their position. Panamá was impressed upon the public imagination as a great swamp where "monkeys play tag with female mosquitoes and parrots"[55] among the palm trees. The extent of the agitation revealed the general ignorance of the public concerning the Canal work and their failure to realize the necessity for its careful preparation.

In July, when the panic was declining, Governor Magoon assumed his duties as Minister to Panamá and inaugurated the new era by starting work on forty-two school buildings. The Isthmus celebrated its second Fourth of July under more somber circumstances than in the preceding year. In Panamá there was a *Te Deum* at the Cathedral, celebrating the "success" of the first year's work on the Canal and the turning on of fresh water from the new waterworks. It was fresh-water day. In the Zone, residents gathered at Corozal to hear Judge Gudger orate, to witness a few races, and to "uncork some fresh U.S. enthusiasm."[56] They knew the worst was over.

[54] Magoon to Secretary of War, March 30, 1906 (P.C. Rec. Bur., File 2-C-4) (MS).

[55] *Panama Star and Herald*, July 21, 1905.

[56] *Ibid.*, June 27, 1905.

From Washington came the most reassuring words. Taft cabled Magoon not to be alarmed by the transfer of power, as he had a good engineer on the way and felt that the resignation offered an opportunity to infuse new life and enthusiasm. He wanted a restoration of work and progress. He evidenced his own confidence in these words: "Shonts and Stevens will soon be with you, and the mountains will move."[57]

[57] Taft to Magoon, June 30, 1905 (P.C. Rec. Bur., File 2-C-4) (MS).

CHAPTER IX

JOHN F. STEVENS RESTORES ORDER
AND CONFIDENCE

To provide housing for this army, to properly feed, to distil into them faith in the ultimate success of the work, to weed out the faint-hearted and incompetent, to create an organization fitted to undertake the tremendous work, and to fill its ranks with the proper material was a task of heroic proportions.—JOHN F. STEVENS, Chief Engineer of Isthmian Canal Commission.[1]

I have endeavored to [prepare before starting construction], and regardless of clamor and criticism, I propose so to do as long as I am in charge of the work; and all the criticism, from any source whatever, of my course in adopting such a policy, will have no effect on me whatever; and I am confident that if this policy is adhered to, the future will show its absolute wisdom.—JOHN F. STEVENS.[2]

THE DRAFTING OF STEVENS AS CHIEF ENGINEER

When Wallace resigned, John F. Stevens, then in the service of the Philippine Commission as railroad expert, was in Chicago on his way to the Islands. To be ready in the event of the resignation of the chief engineer, Taft and Shonts had examined the records of about twenty men and had consulted leaders in transportation. The great railroad builder, James J. Hill, told Taft that no man could be found in the entire country "better adapted" to build the Panama Canal than Stevens. Others likewise spoke highly of that well-known railroad engineer.

Again the lawyer, Cromwell, came to the assistance of what he liked to call "my canal." He called on Stevens and outlined the embarrassing situation facing the Roosevelt administration, which, he intimated, feared the public reaction in case of failure to build the Canal. It was his "persuasive tongue" that overcame Stevens' disinclination for the position, and only two days after

---

[1] Quoted in W. L. Pepperman, *Who Built the Canal?* pp. 11–12.

[2] Stevens to Secretary of War, March 22, 1906 (P.C. Rec. Bur., File D-5-25) (MS).

acceptance of Wallace's resignation, Chairman Shonts telegraphed Stevens his appointment as chief engineer at a salary of
$30,000, effective July 1, which Stevens promptly accepted on
June 30, 1905, and the Commission at once approved.[3]

On the same day that Stevens accepted, Secretary Taft, at the
suggestion of Chairman Shonts, wrote a memorandum to the
Chief of Staff and the Chief of Engineers, directing the assignment of Major G. W. Goethals as one of the chief assistant engineers on the canal work, should his service be desired by the
Commission. Taft was convinced that Goethals could be of
"great use in the construction of the Panama Canal."[4] Goethals
apparently did not know of this and remained at work on the
General Staff undisturbed, although knowledge of this document
must have reached him later.

Shonts did not act on the suggestion but on July 5 advised
Stevens of the arrangement and left it to him to decide. Stevens
apparently decided not to accept this proffered assistance of the
"ablest construction engineer in the army." In the light of after
events it is interesting to conjecture what would have happened
had these two men formed a working team at that early date!
Would it have combined the genius of Stevens as a leader,
organizer, and engineer with the high administrative capacity of
Goethals to produce great results, or would there have been
friction?

Immediately, Shonts sent instructions to the Isthmus not to
make any appointments or changes, pending arrival of the new
chief engineer. He also issued a press statement lauding Stevens'
capacity, executive ability, and character. What he wanted on
the Isthmus was a "leader of men; a man who knows how to
drive, what to expect from his subordinates, and how to enlist
their enthusiasm and support."[5] He knew Stevens and knew
Stevens was that man.

[3] I.C.C., *Minutes*, 98th meeting, July 1, 1905, pp. 37–38 (U.S.).

[4] Taft Memorandum, June 30, 1905, and Shonts' Letter to Stevens, July 5;
quoted in J. B. and F. Bishop, *Goethals*, pp. 129–31.

[5] *Panama Star and Herald*, July 12, 1905.

The appointment had come so suddenly that Stevens had no opportunity to make plans before reporters called for an interview. He realized the vastness of the undertaking and that it was the "greatest of its kind in history,"[6] but he hoped to carry out his part. That was no idle statement, for he had studied almost everything in print on the Canal since the time of Philip II of Spain. He expected to make his family residence on the Isthmus for the next decade and to dedicate his life to that purpose.

Stevens was a man of imposing stature and fine physique and a natural leader of men. His record had been one of astonishing accomplishments. Without a college training, he had started engineering at twenty-one in the City Engineer's Office in Minneapolis, and later went to Texas on railroad-location surveys. He worked on the Denver & Rio Grande and on the Chicago, Milwaukee & St. Paul. He worked with James J. Hill, and became an engineer for a contractor on the Canadian Pacific. He became chief engineer of the Great Northern and built it over the Rockies to the Pacific through Marias Pass, which he discovered, and was made general manager. In 1902 he was chief engineer of the Chicago, Rock Island & Pacific, and its vice-president in 1904.[7] His record was known to every engineer on the Isthmus.

Widely read on Isthmian conditions, it is not strange that Panamá was no terror to him, or that he could say: "For three years in Mexico I stood the test of chills and fever incident to malaria. I have slept under wet skies on the Western plains— rolled only in a single blanket, and I have experienced the rigors of a far Northern winter under primitive conditions."[8] Certainly, to rugged Stevens, tropical Panamá could be no worse than the Philippines.

He launched into his work with characteristic energy. Early in July he was in Washington, organizing a corps of engineers

[6] *Panama Star and Herald*, July 13, 1905.
[7] Stevens, *An Engineer's Recollections*, pp. vii-ix.
[8] Quoted in *Panama Star and Herald*, Oct. 22, 1905.

for practically an entire staff. He did this on the basis of fitness—an action that was not very popular in certain circles. The head of the American Federation of Labor tried to intimidate him into making a closed shop. When Stevens refused, the labor leader "threatened to take the matter to the President, and was told that he could take it to the Lord, if he chose, but that it would make no difference, and to close the door when he went out."[9] Nothing more was heard on the subject at the time. He had been given a free hand by Shonts.

Stevens knew about the food situation on the Isthmus, and before leaving he arranged for a contract with a Chicago house for fresh meat to be sent via Panama Railroad steamers at a cost about 60 per cent of Chicago retail prices.

He then called upon the President at Oyster Bay. Roosevelt told him affairs at Panamá were in a "devil of a mess." Stevens stated the conditions of his acceptance to the President: First, he was to have "a free hand in all matters" and not be hampered by anyone in authority, high or low; second, he agreed to remain until the "success or failure" of the project was determined according to his own judgment. To these Roosevelt acquiesced and, to impress his views, told an anecdote of a man of sudden wealth speaking to his butler: "I don't know in the least what you are to do—but one thing I *do* know, you get busy and buttle like Hell."[10] He directed Stevens to communicate directly with him instead of through official channels. When Stevens pointed out the possible resulting conflict with the War Department, Roosevelt waved it aside, as all hands there knew his views.

With these injunctions and confident of his future, Stevens sailed for Panamá, along with Chairman Shonts and Colonel Ernst, a new member of the Commission. With him went also the sympathy of Wallace, who considered that Stevens' experience "more nearly" matched his own than that of any other engineer connected with the Canal.

9 Stevens, "The Panama Canal." A.S.C.E., *Transactions*, XCI, 950.
10*Ibid.*, pp. 949–50.

STEVENS AND SHONTS ARRIVE AND SWING INTO ACTION

When the new chairman, with Chief Engineer Stevens and Commissioner Ernst, arrived at Colón on July 25, the Isthmus had just passed the height of the yellow-fever epidemic, with sixty-two cases in June. There was no spectacular reception for the new officials. Instead, they hurried across the Isthmus to the home of Governor Magoon.

All along the line employees were in a state of alarm. On the very ship that carried Shonts and Stevens to Panamá, more employees were booked for return to the United States than had been brought down. Stevens sensed a dangerous psychological situation. As he expressed it, employees were simply "scared out of their boots, afraid of yellow fever and afraid of everything."[11] Quick action was needed.

After dinner that evening Shonts called a conference at the Governor's residence. Stevens, Magoon, Gorgas, and Ross were there, as discussions on the future of the Panama Canal began on the wide veranda of Magoon's house. The Governor explained the troubles on the Isthmus—that prices for food had risen, that pay raises had been granted twice, and that Panamá merchants had raised prices each time. He told about men going into the jungle for wild bananas or into swamps for sugar cane, because they were unable to sustain life on their pay. Eggs were selling for $1.50 a dozen. Even fish prices had risen, because fishermen refused to make two catches a week. They had discovered that with the large number of arrivals they could make as much in one haul as in two. "What are we going to do?" the worried Governor asked.

Shonts answered that commissaries would be opened to all employees. Magoon explained that such action would be in violation of an order of the War Department. Shonts insisted and ordered Stevens to load a car with food at Colón the next day, "go along the line and condemn a building where you can find one satisfactorily located, and plan to distribute these supplies

[11] Stevens' Statement, Jan. 16, 1906 (Hearings No. 18, I, 38) (U.S.).

to the Canal employés at cost."[12] Magoon predicted trouble
with the merchants, but Shonts was willing to accept that and
was ready to go to Congress if necessary.

Near by, a great palace for the new Governor was under construction. Magoon had ideas of establishing a model government
in the tropics as an object lesson in government to the small countries. Turning to the Governor, Shonts stated that was not one of
his duties, that there would be no more government than that
needed to maintain order, and that the sole purpose of the Commission was to build the Canal.

Then, shifting to Gorgas, Shonts found that in spite of the
support given by Magoon, the sanitation campaign was not progressing. Yellow-fever cases had continued at such a rate that
employees discredited the theory of mosquito propagation of the
disease. Gorgas had been characterized as "that crank" who
was "wasting money in trying to drain pools, in cutting grass
and weeds, and insisting that every house and quarters should be
screened."[13] Along with criticism from beneath, there had been
considerable derision on the part of superiors to overcome.
Shonts wanted to do everything necessary to eradicate yellow
fever and promised to place Gorgas' orders by cable for delivery by the next steamer. He wanted quick action and directed
Gorgas to "commence with the Palace and disinfect every
house" in both terminal cities down to the "lowest hovel."[14]

Shonts and Stevens that very night accurately estimated the
situation on the Isthmus. The most urgent need was for housing
and feeding of employees. It was a great problem of sanitation,
homes, markets, and entertainment; of procuring supplies to
keep the working forces contented and in good health; and of
forming an organization for gathering and augmenting these
forces.[15]

Before the meeting was over that night Shonts called for a

[12] Pepperman, *op. cit.*, pp. 133–34.
[13] Stevens, "The Panama Canal," *op. cit.*, pp. 951–52.
[14] Pepperman, *op. cit.*, p. 137.
[15] *Ibid.*, p. 20.

meeting of heads of departments for the next afternoon. Word of the conferences spread over the Isthmus rapidly, and hopes began to rise.

Stevens' first step was to become familiar with the work. He looked over the Isthmus and saw the work of government under Magoon, sanitation under Gorgas, materials and supplies under the purchasing agent in Washington, and what there was of engineering. The organization he found was "top-heavy,"[16] with overlapping responsibilities and bureaus and with a "wild scramble" for more pay. Supplies were arriving in great quantities, but no one knew where they were to go.

Large forces of men were fighting filth and mosquitoes and cutting grass, but there was neither organization nor results, owing to several causes—sudden changes of officials, yellow fever, and rumors. This abnormal feeling was indicated among employees by "lack of interest," "absence of harmony," profound discouragement, and a lack of confidence in Canal policies. There had been no start on the Canal, and no plans. The work in progress was "merely colorable" and of no value toward the Canal. Worse than all, as Stevens expressed it, in the "diseased imagination of the disjointed forces of white employees, hovered the angel of death in the shape of yellow fever."[17]

He searched for a plan for the work in Culebra Cut but could find nothing definite as to either tracks or dumps. Dumps were poorly located, and locomotives had to pull loaded trains uphill to dumps that were too high, especially in the rainy season. Work under way was not in conformity to any plan, but was haphazard, over poor tracks, and undertaken in answer to the popular demand to "make the dirt fly," which Stevens aptly called the "clamor of ignorance."

French equipment in use was hopelessly antiquated, but there were eleven steam shovels purchased by Wallace; how-

[16] Stevens to Secretary of War, March 22, 1906 (P.C. Rec. Bur., File D-5-25) (MS).

[17] Bennett, *History of the Panama Canal*, p. 204.

ever, these were too large for the small French cars used to haul spoil to the dumps. Both Stevens and Shonts felt that it would have been better if Wallace had never found any old French equipment, and if he had never started any operation at all.

Shortly after his arrival, Stevens viewed Culebra Cut from a high point on a bank. He counted seven work trains derailed and all shovels in sight idle. Workers were struggling to get the trains back on the tracks. Seeing instantly what to do, he suspended operations on all excavation in the Cut and reorganized the force there into track gangs to install a trackage system that he had planned.

Although the Commission already had a few steam shovels and 60 or 70 western dumpcars of the 300 ordered by Wallace, Stevens found that these would not dump on the side. Clay would stick in the rain. Of 500 flatcars ordered, 250 were in service, not on the canal work but on hauling railroad supplies. The double-tracking of the railroad had started; a few light cuts had been made, but no fills. Wallace had ordered only 24 locomotives and several types of dumpcars, as he had wanted a long experiment before deciding what type to adopt. Stevens' past experience qualified him to decide without experiment.

Only 350 of the 2,100 French houses had been repaired, because of long delays in receiving lumber. There was congestion on the docks, with insufficient laborers to unload ships; but Shonts transferred about 125 men working on the foundation of Magoon's palace to the more pressing task of unloading ships.[18]

Within a week the new Commission had decided what to do—double-track the Panama Railroad and obtain new terminal equipment, establish commissaries for all employees, construct a new hotel (the Tivoli) as a temporary emergency measure and then erect permanent quarters, place all available labor on sanitary work, and, most important, in Culebra Cut make thorough preparation of levels that would receive the greatest number of steam shovels.

[18] Shonts' Statement, Jan. 26, 1906 (Hearings No. 18, I, 366, 388) (U.S.).

The criticism of Gorgas bore fruit. Shonts notified Stevens that Gorgas would have to go and that a "young osteopathist"[19] would take his place. Stevens intervened forcibly, and Gorgas was retained. Stevens knew the importance of sanitation and quarters for men in undeveloped territory and turned over almost all the Engineer Department to Colonel Gorgas for sanitation work. The rest of the Engineer Department was set at work on repair and construction of quarters. Later he suggested Gorgas for membership in the Commission.

Within a few days Stevens and Shonts had seen enough. On August 1 all canal excavation ceased. Shonts returned to Washington and left Stevens in full charge of the struggle on the Isthmus.

After Stevens became familiar with the problem he inclined toward the 85-foot high-level lock canal. For this he was pitied by many as a scapegoat for future failure. On all sides people remarked: "What does he know about building a canal? He may be a good railroad man, but as for a lift of 85 feet—why the man's crazy." His reply was, "Well, we'll see."[20]

STEVENS STARTS WORK

The new chief engineer quickly proved himself to be a man of action as well as ideas. After stopping all excavation, there were too many employees. Excess men were returned to the United States, with instructions that they would be notified when to come back.

Stevens' wide background made him strong. Many of his ideas of organization came from his railroad and mining experience in undeveloped country. He knew the urgency for proper quarters for employees and stressed the Building Division as first in importance. He realized the necessity for health and sanitation and gave full support to Colonel Gorgas, who up to that time had been waging a losing battle with the authorities in Washington. As general manager of the Great Northern he had faced

---

[19] Stevens, "The Panama Canal," *op. cit.*, pp. 951–52.
[20] *Panama Star and Herald*, March 27, 1937.

the problem of stripping iron-ore properties quickly. He had consulted with the Bucyrus engineers, and together they had planned large-capacity steam shovels with great mechanical power for this mining work.[21]

To Stevens the excavation of Culebra Cut involved only a problem of applying steam-shovel, mining-excavation methods as used in making a large railroad cut. All he had to do was to use shovels of similar design to those developed for mining and to devise the transportation system for rapid disposition of the spoil. These were problems with which Stevens had had years of experience. He knew exactly what to do and what equipment to order.

Constructing the Canal in the Isthmian jungle and building railroads in the Far West were both enterprises in undeveloped territory. Stevens saw the similarity and decided instinctively on careful preparations with sufficient equipment before starting construction. He realized immediately that the previous construction had been simply throwing away money by using the worn and out-of-date equipment, and he refused to continue wasting time and money in that manner. He said he would prefer to "take the money and throw it into the river or put it into the furnace."[22]

One of the early actions of Shonts and Stevens was to place the Division of Materials and Supplies under a new man. Paymaster Tobey returned to active duty with the United States Navy and his position was given to W. G. Tubby, formerly general storekeeper of the Great Northern, at $9,000 a year. For disbursing they employed E. J. Williams of the Chicago and Northwestern Railroad.

The greatest problem was to restore morale. Stevens went out along the line, viewed the various projects, tramped in overalls through jungle and over hills, rode the trains, and talked with the men. He walked with energy and was confident. He was

[21] John F. Stevens, Jr., Letter to author, Dec. 25, 1943.
[22] Stevens' Statement, Jan. 16, 1906 (Hearings No. 18, I, 22) (U.S.).

the type of man that other men naturally look to as leader and whose presence is felt. There were only three diseases on the Isthmus, he told them—"yellow fever, malaria and cold feet; and the greatest of these is cold feet."[23]

The reorganized commissaries did not work smoothly at first. At Empire the old system had been suspended, but the new one had not been put into effect. As a result, employees were out of food and faced starvation, yet the auditor in charge would not open the store. Stevens went there in a special train, took matters into his own hands, overruled the auditor, and opened the store.[24]

The Isthmus had no refrigerator service at that time, and local sources were inadequate. Something radical had to be done in that sphere for these employees in the tropics. Cold-storage equipment was installed on the Panama Railroad steamers, a cold-storage plant was built at Colón, and refrigerator cars were procured for the railroad.

Soon frozen products were brought from New York and deposited in cold storage at Colón, and daily deliveries of perishable food and ice were made at towns across the Isthmus. Many Panamá merchants vainly protested, but President Amador and disinterested Panamanians approved the actions of the Commission.

At first deliveries were slow. On one occasion some supplies that Mrs. Stevens had ordered across the Isthmus were late, and Stevens wanted to know why. To the manager of the commissary he wrote that "if this is the way the Chief Engineer's requests are to be handled, I cannot imagine what attention any requests from any of my subordinates would receive."[25] He added that he presumed the situation would be corrected.

Feeding about 17,000 men 2,000 miles away from home was a gigantic problem, because the local community could supply little and indolent natives never planned for the future. The

[23] Farnham Bishop, *Panama, Past and Present*, p. 159.

[24] Pepperman, *op. cit.*, p. 52.

[25] Stevens to R. Bermudes, Aug. 11, 1905 (P.C. Rec. Bur., File Personnel, Stevens) (MS).

only arrangements for these men up to this time had been small privately operated messes. Something had to be done for this service.

One of Mr. Wallace's friends, Jacob E. Markel, an experienced railroad-construction mess-hall operator, was on the Isthmus when Stevens arrived and was still looking for a contract to feed all the Canal forces. He had accompanied Stevens across the Isthmus on July 27 and had worked out plans for extending the Colón commissary along the railroad by providing branches as well as building small hotels with dining rooms. Markel had big ideas. He was going to plant gardens by each hotel and raise vegetables and get fishermen to come down from Gloucester, Massachusetts, to establish a fishing industry. He was going to make the country self-sustaining.[26] He returned north with Shonts, confident that he had obtained the feeding contract.

In the meantime employees had to be fed. Stevens, unable to obtain action from Washington by cable, established and operated mess halls along the Canal. He was surprised to find that he could feed gold personnel at 30 cents a meal. Employees liked the arrangements.

In Washington the contract plan for feeding received serious attention, and the Commission asked for bids. When the bids were opened in September, Markel was low bidder at $36 a month. Stevens was notified; but meanwhile, during these trying weeks Stevens had succeeded in feeding gold employees for $27.50 a month—a most satisfactory solution for the employees.

Among employees the Markel bid met instant reaction, creating tremendous dissatisfaction. Stevens protested the awarding of a contract to Markel, as it would necessitate increase of pay; besides, there was a "million dollars a year clear profit" for the contractor. The contract was canceled with the consent of Markel, who stated it would be impossible to do the work with Stevens "cutting his bowels out."[27]

[26] Markel's Statement, March 2, 1906 (Hearings No. 18, II, 1256, 1264) (U.S.).
[27] Ibid. (II, 1290-91).

Following the precedent of the French, in June it was decided to equip the old Aspinwall House at Taboga as a sanatorium, so that recuperating employees could receive the benefit
of that island's more salubrious climate. Progress was slow,
because the Canal divisions working on the building and water
supply needed a "handful of material" that should have been
placed on the ground ready for use before starting. Stevens
wrote the division heads, deploring the situation and asking for
a list of needed materials, so all of it could be taken over at one
time. He did not like to have "small jobs dragging when men
are required elsewhere for more important work."[28] The Taboga
Sanatorium was opened in September.

Employees required additional recreation facilities, as there
was nothing to do for recreation except to visit Panamá. Stevens
advocated clubhouses. He secured a building for the Cristóbal
Club and went over plans for new buildings. He recommended
two-story buildings with wide verandas on both floors, with
space for "billiards, bowling alley, cards, reading, and smoking
rooms."[29] The Commission approved at its one-hundred-and-
first meeting on November 9, 1905, and Stevens started club
buildings at Cristóbal, Gorgona, Empire, and Culebra.

There was no band on the Canal Zone, but many of the
employees were musicians who wanted a chance to play. A plan
was proposed for a volunteer band. Stevens was interested, and
Governor Magoon assisted by obtaining instruments. As a result,
the Isthmian Canal Commission Band was organized in September 1905, with Dr. Sumner Coolidge as director. At first
the men liked to play together, but before long it became difficult to hold them. Stevens appreciated the value of the Band
and prevented its disintegration by reorganizing it with thirty-
five paid members and a full-time director and librarian. The
Band gave concerts at various towns along the Canal, played

[28] Stevens to C. E. Davis and W. M. Belding, Sept. 11, 1905 (P.C. Rec. Bur.,
File 13-H-65) (MS).

[29] Stevens to Shonts, Oct. 23, 1905, I.C.C., *Minutes,* 101st meeting, Nov. 9,
1905, p. 17 (U.S.).

at dances, and became a well-known Construction Day institution.[30]

Construction on Governor Magoon's palace was resumed.
The Governor wanted an equally palatial residence built for
the Chief Engineer, overlooking the waters of Panamá Bay.
Stevens bluntly objected. He did not want a palace; he wanted
a corrugated-roof residence on the side of Culebra Cut, where
he could watch the work progress. This was embarrassing to
Magoon, who then refused to live in his palace. When it was
completed, the palace was used as an Administration Building
for the Civil Government and was never used as a governor's
residence.[31] Today that imposing building is a Court House.

In Panamá City there was only one hotel—the Hotel Central. It was always filled to capacity, had no conveniences, and
the table was "execrable." People who visited Panamá stayed no
longer than necessary. A hotel at Ancon for employees and
guests was a necessity. Chairman Shonts and Governor Magoon,
sitting as the Executive Committee on August 2, 1905, authorized "building an hotel on a small hill at Ancon" as an emergency measure, and the next day Stevens received his instructions
to build.

A young architect was sent up to the hill to look over the
land and prepare plans. He saw a small building run as a
saloon and gambling house. It was marked *Tivoli*, after Tivoli
near Rome. Someone had to name the future hotel, and the
young architect, without instruction and not knowing the name
would be adopted, selected *Tivoli* and entered it on the drawing.
The name has remained through the years.

Construction of the hotel was supposed to start in August,
but progress was slow. On the first of September Stevens looked
over the ground. Grading had not started, and it was evident
that the men handling the work had never seen any grading. He
wrote the master builder to "get some mules and scrapers and

---

[30] Haskins, *Canal Zone Pilot*, pp. 389–92.
[31] S. M. Hitt, Conversation with author, March 19, 1941.

get this work going."[32] This was a rush job, and Stevens wanted it pushed. The letter had its desired effect.

In the meantime there was difficulty in obtaining material to meet the architect's specifications, because of the time required to get plaster and metal. Stevens directed that these materials be omitted from the specifications, as he expected this hotel to "pass out of existence and be wiped off the books" on completion of the Canal. He directed that no attention be paid to "rules or plans" and "no time or money spent on frills," as the situation was serious. He admonished the master builder, "take matters into your hands promptly and decisively, and let no other policy or person stand in your way."[33]

Stevens inspected in the vicinity of Ancon. He observed delays in transporting lumber to other buildings by the mule-and-cart method, which he thought crude at best. But what he actually saw infuriated him. Transportation was being delayed by black drivers giving their black friends rides up Ancon Hill. Stevens wrote the acting chief of supplies that those mules were required to "drag not only the driver, but another lazy nigger up the steep hill."[34] The drivers as a result became less generous.

Another difficulty had to be handled. Men working on the Canal were required to take quinine. They rebelled. They were given the quinine with a "little gill of rum." The rebellion ended.

The railroad, as inherited by the Commission, was hopelessly antiquated. To Stevens it was only a "phantom railroad,"[35] with light engines and small light cars built thirty-five years before, the only exceptions being a few flatcars and locomotives recently bought for the Commission. Without terminal facilities, congestion was acute, and freight piled up in Colón in a "hopeless mass of confusion." Some freight had not been delivered for eighteen months, cars were tied up for ninety days,

[32] Stevens to Belding, Sept. 2, 1905 (P.C. Rec. Bur., File 13-K-25) (MS).

[33] *Ibid.*, Sept. 30, 1905.

[34] Stevens to V. S. Jackson, Oct. 18, 1905 (*ibid.*).

[35] Sibert and Stevens, *Construction of the Panama Canal*, p. 48.

and in certain cases even the shipment papers were lost. Stevens said the only good thing he heard about the railroad was that "there had been no collisions for some time." On this he commented: "A collision has its good points as well as bad ones—it indicates there is something moving on the railroad."[36]

The first task on the railroad was to clear out the congestion. He persuaded steamer lines to take portions of the delayed freight, locate the owners, and deliver. He found much freight for local merchants undelivered because of the old practice of using the railroad property as storage warehouses.

The old personnel of the railroad had failed completely to meet new demands, and Stevens acted to correct the condition. It took him only thirty days to get a new railroad manager, W. G. Bierd. It was not long before the congestion was reduced, and Panamá merchants complained because their freight arrived too soon. "We don't like that, because we don't want that freight yet,"[37] was their cry.

In his desperate efforts to relieve congestion, Stevens had to use old French dumpcars to haul coal from Colón to Panamá. These small cars jumped the tracks. They could go only four or five miles an hour and required about ten hours to cross the Isthmus. At times he had to stop all passenger trains. The situation was so acute that Stevens stated that if he had had "all the steam shovels in the world, all the money in the world, and all the men in the world,"[38] nothing could have been done because there was no plant to haul material away; and transportation was the key to building the Panama Canal.

Stevens double-tracked the railroad all the way across the Isthmus, except over Culebra Hill and from Mount Hope to Gatun. He increased the dock capacity at both Cristóbal and La Boca, replaced the light 56-pound rail with 70-pound rail, and strengthened the bridges all along the line to enable them to carry the heavy loads. By December 1905, the congestion was

[36] I.C.C., *Annual Report*, 1905, Pt. 1, p. 121 (U.S.).
[37] Stevens' Statement, Jan. 16, 1906 (Hearings No. 18, I, 39) (U.S.).
[38] *Ibid.* (I, 27).

cleared out and the railroad was well on its way to rehabilitation, ready to establish its phenomenal record as an adjunct to the building of the Canal.

When lumber began to arrive, everyone who could "wield a plane or drive a nail" was placed in housing work, and by the end of the year about 1,000 French houses had been repaired, hotels were under way, and the canal line began to look like a continuous city under construction from one end of the Zone to the other.

Stevens began ordering the construction plant the month after his arrival. He had decided that "the only car that could be used, the only car that wet material could be unloaded from, was a flat car with a plow."[39] He placed orders for 120 locomotives, 800 flatcars with steam-operated plows for unloading, and installed an eight-mile air line in Culebra Cut for pneumatic drills.

Shonts was put under political pressure to award contracts to particular parties who represented their products as especially designed for the work. Stevens insisted upon proved equipment and no experimentation.

The Wallace skeleton engineering organization was continued for a few weeks, but in August Stevens began working on a new organization. He planned to select men of ability— men who could "follow general instructions and continue work without constant presence of an immediate superior."[40] He wanted to be relieved of details. His policy was "to give an official ample authority, and then to hold him responsible for results."[41] He did not want any "passing of the buck." His first plan of organization was issued August 29, effective September 1, 1905. When established it was as follows: Colón Division, from the Atlantic to Bohío; Chagres Division, from Bohío to Bas Obispo and also to Alhajuela; Culebra Division, from Bas Obispo to Miraflores; La Boca Division, from Mira-

[39] Stevens' Statement, Jan. 16, 1906 (Hearings No. 18, I, 29) (U.S.). Lidgerwood Mfg. Co., *Rapid Unloader, ca.* 1919, pp. 3–7, 16.

[40] *Panama Star and Herald,* Aug. 12, 1905.

[41] Stevens, "The Panama Canal," *op. cit.,* p. 954.

flores to the Pacific; and Mechanical Division at Panamá, in charge of all machinery and equipment. There were also divisions of Municipal Engineering, Building Construction, Meteorology, and River Hydraulics, and a Branch of Labor and Quarters. Competent men were placed in charge of each.

By October Stevens estimated he had arranged for 60 steam shovels, but planned on having 100—80 for working and 20 under repair. At this time he did not know what type of canal would be adopted and worked out three sets of plans to be ready for any decision that might be made. He expected the entire plant would be installed by July 1, 1906. He refused to be rushed into premature construction and warned that the "French Company fell down because they could not dispose of the material"[42]—a matter of transportation.

Improved conditions on the Canal were noted in the press of the United States, and papers became less critical. One of Stevens' former associates wrote that only death or breakdown could cause Stevens to leave the Canal. "Grant him length of days and good health and he will build that canal—build it honestly and well. He has the soldier instincts of bravery, loyalty and obedience to his superiors. He is rugged as the hills. In all the equipment of experience, aggressiveness, tenacity and mental strength that go to make a great engineer he is qualified for the momentous task."[43] He was rugged enough to push a drunken employee out of his office with his fist.[44]

Conditions looked more hopeful in December. There were 2,600 men employed at Culebra; railroad yards and much track had been laid; dredging was under way in both the Atlantic and the Pacific sea-level portions of the Canal; examinations had started in Colón Harbor and on Gatun Dam site; and the Culebra transportation system was under way.

Men began writing home to their friends to come down and work and bring two good men with them. The yellow-fever

[42] Board of Consulting Engineers, *Report*, 1906, p. 289 (U.S.).
[43] *Panama Star and Herald*, Oct. 22, 1905.
[44] *Ibid.*, Nov. 30, 1905.

epidemic was over, with only three cases in November. Refrigerated food and ice were being delivered along the line. Men's families were arriving on every boat and anxious to make homes.

President Roosevelt was impressed with the progress. In his Annual Message to Congress on December 5, 1905, he stated: "Gratifying progress has been made during the past year, and especially during the past four months."[45] Things were going along fine. Stevens did not want to leave his work at this stage; but he was called to Washington and left the Isthmus on December 12, 1905.

In Washington, Congress was investigating the Canal, and Stevens expected to have some trouble. He could not understand why interferences were placed in his way and expressed his feelings in a letter to Governor Magoon. He wanted to go ahead with the work if it could be done in a "businesslike way; but if I have got to mix and mingle with every politician in the United States, the sooner I will be able to drop it the better I will be satisfied."[46]

TAFT VISITS THE ISTHMUS WITH GOETHALS

In the fall of 1905 Secretary Taft decided to visit the Canal Zone a second time. He had to clear up some questions with Panamá, to check progress of the Canal, and to decide questions of fortifications. He brought with him a party including General John P. Story, Chief of Artillery; Colonel Clarence R. Edwards, Chief of Insular Bureau; Lieutenant Colonel W. M. Black, Major George W. Goethals, and Lieutenant Mark Brooke.

The party arrived at Cristóbal on November 2 and crossed to Panamá in the latter part of the wet season. At Colón garbage was floating. Both terminal cities were in the midst of street improvements. Houses showed evidences of recent sealing during the fumigation campaign, and the Secretary's train was a "rattling relic." To Major Goethals, conditions appeared "chaotic." He later stated the prospects of a canal at that time seemed

---

[45] *Messages and Papers of the Presidents*, X, 7021 (U.S.).
[46] Stevens to Magoon, Dec. 29, 1905 (P.C. Rec. Bur., File D-5-25) (MS).

"rather hopeless."[47] Mr. Taft, however, had seen the Isthmus the year before, and he knew there was a marked improvement that indicated the new organization was effective.

Goethals was on this trip as special assistant to Mr. Taft, who, according to George M. Wells, wanted his advice about affairs on the Isthmus. Mr. Taft had already formed a high opinion of Goethals' ability, and Mr. Wells, who was later Goethals' partner, thought it was this trip which later resulted in Goethals' appointment to the Canal. Colonel Black, who roomed with Goethals during the voyage, has stated that Goethals made no special comments about the Canal and did not show any special interest.[48]

It was, however, Goethals' first introduction to the Canal. He was not there long enough to obtain detailed information, but the seeds of his future had been sown.

POULTNEY BIGELOW ATTACKS THE CANAL'S "MISMANAGEMENT"

On Thanksgiving Day, November 30, 1905, the steamer "Trent" arrived at Colón at 10 A.M. Among her passengers was a well-known writer. It being a holiday and little going on, this writer crossed the Isthmus the same afternoon, viewed the wrecks left from the French effort, visited Panamá and the Ancon Hospital, talked with Executive Secretary Harry D. Reed, called at the Governor's House but found Magoon out at the time. In the evening he returned to Colón, where he met Tracy Robinson and John Lundie, two local businessmen who had been disappointed by the Commission in some business deals. They showed him the sights of Colón, and the writer departed from Cristóbal on December 1 at 2:10 P.M.; his total time on the Isthmus was twenty-eight hours and ten minutes.[49] His name was Poultney Bigelow, one of the more competent and better-known American writers of his time.

The local press, after his departure, stated that he had taken a great interest in conditions at Colón but that he was surprised

[47] *Panama Star and Herald*, March 19, 1907.

[48] J. B. and F. Bishop, *Goethals, Genius of the Panama Canal: a Biography*, pp. 134–5.   [49] I.C.C., *Annual Report*, 1905, Pt. 2, p. 15 (U.S.).

to see so little done toward improving that "Gateway of the Universe."[50] During his wallowing in the mire of that city, he visited a hundred or more huts and latrines. He had talked with many Negroes, viewed the torn-up streets of the city, and looked over near-by swamplands. He had been there long enough and had seen enough to write about everything on the Isthmus from the "smell of Colón" to the sewer system of Panamá.

Upon return from his venture he submitted his article to *Harper's Weekly* and to *Collier's*, but it was rejected.[51] He afterward met the editor of a small reliable magazine, *The Independent*, which published the article on January 4, 1906, under the title "Our Mismanagement in Panama." In it Bigelow attacked most bitterly nearly everything on the Isthmus. Filled with incorrect statements and replete with implications, the article received wide attention from the credulous, particularly because it was published in *The Independent*. It created a national sensation.

Stevens was in Washington at the time, busy at Congressional hearings with no time for such nonsense, and he ignored the article altogether. But Roosevelt insisted on a reply. Stevens drafted a scorching memorandum to Secretary Taft, tearing Bigelow's statement to pieces with the strength and accuracy of statement inherent in his nature. Taft added further information in a long statement to the President, who sent a special message to Congress.[52]

The Senate Committee on Interoceanic Canals called Bigelow before it. He was embarrassed. He floundered. He talked about Russia and New York police and gave plenty of hearsay evidence. Members protested and tried to force him to state facts to support the truth of his article. They tried to make him reveal the names of eminent engineers who, he alleged, had refused to work on the Canal.

At first Bigelow refused to answer. He replied that they

[50] *Panama Star and Herald*, Dec. 3, 1905.

[51] Bigelow's Statement, Jan. 18, 1906 (Hearings No. 18, I, 101) (U.S.).

[52] I.C.C., *Annual Report*, 1905, Pt. 2, of which pp. 79–91 contain a reprint of Bigelow's article (U.S.).

could put him on bread and water, even condemn him to Colón, but they could not make him betray people who had confided in him. The Committee went into executive session, and later he was grilled by Senator Morgan, to whom he revealed the names of W. B. Parsons and J. R. Freeman. Then, having given their names, he wanted to withdraw them from the record but was told by Senator Morgan that he could not swear to a thing and then withdraw it.

"Well," replied Bigelow, "I have committed an indiscretion for the first time in my life then."

"I do not know about your indiscretions; that is a question for another tribunal, perhaps,"[53] answered the Alabaman.

The Committee could not agree on procedure; the matter was dropped, and Bigelow was forgotten.

STEVENS PUSHES PREPARATORY WORK

In Washington, Stevens, anticipating that Congress would adopt the lock-type canal, scouted around for someone to take charge of the design of locks. He offered the position to Joseph Ripley, Lock Superintendent at Sault Ste. Marie, who accepted.[54] Stevens was delighted but held the appointment in abeyance until Congress acted.

After attending Committee hearings in Congress, Stevens returned to the Isthmus on February 5, 1906. There he noted much improvement in Colón, and his organization began to function smoothly. At Culebra his home was nearing completion, which would enable him to live with his force that was working on Culebra Cut. The increase in yardage began to show up. In January 1906 excavation in Culebra Cut was 120,990 cubic yards at 72 cents, as compared with 70,630 at 93 cents in December.

Even yet he did not know the type of canal. He wanted the lock type and believed that would be selected; he made plans for it, but did not know. Excavation in Culebra would count

[53] Bigelow's Statement, *op. cit.*, I, 114.

[54] Ripley to Shonts, Feb. 3, 1906 (P.C. Rec. Bur., File Personnel, Ripley) (MS).

toward either plan, and Stevens was able to get that under way. Even so, he was hindered at every turn by this uncertainty.

In March he moved his home and office to Culebra, which became headquarters for construction. The Accounting Department was moved to Empire. The Governor moved his office into the new Palace, which then became the Administration Building and later the Court House. The old Administration Building in Panamá City, received from the French, was abandoned. In Culebra there were fewer distracting influences for the Construction Staff than there had been in Panamá.

Serene, calm, and never hurried, Stevens was always ahead of his work. He took a paternal interest toward employees and started the practice of interviewing all workers who wanted to see him about their problems. Sometimes he had to decide an important matter; more frequently it was small. He would assuage the sorrow of a wife who had one rocking chair less in her home than the wife of another employee with the same salary. Such problems, though small, were the ones that made living in the stiflingly close association on the Isthmus difficult.

Gradually, Stevens won enthusiastic supporters among the workers in whom he showed so much interest. But he could also be forceful and hard, well illustrated when he put down a steam-shovel strike in 1906 by deporting the engineers.[55]

Stevens opposed the eight-hour day for the Isthmus. He wanted men to work longer and build the Canal quicker and advocated Chinese labor. When asked in Congress if he thought it would be well for both black and white to work ten hours, Stevens replied: "I gauge everybody by myself. I work from fourteen to eighteen hours."[56]

He realized the psychological change that had come over his employees when they found a leader to take them out of chaos and to make decisions. He had praised them before Congress, stating that in his thirty years of experience he had not seen "a more faithful, hard-working, loyal set of men."[57]

[55] Pepperman, *op. cit.,* pp. 89-90.
[56] Stevens' Statement, Jan. 23, 1906 (Hearings No. 18, I, 55) (U.S.).
[57] *Ibid.,* Jan. 16, 1906 (I, 38).

Double-tracking of the railroad was pushed. Paving of Panamá streets with brick from Peoria, Illinois, was rushed. Empire and Culebra rapidly came to the front as construction towns, after removing headquarters and other activities to towns along the line and after starting real excavation over the new rail system in the Canal. Meanwhile, recurrent rumors spread of Shonts's resignation.

Plans had to be made for relocating the Panama Railroad. They would be different, depending upon the type of canal. At first it was planned to place the rail line on a berm in Culebra Cut. North of the Cut it would skirt the east edge of the lake. South of the Cut the railroad had to cross some rough country. There was a hill on the line near Miraflores, and Stevens had to decide what to do. He had built a large railroad with many tunnels in the Pacific Northwest. The Panama Railroad did not have a tunnel. It was only natural for him to say that "a railroad without one tunnel was not a railroad."[58] The Panama Railroad was built with that one tunnel.

In April 3,000 men were working on Culebra Cut, making inroads into the sides with seventeen steam shovels between Bas Obispo and Pedro Miguel. As described by a witness: "The groan of the giant shovel, the sharp tap, tap, tap of the power drill, the rumble of underground explosions, are not unfamiliar sounds along the canal route."[59]

Just as this activity on the Isthmus was starting, the management of the Canal was offered to Secretary of State Root, but he declined. He did not wish this "graveyard of reputations."[60]

In June 1906, excavation in Culebra was up to 212,623 cubic yards, and in the same month Congress was nearing its decision as to the type of canal. When the outcome of the debate became clear and the success of the undertaking apparent, late in the month the White House announced that President Roosevelt would visit the Canal in November.

---

[58] H. H. Evans, Conversation with author, Sept. 30, 1942.
[59] *Panama Star and Herald*, April 6, 1906.   [60] *Ibid.*, March 29, 1906.

Chapter X

THE BATTLE OF THE LEVELS AND THE GREAT DECISION

Nature has interposed only two formidable engineering difficulties on the line of the canal, the cut at the continental divide and the regulation of the Chagres River.—Henry L. Abbot, Brigadier General, United States Army, Retired, formerly member of the Comité Technique.[1]

The one great problem in the construction of any canal down there is the control of the Chagres River. That overshadows everything else.—John F. Stevens.[2]

I have been privileged to be of some little service to my country, and the greatest service I ever gave to it, was the part I took in preventing foreign votes from foisting a nameless, useless thing [sea-level canal as proposed by the majority of the Consulting Board] upon a too credulous American people.—John F. Stevens.[3]

WALLACE RESURRECTS THE SEA-LEVEL CANAL

When the Spooner Act was passed in 1902, Congress, following the recommendations of both French and United States Commissions, contemplated a lock canal, as shown by the language of the Act. The lock plan had been evolved by the French from their long experience on the Isthmus. The sea-level plan of De Lesseps, started with so much vigor and enthusiasm, had been discredited. The "battle of the levels" that loomed up so strongly at the Paris Congress in 1879 appeared to have been decided. But the lock plan had not been specifically adopted by Congress as the type to be constructed. There was still some doubt as to the intent of Congress.

But it was not long before Congressional interest was evident. In the fall of 1904, before work on the Isthmus had started, the Committee on Interstate and Foreign Commerce, under that ardent champion of the Nicaragua Canal, William P. Hepburn,

[1] Abbot, *Problems of the Panama Canal*, p. 108.
[2] Statement, June 5, 1906 (Hearings No. 10, p. 17) (U.S.).
[3] Stevens, "The Panama Canal," A.S.C.E., *Transactions*, XCI, 966.

visited Panamá on the transport "Sumner" on the first Congressional "junketing"[4] trip, accompanied by wives and relatives. They were greeted by high officials of the Canal Zone and Panamá, and took in the sights of Colón. They found that yellow fever was starting. Not caring to risk their lives or to endure the hardships of living in the primitive hotels of that time in Panamá, the Congressmen decided against residing ashore and made their headquarters on board the transport. They did take one day, however, to cross the Isthmus to Panamá City where Governor Davis, Chief Engineer Wallace, Minister John Barrett, and a Panamanian delegation headed by Pablo Arosemena, received the distinguished guests. They called upon President Amador, made the usual drive around Ancon Hill, and returned to their ship the same day.[5]

They held hearings on board ship. Wallace made what General Abbot called "suggestive references"[6] to a sea-level canal. The Committee learned a few facts about the Isthmus. When they returned, they became a source for much criticism of the Canal. The Isthmian Canal Commission decided to prepare definite plans and directed its Committee on Engineering to visit the Isthmus and obtain data to determine the type of canal.

The two committee members, Burr and Parsons, arrived at Colón on January 24, 1905, and Governor Davis became a member. They examined the Canal and held sessions. They witnessed a severe norther at Colón and obtained a firsthand demonstration of the power of the sea.

Wallace, on February 1, 1905, submitted a special report on the work since June 1, 1904. The part dealing with the type of canal was very brief. For a sea-level canal he estimated the total excavation in Culebra Cut at 186,000,000 cubic yards. With 100 steam shovels, he expected to excavate 30,000,000 cubic yards a year at a cost of 50 cents per cubic yard. Allowing two

[4] *Engineering Record*, Jan. 7, 1905, LI, 2.
[5] *Panama Star and Herald*, Nov. 25, 1904.
[6] Abbot, *Problems of the Panama Canal*, pp. 24–25.

years for preparation, two for contingencies, and six for excavation, he predicted the Canal could be opened for traffic in ten to twelve years. He claimed it was the most economical type of canal and the simplest in "design, plan, and execution."[7] However, his report did not consider the overwhelming importance of the Chagres. He accepted the excavation of Culebra Cut as the controlling factor and seemed not to have realized the influence of the Chagres on canal history.

On February 14 the Engineering Committee made its report to Admiral Walker. Although it considered several lock projects, it submitted a resolution recommending a sea-level canal with bottom width of 150 feet, a minimum depth of water of 35 feet, with twin tidal locks at Miraflores 1,000 feet long by 100 feet wide, and a great dam at Gamboa; the total cost was estimated at $230,500,000.[8] This was the first definite plan for construction of the Canal submitted to the Commission by its Committee on Engineering. By it the sea-level plan was rescued from oblivion, largely through the efforts of Mr. Wallace. But he must not have realized it at the time, for in March he wrote Commissioner Parsons lamenting that he had heard nothing of the "more important recommendations"[9] he had submitted. The Committee, however, had resurrected the question of the levels and by so doing had caused the long delay in getting canal work started and had become the source of a bitter struggle in Congress.

The first Commission, even when nearing the end of its official existence, continued meetings with all formality, in apparent unconsciousness of its impending fate. At its eighty-sixth meeting on March 15, the sea-level resolution was referred to a committee on engineering plans for study, but no other action was taken.

[7] Wallace to Admiral Walker, Feb. 1, 1905; quoted in his Statement, Feb. 6, 1906 (Hearings No. 18, I, 661, 663) (U.S.).

[8] I.C.C., *Proceedings*, 80th meeting, Feb. 23, 1905, pp. 383–84 (U.S.).

[9] Wallace to Parsons, March 18, 1905 (P.C. Rec. Bur., File Personnel, Wallace) (MS).

At its final meeting on March 29, in the midst of discussion of salaries, bids, sanitation, and other Canal business, the Commission passed a resolution authorizing the design of a seal for the Canal Zone under direction of Gaillard Hunt of the Department of State, and then adjourned *sine die* at 4:10 P.M.

The seal was designed by the artists of Tiffany,[10] after considerable historical research that was not used. The shield showed a Spanish galleon of the fifteenth century passing, head on under full sail, between the high banks of Culebra Cut and into the swells of the Pacific. The sky was aglow with the colors of a tropical sunset. On the upper edge of the shield was a blue band under which were 13 red and white bars—the significant colors of the flag of the United States. Below the shield, inscribed on a banner, were the words: "The Land Divided—The World United." The symbolism was that of the sea-level canal constituting the Strait of Panama. Only a Commission with that idea in mind would have approved that design.

THE BOARD OF CONSULTING ENGINEERS

When the Commission was reorganized by President Roosevelt in April 1905, he also announced the appointment of a Board of Consulting Engineers to consider the type of canal. Following the precedent of De Lesseps in 1879, Roosevelt decided upon an International Board, which he appointed on June 24, 1905. General Davis was selected as chairman, in recognition of his contributions as the first Governor of the Canal Zone. The Board included distinguished engineers from the United States, England, Germany, France, and The Netherlands. One member, Henry L. Abbot, had served on the Comité Technique, had made a profound study of the hydrography of the Chagres River, and was eminently qualified to advise on building the Canal.

The other important event at this critical time in the history of the Canal was the appointment of John F. Stevens as chief engineer.

[10] Gaillard Hunt to Shonts, July 14, 1905 (P.C. Rec. Bur., File 94-A-121) (M.S.).

When Stevens first arrived on the Isthmus in 1905 he was a sea-level-canal man. He had read almost everything written about the Panama Canal since the time of the early Spanish and went to Panamá with a mental picture of a "wide expanse of blue, rippling water and great ships plowing their way through it, like the Straits of Magellan, minus the current."[11] He could not resist asking himself, why not dig a little deeper and get a better canal at sea level rather than save a little time and money by constructing a temporary lock canal. He had not lived on the Isthmus and did not know the problems from firsthand observation. His early opinions were based largely on the study of documents.

But not long after arriving on the Isthmus and talking with engineers, he realized how much the digging of the Panama Canal differed from that of Suez. At Panamá there was a mountain range of irregular hills to cross. He found about twenty streams entering the Chagres valley but had not fully appreciated the great floods and the current they could cause during tropical deluges. Now he saw the enormous task involved in the construction of diversion canals of sufficient size to handle the flood waters.

After discussing the problem with nearly every engineer on the Isthmus he could not find one sea-level advocate in the entire force. He valued their opinion more highly than that of more eminent engineers which had been gleaned from textbooks. He studied the lock project and inclined toward it. Recognizing the problem of the Chagres as the real key to the Canal, he saw the high-lake idea as the solution, which would enable the Chagres to form a great lake instead of being the potential destroyer of the Canal.

But Bohío had been accepted for a long time by the New French Company as the best location for a dam on the Atlantic side. It was also recommended by the Walker Commission of 1901–2.

[11] Stevens' Statement, June 5, 1906 (Hearings No. 10, pp. 13–14) (U.S.).

Stevens questioned this idea on his very first examination of the Canal. "Is it a fact or is it an assumption?"[12] he asked. He compared Bohío and Gatun. On asking his assistants why Bohío was selected over Gatun for a dam site, he was told that it was better; but when he asked why, he received no definite reasons. After checking and finding that no borings had been taken at Gatun, he concluded that his assistants could not have based their statements on practical knowledge.

He had borings made at Gatun and decided that it was the better site, as a lake formed by a dam at Gatun would handle the problem of the torrential Chagres and other streams more effectively. Why not use Gatun for a dam site and make the Chagres the "servant, instead of the master of the situation,"[13] asked Stevens; and from his early days on the Isthmus he became a leading advocate of the lock canal as opposed to the sea-level canal.

The Consulting Board convened at the Commission office in Washington on September 1, 1905. Chairman Shonts forwarded some "well-digested" plans to the Board. They included reports of the Comité Technique, the first Walker Commission of 1901–2, plans for a lock canal by L. W. Bates, one by P. Bunau-Varilla, and more recent data gathered on the Isthmus. But Shonts's letter did not escape criticism in the press. It was considered as indirectly favoring a lock canal and opposing a sea-level canal.

The Board completed its organization and assigned tasks to its committees. It then called upon President Roosevelt on September 11, 1905, at Oyster Bay. When addressing the members, Roosevelt indicated he did not want the recommendations of sycophants. ". . . . I expect you to advise me, not what you think I want to hear but what you think I ought to hear."[14] He expressed hope for a sea-level canal ultimately and stated that

[12] Stevens' Statement, Jan. 23, 1906 (Hearings No. 18, I, 292) (U.S.).

[13] Stevens, "The Panama Canal," op. cit., p. 955.

[14] Board of Consulting Engineers, Report, 1906, p. 12 (U.S.).

the chief advantage of the Panama route was its possibility for a sea-level canal. He urged expedition in their decision.

The Board would have to decide on matters affecting dams on the Isthmus and wanted firsthand impressions. They visited the Wachusetts Dam in Massachusetts and then sailed for the Isthmus, where they arrived on October 4 and spent a week inspecting canal works and holding sessions. Their visit came only a few months after the great crisis on the Canal and at a time of strenuous effort to reorganize and restore progress.

When Stevens appeared before the Board, he was tired, having had only five hours' sleep during the preceding sixty hours. He explained that he had come to the Canal on only thirty-six hours' notice and had spent most of his time trying to create an organization out of chaos and that therefore his experience would not yet justify an opinion. He described the Culebra excavation and how the French had fallen down because they could not dispose of their material. His comparison of their spoil-removing plant to a modern one as "baby carriages to automobiles"[15] was made not as a reflection on the French but as an expression of admiration, for he could not understand how they had accomplished so much with the small plant they had.

He was critical of Canal labor conditions as compared with those in the United States, where rainfall does not stop work; but on the Isthmus, when a cloud appears the men "start out with an umbrella as well as a cigarette."[16] He considered thirty-six hours per week an excellent record for one laborer. When asked if he had any ideas differing from projects submitted to the Board which he desired to incorporate in the final report, Stevens replied he had not, but added "I guess I am the only man in the United States who has not."[17] He appealed for an early decision as to type of canal. ". . . . I cannot, and I do not believe any human being can, do much more than mark time until that is done. I can fix my quarters, and as far as my limited intelli-

[15] Board of Consulting Engineers, *Report*, 1906, p. 286 (U.S.).
[16] *Ibid.*, p. 287.   [17] *Ibid.*, p. 294.

gence permits me I can contract for certain rolling stock. I have contracted for two or three million dollars' worth of plant the last month, but beyond that I cannot go."[18]

After the Board returned to Washington, they continued sessions, and former Chief Engineer Wallace testified on November 3, 1905. He advocated the sea-level canal, answered questions of the members, placed some prepared statements in the record, and received a vote of thanks for the "free frank manner"[19] in which he had presented his contribution. He was restoring his reputation.

When the Board met on November 18, the members were ready for voting and explained their views. Mr. Parsons, a sea-level advocate, pointed out that in building the great railroads and other great enterprises of the world "there is scarcely a case where the projectors have overshot the mark"[20] and did not regret afterwards their failure to build a large size. Would the Panama Canal profit by their experience through constructing a sea-level canal instead of a lock canal?

Chairman Davis made an eloquent plea for a sea-level canal. He was confident that the Chagres—the "lion in the path"[21]— could be handled with the greater knowledge of that turbulent river. He also saw no difficulty in excavating Culebra Cut to sea level.

The vote of the Board was eight for sea-level type and five for lock. The five European members voted for the sea-level. The United States members split, three—Burr, Parsons, and Davis — voting for sea-level and five — Ripley, Randolph, Stearns, Abbot, and Noble—voting for lock.[22] The Board unanimously rejected the plans of Bunau-Varilla and Bates as inexpedient.

Its real work now was over. Only the preparation of a majority report and a minority report remained, and these were submitted to the Commission on January 10, 1906. Alfred Noble wrote the report of the minority for the lock canal.

[18] *Ibid.*
[19] *Ibid*, p. 393.   [20] *Ibid.*, p. 141.   [21] *Ibid.*, p. 143.   [22] *Ibid.*, p. 144.

In the United States the idea of a sea-level canal had a tremendous popular appeal. In Panamá people were decidedly more realistic. The foreign members of the Board were accused of "spending American money, not their own."[23] Panamanians feared that this act had made more distant the day of completion. Roosevelt was disappointed at the result. The Nicaragua Canal promoters and the transcontinental railroads saw it as a chance to delay again the completion of the first waterway across the Isthmus.

Meanwhile Stevens went to Washington, and the report was referred to him. He supported the minority report for an 85-foot summit-level lock-type canal, as preferable for safety and quick passage of ships and as offering the best solution for controlling the flood waters of the Chagres[24]—the fundamentals of the Canal—and at less cost for operation, maintenance, and fixed charges.

The Isthmian Canal Commission also approved the minority report, but even they were not unanimous. The Navy representative, Admiral Endicott, a civil engineer, supported the sea-level plan. Secretary Taft, in forwarding the report to the President, explained that he had been a sea-level man on his first trip to Panamá in 1904 but the report of the minority had changed his views. President Roosevelt studied the report and decided the minority was right. On February 19, 1906, he forwarded the report to Congress, recommending a lock canal and stating that unless otherwise directed a lock canal would be built as contemplated by law. He emphasized in his message the positive views for a lock canal by Chief Engineer Stevens "who will be mainly responsible for the success of this mighty engineering feat, and who has therefore a peculiar personal interest in judging aright."[25]

The issue was now up to the legislators.

---

[23] *Panama Star and Herald*, Dec. 13, 1905.
[24] Board of Consulting Engineers, *op. cit.*, p. xxi (U.S.).
[25] *Ibid.*, p. iv.

THE STRUGGLE IN COMMITTEE

The publication of Poultney Bigelow's article in *The Independent* precipitated a Senate investigation in the form of a resolution on January 9, 1906, calling for an investigation of "all matters" relating to the Panama Canal. Two days later the inquiry started before the Committee on Interoceanic Canals, with Secretary Taft as first witness.

Congressional interest was general, and much information on the Canal was presented to other committees as well. In the House, Mr. Taft opposed vigorously any attempt to excavate until the plant was ready. He quoted James J. Hill as saying the officials would have been "fools to begin any sort of work down there for two years,"[26] until after fullest preparation. The Secretary added that was what Mr. Wallace had done.

Stevens was the first key witness. Senators questioned him on all angles of the Canal and life on the Isthmus. He had ready answers and was judicious and fair. He described how the University Club of Panamá, 300 members strong, had been formed of members that had to be college graduates; he was not eligible under the rules as he was not a graduate, but they made him an honorary vice-president.[27] He opposed changing the five-foot gauge of the Panama Railroad to standard gauge, but suggested that a six-foot gauge would be better than a five-foot.

He outlined his plan to construct Gatun Dam with earth and rock from Culebra Cut and fill from hydraulic pumps. When questioned by Senator John T. Morgan as to the strength of such a dam, Stevens said it was so strong no power could even move it. As for making it stronger, he said, "It is like killing a duck; when you kill him he is dead; there is no use in trying to kill him any 'deader'."[28] He declared that the French canal alignment had been excellently done and predicted the lake would form a "body of dead water"[29] that would be safe from currents.

[26] Taft's Statement, Jan. 15, 1906 (Hearings No. 9, p. 218) (U.S.).

[27] Stevens' Statement, Jan. 16, 1906 (Senate Committee Hearings No. 18, I, 55) (U.S.).

[28] Stevens' Statement, Jan. 23, 1906 (*ibid.*, I, 251) (U.S.).

[29] *Ibid.* (I, 258).

Stevens made a strong case for the superiority of the lock canal and pinned his faith on it, telling the Senators that "for a less price you are getting a superior article."[30] He opposed vigorously the building of a dam at Bohío, because that location would place "percolating material" beneath it and cause loss of water by seepage.

When he was questioned by a Senator about the use of masonry core for the dam, Stevens recommended an earthen dam in spite of the opinion of eminent engineers. "It seems to me when you get a thing that you feel in your own mind to be absolutely safe, when you have not a shadow of a doubt about it, that any additions are superfluous," he continued.

"Yes, if it is absolutely safe. Here I suggest that that is a very positive opinion or conviction that you have," the Senator replied.

"Well, I am a positive man," answered Stevens.

"So I observe. That is the kind of man we want, I think,"[31] said the Senator.

When asked about the effect of Gatun Lake on the population of the Canal Zone, Stevens had definite ideas. He answered: ". . . . I cannot see for the life of me where there are ever going to be any centers of population in the interior of the Isthmus of Panama—not of white people."[32] No white people were going there to farm, and he predicted the population would always consist of natives.

The consulting engineers had recommended dams and a set of locks at Sosa Hill, to form an intermediate-level lake between the summit level and the Pacific. This proposal received Stevens' special disapproval. He recommended all locks be located at Miraflores. He recognized the fundamental error of separating the Pacific locks into two groups and urged that these locks be constructed in one structure, as a desirable change in the plan.[33]

[30] Stevens' Statement, Jan. 23, 1906 (Senate Committee Hearings No. 18, I, 284) (U.S.)

[31] *Ibid.* (I, 296).   [32] *Ibid.* (I, 243).

[33] Stevens to Shonts, cable, Feb. 20, 1906 (P.C. Rec. Bur., File 9-A-1) (MS).

Concluding his statement with a strong plea for the lock canal, he said, "If I had to build that canal with my own money, as between the two plans I should take the high-level plan, even if I expected that my family to come after me for generations would operate it." He had made a great impression on the Committee and was congratulated. Stevens remarked, "I have talked a great deal, and I am not a very good talker"; to which a Senator exclaimed, "I am not so sure of that."[34]

But Stevens was entitled to talk. During his railroad-building days he had seen construction in mountains. He knew the nature of pressures created by deep excavations and the havoc that could be caused. He had made daily trips along the Canal, had trudged along its narrow valleys, and understood the problems involved in its construction. He considered the rock formations of the mountains of Culebra Cut treacherous and the risk too great to venture. He feared that, if a sea-level canal were attempted, slides would occur in such proportions as to endanger the whole undertaking.

Stevens returned to the Isthmus, but had not been there long when the harrassed Shonts cabled that he would keep him advised of developments in Congress and would summon him by cable if he were needed. Stevens did not like this and wired back, "I have said all I can to the committee about the type and protest against being called to leave work, as it will be of no benefit."[35]

Wallace also appeared before the Senate Committee and used the opportunity for a reply to the Taft-Cromwell attack, which he said was so "uncalled for and unjustifiable" that he suddenly had found himself placarded over the country as "utterly lacking in personal and professional honor," and that it might have prevented him from "earning bread for myself and those dependent upon me."[36] He made a special plea for the support of Stevens and for giving him a free hand with fewest possible re-

[34] Stevens' Statement, Jan. 23, 1906 (Hearings No. 18, I, 331) (U.S.).

[35] Stevens to Shonts, cable, March 8, 1906 (P.C. Rec. Bur., File 9-A-1) (MS).

[36] Wallace's Statement, Feb. 5, 1906 (Hearings No. 18, I, 551) (U.S.).

strictions as to hours and pay of workers. He must have had some of his own unfortunate experiences in mind, for he stated that the only successful way to build the Canal would be to place the work in charge of a "pure, absolute despot, and hold his hands up, and keep the wolves off his back." Nor had Wallace changed his views on the sea-level canal, for he advocated that scheme again.

When Parsons appeared he also made a strong plea for a sea-level canal, explaining that the twelve to thirteen years estimated for completion was adopted in order to get a unanimous vote in the Consulting Board. He thought a lock canal would take longer, owing to the manufacture of complicated lock machinery. Nor did Parsons like the dam at Gatun. Senator Morgan wanted to know if the dam was strong enough to bear the water pressure from the wide expanse of the lake. Parsons had to explain to the Senate Authority on Canals that water "pressure is due to the height of the water, and not to its width."[37]

Parsons also attacked the plan for flights of locks in one structure as being fundamentally wrong. He was as positive as he could be and wanted them to understand right then and there. He wanted it recorded as being against his "emphatic protest as a matter of safety."[38] These views were expressed also by Burr.

Shonts was worried; he cabled Stevens on the Isthmus that Burr and Parsons had testified for the sea-level canal and had asserted that the Gatun lock site was not large enough for locks in series. Stevens replied that he had just made a personal examination and urged Shonts to contradict on his authority, stating "if nature had intended triple locks there she could not have arranged matters better."[39]

But Taft was not satisfied with that indefinite rebuttal. He cabled Stevens to measure Gatun Hill. In a few hours Division Engineer Maltby was collecting data, and Stevens cabled Taft

[37] Parsons' Statement, March 13, 1906 (Hearings No. 18, II, 1752–74) (U.S.).
[38] Ibid. (pp. 1779–80).
[39] Stevens to Shonts, cable, March 17, 1906 (P.C. Rec. Bur., File 9-A-1) (MS).

that length for twin triple locks, 3,100 by 300 feet, had been developed by 100 borings; that foundations were perfect and "ideal for construction and permanency."[40]

Wallace testified again in March, attacking Gatun as the site for a dam and locks, because rock foundation was not attainable, earth structure would not prevent seepage, and three locks in flight with a mile-long concrete construction was dangerous unless there was uniform settlement. Shonts again cabled Stevens for support, and Stevens replied with his usual definiteness that the character of foundation for Gatun locks "absolutely prohibits the slightest chance of any settlement. This can not be too strongly emphasized."[41]

April came, and still there was no decision. Again Stevens cabled Taft for a "quick decision for high-level lock type and no mandatory legislation compelling contract work,"[42] as being indispensable for progress. He was becoming irritated at the "vexatious manner" in which the Canal was being handled in Washington. He saw no reason for such dilatoriness on that pressing decision.

It was not until May 17, 1906, that the Committee reported to the Senate. It favored a sea-level canal by the close vote of six to five. The battles in committee were over, and the others were on the floor of Congress. The lock canal appeared defeated.

THE GREAT DECISION

Stevens, who in the meantime had returned to Washington, still banked on the eventual adoption of the lock canal and even then was planning to build the town of Gatun. Because he advocated the lock canal so strenuously and fearlessly he was criticized for wanting to attain glory more quickly by a lock canal than was possible by a sea-level canal. He knew there would be glory, but he was not interested in glory. He knew what he was saying when referring to the glory of building the Canal, he

[40] Stevens to Isthmian, cable, March 20, 1906 (*ibid.*).
[41] Hains' Statement, March 27, 1906 (Hearings No. 18, III, 2111) (U.S.).
[42] Stevens to Taft, cable, April 23, 1906 (P.C. Rec. Bur., File 9-A-1) (MS).

stated before a House Committee on June 5, 1906, "There is a lot of hard work in it; and for any man that goes down there and builds that canal there is nothing left after he gets through."[43]

Senators criticized from the floor of the Senate much of what he had advocated. He assumed he was being criticized also for being in Washington instead of being at work on the Isthmus. He did not care about criticism. "When I am asked my opinion I have got to give it,"[44] was his only comment on this score.

As to the kind of labor, Stevens advocated hiring several nationalities—Italians, Japanese, or Swedes—anything to place them in competition with each other, so that no one group could think it was the only source of labor.

Even in the last stages of this struggle he was not dogmatic about his views concerning the type of canal. If the sea-level canal, as imagined by many people, could be built for $404,-000,000 in ten or twelve years, he stated, "I would say to build it that way and drop all other plans; but you cannot do it."[45] It would depend, he stated, on developing something in the way of excavation and handling of material not then possessed; but any lock canal could be transformed later to sea level.

Stevens faced a real crisis and became a "lobbyist" to help steer the plan through Congress. He went to Roosevelt for assistance but found him "luke-warm" to the lock idea. Stevens said: "I talked to Teddy like a Dutch uncle." Roosevelt was convinced and stood behind him "like a brick."[46]

The first break in the legislative battle came in the House on June 15, 1906, when an amendment to the Canal Appropriation Bill, providing that none of the money appropriated should be used for a sea-level canal, was adopted.

Stevens worked many hours assisting Senators to write speeches on the Canal. The most important was that of Senator Knox, who made the great speech during the Senate debate. To assist him in the explaining, Stevens supplied a large map of the

[43] Stevens' Statement, June 5, 1906 (Hearings No. 10, p. 32) (U.S.).
[44] *Ibid.*, p. 33.   [45] *Ibid.*, pp. 32–33.
[46] *Panama American*, March 20, 1936, pp. 1, 8.

Canal that was placed on the wall of the Senate Chamber. It showed the lock plan and lake in blue; the sea-level canal was shown in red. Knox compared the two plans in a strong and factual analysis. In his final summation of the points of superiority in the lock plan over the sea-level, he supported the Gatun Dam as a safe feature.[47]

On June 21 the Senate bill came to a vote and passed, thirty-six to thirty-one, a narrow margin for an issue so important. The House approved on June 27, and it was signed by President Roosevelt on June 29, 1906. The law provided for a high-level lock-type canal with a summit level of eighty-five feet, as proposed by the minority, consisting of a large summit-level terminal lake on the Atlantic to be formed by damming the Chagres River at Gatun, a 200-foot cut through the central mass, and an intermediate-level lake on the Pacific known as Lake Sosa. Locks were to be located at Gatun, Pedro Miguel, and Sosa Hill. Except for the intermediate-level lake on the Pacific, the plan was essentially the same as that first advanced so eloquently by the Frenchman, Godin de Lépinay, twenty-seven years before at the Paris Congress in 1879.

This was the great decision in building the Panama Canal.

STARTING THE CANAL

Stevens and his engineers had already worked out several plans in advance, and when the decision was made the canal forces were ready. Within twenty-four hours the construction of the town of Gatun was under way, soon to be followed by towns for the Pacific locks, and work was pushed vigorously. Stevens was now free to complete his organization. He selected Joseph Ripley to organize a force for designing locks and dams, and work began on this in August. Ripley, in turn, searched for other men to form a design section; among them were L. D. Cornish, Henry Goldmark, and Edward Schildhauer.

[47] P. C. Knox, "Panama Canal," speech, June 19, 1906 (Reprint from *Congressional Record*, XL, Pt. 9, pp. 8702–8; 59th Cong., 1st sess.) (U.S.).

With his labors in Congress over, Stevens sailed back to the Isthmus with Chairman Shonts, arriving July 4, 1906. He was confident now of the future of the Canal. No longer would uncertainty cause doubt and delay for the builders. No longer could the enemies of any canal at all seize upon that issue to confuse and delay. Stevens was at last free to launch his plan unhampered.

The critical sanitary problem had disappeared, the housing problem for both gold and silver employees was solved. Supplies were being procured with a promptness hitherto unknown, and the Panama Railroad service had shown the improvement to be expected from experienced railroad leadership. Refrigerator cars were making daily trips from the cold-storage plant at Colón to points along the line. An effective Mechanical Division was functioning, with shops at Cristóbal, Matachin, Empire, and Paraiso.

Equipment for excavation had been purchased or contracted for, as follows: 1,100 flatcars, 120 locomotives, 43 steam shovels, and unloaders, spreaders, and dipper dredges. Hotels for gold employees, messes for Europeans, and kitchens for the West Indians were operating, with meals for gold employees at 30 cents each and for silver employees at 30 cents a day. The total force on June 30, 1906, numbered 19,600.

Water had been supplied not only in Colón and Panamá, but in the line towns of Empire, Gorgona, and Bas Obispo. On the reservoir near Mount Hope the only boat that graced its waters was christened "Poultney Bigelow," in honor of its great detractor.

Magoon's and Gorgas' energetic measures for sanitation had produced results. Double-tracking of the railroad and the preparing of terminals and yards for vast quantities of cargo and earth were being pushed with "great vigor." In Culebra Cut the tracks had been laid and ballasted. Air lines had been installed in the Cut for pneumatic drills. The Engineer Department had been moved from Panamá to Culebra and located at the scene of the work on a hill which Governor Magoon called "brains hill."[48]

What a contrast with the previous year Stevens must have sensed as he arrived on July 4! It is not strange that General Abbot wrote, expecting a "rapid and decided progress in works of construction."[49] Stevens was now a member of the Commission, as well as chief engineer. This made him a member of the Executive Committee, which practically made him the Commission, as Chairman Shonts was on the Isthmus very infrequently and only for short intervals.

The decision for a high-level canal meant that, with the closing of the Chagres valley by a great dam at Gatun, the waters would rise and cover the surrounding country to form a great lake. It would cover much of the railroad and many towns and transform mountains into large islands.

It would be necessary to relocate about forty-two miles of railroad. Surveys were started promptly in July by two parties working from opposite ends. To avoid crossing the Canal, the railroad had to be relocated entirely on the east side of the Canal. To enable the hauling of long trains across the Isthmus it was planned to lay the rail on the east berm through Culebra Cut— a route that would afford strange sights to the thousands who would transit by rail.

After the great decision, matters of organization naturally arose. Assistant Chief Engineer John G. Sullivan, in a long memorandum, requested Stevens to establish an office engineer— up to that time nonexistent. But now the time was ripe for starting an office engineering force to plan for engineers in the field. Stevens scribbled in pencil on the margin, "Do it soon as possible. JFS 7/9/06."[50] With only eight small and two large drafting tables for equipment the office was started. Stevens thought also of forming large construction divisions but delayed decision pending exact location of dams and locks on the Pacific.

---

[48] *Panama Star and Herald,* Oct. 24, 1906.

[49] Abbot, *Problems of the Panama Canal,* p. 35.

[50] Sullivan to Stevens, July 7, 1906 (P.C. Rec. Bur., File 2-C-13) (MS).

With all three members of the Executive Committee—Shonts, Stevens, and Magoon—on the Isthmus, discussion centered on the organization of the Commission. Stevens drafted a proposed executive order to amend the order of April 1, 1905.[51] It arranged the permanent construction organization into departments under the chairman. It gave the chief engineer power to act on the Canal Zone in the absence of the chairman. It separated government and sanitation, and abolished the Executive Committee.

Shonts forwarded the draft from Culebra, adding his desire to separate the governorship from the position of Minister to Panamá. He suggested that the organization consist of Chief Engineer, Governor, Chief Sanitary Officer, General Counsel, General Purchasing Officer, General Auditor, and Disbursing Officer. The Commission should consist of Chairman, Chief Engineer, Chief Sanitary Officer, General Counsel, Manager of Labor and Quarters, an Army Engineer and a Navy Engineer.

Relations between Stevens and Magoon had not been smooth, and Shonts expected trouble with Magoon when it became apparent he was left out in the reorganization. Fortunately, Taft had advised Shonts in May that Magoon was going to the Philippines and a change would be easy to make.

At this time Shonts wrote to Taft that preparatory work on the Canal was finished and actual construction was starting. For these reasons it would be "suicidal to commence the great task before us without a clear-cut organization with centralized power."[52] He asked Taft to arrange with the President to issue the reorganization order so as to fit in with Magoon's transfer.

Stevens wrote directly to Roosevelt, supporting Shonts and urging subordination of everything to construction. He wanted it a "one-man proposition." Although he advised the President that he had collaborated with Mr. Shonts, the statement was a

---

[51] C. A. McIlvaine, Conversation with the author, March 20, 1941.

[52] Shonts to Secretary of War, July 31, 1906 (P.C. Rec. Bur., File 2-C-13) (MS).

"polite fiction,"[53] for he himself had drafted the proposed order.

Governor Magoon did not like some features of the reorganization. He wrote Mr. Taft, requesting him not to act until after they had conferred, stating, "Things are moving smoothly, and there is no reason for making changes"[54] until after a conference at least. Taft concurred with Magoon and replied that he was anxious to see him and wanted him to talk with the President before reorganization was put into effect. Taft also stated that, although he agreed with much of what Shonts and Stevens planned, there were "some aspects of it that they do not fully appreciate the importance of." Ominous words! What did he mean?

In spite of Magoon's efforts, after Shonts returned to Washington he was able to write Stevens that both Roosevelt and Taft approved subordinating the governorship to the Commission and separating that office from the post of Minister to Panamá.[55]

The problem of eliminating Magoon was solved earlier than Stevens expected. A revolution had broken out in Cuba in August, and United States forces occupied the island. Magoon's departure was hastened, and he left the Isthmus on September 25, 1906, without relief, after turning over his duties to Executive Secretary Harry D. Reed.

Magoon had endeared himself to both Panamanians and North Americans on the Isthmus. He received an impressive send-off, with school children lining the streets, bands playing, and a Marine Guard of Honor. He had produced excellent results in sanitation and had done well as the second Governor of the Canal Zone. It was not surprising to hear of his appointment to a better position as Provisional Governor of Cuba, in recognition of his work.

His transfer without relief represented the first important break in the Shonts Commission. Coupled with the failure to fill

[53] Bennett, *History of the Panama Canal*, p. 222.

[54] Magoon to Taft, Aug. 20, 1906 (P.C. Rec. Bur., File Personnel, Magoon) (MS).

[55] Shonts to Stevens, Aug. 22, 1906 (P.C. Rec. Bur., File 2-C-13) (MS).

an earlier vacancy caused by the transfer of Colonel Ernst, speculation quickly arose as to the nature of what was to come.

Work on the Canal took shape rapidly, changing the appearance of the Isthmus as tracks and plants for excavation of Gatun, Pedro Miguel, and Sosa lock sites were assembled and installed. The dam site at Gatun was cleared, and tracks were laid for dumping spoil from Culebra Cut. Stevens obtained an option on a rock quarry at Porto Bello and ordered a crushing plant to prepare rock for concrete to be used in the Atlantic locks. In October 1906 excavation started at Gatun Lock site, the yardage at Culebra Cut mounted to 327,009 cubic yards, and forty-eight steam shovels were at work on the line of the Canal. People called Culebra "Stevens City."[56]

Steam shovels, unloaders, and spreaders were being assembled as they arrived on the Isthmus. W. G. Bierd, the General Manager of the Panama Railroad, was developing the track-shifter, the machine which—later manufactured in the shops at Gorgona—completed the set of these four great instruments of excavation.[57] Assistant Chief Engineer John G. Sullivan and George D. Brooke of the Department of Motive Power and Machinery devised a side extension to the Lidgerwood flatcars so that spoil could be dumped well clear of the tracks.[58]

In spite of this record of achievement on the Isthmus, there had developed a critical undercurrent at Washington. Secretary Taft did not want Stevens and Shonts to dominate relations with Panamá. He feared they would take the same attitude toward labor on the Isthmus that they would if working for Mr. Hill on the Great Northern. Taft did not want any more difficulties.

Roosevelt recognized Stevens' strength and considered him an "admirable man." But he observed that Stevens had failed to develop anyone to relieve him. He also had noticed Stevens' independence of both Congress and Panamá as representatives of public opinion. Thoughts similar to these were in Roosevelt's mind when he wrote Taft in August that Stevens could "render himself worse than valueless in just one way, and that is by thinking himself indispensable."[59]

Toward the end of 1906 the work of preparation was almost complete. The organization for construction was perfected, with chief control located on the Isthmus. Design work for locks and dams was under way. The plant was ready for actual excavation. The working force was well organized, well housed, and well fed. Morale was high, and the Chief Engineer was giving personal attention to the erection of the Culebra Clubhouse and to encouraging other recreation. It was with this background that Stevens was able to predict, even at so early a date, that the Panama Canal would be opened for traffic by January 1, 1915.

[59] Roosevelt to Taft, Aug. 27, 1906 (Taft Papers: Taft-Roosevelt, Box II) (MS).

CHAPTER XI

ROOSEVELT VISITS THE ISTHMUS AND STEVENS BECOMES DICTATOR OF THE ZONE

They are doing something which will redound immeasurably to the credit of America, which will benefit all the world, and which will last for ages to come. Under Mr. Shonts and Mr. Stevens and Doctor Gorgas this work has started with every omen of good fortune.—THEODORE ROOSEVELT.[1]

BACKGROUND OF ROOSEVELT'S VISIT TO THE ISTHMUS

Beginning with Poultney Bigelow's ill-advised article published in January 1906, the Canal became the object of attacks by systematic propaganda. Some were directed against features of the Canal and some against its location at Panamá. Advocates of Nicaragua did their share, and the transcontinental railroads carried on their own campaigns. Their object probably was to prevent the building of any canal at all by making it difficult to secure canal employees in the United States. The troubles of the first Commission, the chaos following the Wallace affair, and the yellow-fever epidemic gave much material to an army of critics.

Roosevelt had to answer these critics and could do so only after a personal observation of the Isthmus. For a long time he had desired to visit the Isthmus but could not act until after the Senate approved the lock plan. It was not until June 25, 1906, that the White House announced that the President, accompanied by Secretary Taft and Chairman Shonts, would visit Panamá in November, a month he chose because it was one of the two most rainy and most unhealthful months of the year. He wanted to see the Isthmus under its most adverse conditions.

There was much gratification on the Isthmus at this announcement, and Governor Magoon enthusiastically cabled Secretary

[1] President Theodore Roosevelt, *Special Message . . . . to Congress Concerning the Panama Canal . . . . ,* Dec. 17, 1906, p. 28 (U.S.).

228

Taft. In the United States there was much criticism. This trip was a violation of the precedent established by Washington, that the President should not leave the boundaries of the country. But Roosevelt had decided to ignore that unwritten law.

There was one serious drawback. The Zone at that time had no hotel. The Tivoli Hotel was only partly completed, with the main building well under way and the kitchen started. Stevens wanted the hotel ready in October and directed the Master Builder, then going on leave to the United States, to check on supplies and furnishings. Stevens himself checked on details of construction—chef's and servants' quarters, electrical equipment and plumbing, and also organization of the force. It was a task of constant pushing, with Stevens behind every move and the workers supporting him with enthusiasm.

Shonts feared there would be no place ready for the President, and with his delicate diplomatic touch suggested to Mr. Taft that the President's party might prefer to remain on board ship at Colón; but Roosevelt evidently insisted upon living ashore, as he wanted to see everything. Shonts had given Stevens no definite plans but anxiously cabled him inquiring if part of the Tivoli could not be finished for the President's party in November. Overworked Stevens answered with a request for facts: "How many in party? How many rooms needed? Just what date in November?"[2]—and advised him that everything depended upon getting furniture and kitchen gear. Incidentally, these were then on order in Shonts' office.

As the time for Roosevelt's visit approached, it became the main topic of general discussion on the Zone and in Panamá. Quite unexpectedly an opportunity came for a dress rehearsal for the reception of the President, when word was received of an impending visit by Secretary of State Elihu Root. Orders were rushed to all the towns and villages along the line to clean up and make themselves attractive. Houses were to be painted or whitewashed.

[2] Stevens to Shonts, cable, Aug. 20, 1906 (P.C. Rec. Bur., File 28-I-62) (U.S.).

When Secretary Root crossed the Isthmus on September 21, 1906, he saw a more orderly and presentable Canal Zone. Root's itinerary included all stations on the Canal. Points of interest were indicated. School children were paraded in his honor along the line.

The engineers impressed him as being "first-rate specimens of clear-headed, active and competent Americans of the constructing type."[3] Evidently it took more than the building of a canal to make this great North American jurist enthusiastic about the Panama Canal.

Detailed plans for the President's visit began on September 1, when Mr. Taft cabled Governor Magoon that the President planned to arrive in mid-November for three or four days. He suggested that only one entertainment be given for the President, as the purpose of the visit was to inspect the Canal work. He directed Magoon to confer with the Chief Engineer and arrive at a program that would afford a full conception of the Canal project without "overdoing matters."[4]

Magoon conferred with President Amador. He did not know the exact plan desired for President Roosevelt, nor did he know if Roosevelt would enter Panamá. Nevertheless, he wrote Taft a tentative plan, based on using the Tivoli and starting inspections from the Pacific end.[5] But he did not know.

In his dilemma he appealed to Stevens, who dictated a three-day program for the President, designed to show all the Canal works. He assured the Governor of his ability to have the Tivoli ready.[6] Then Stevens cabled Chairman Shonts, "Should know quick needs for Tivoli November party."[7] He also wanted to know if it was intended to touch Panamanian territory.

Affairs in Cuba had taken a bad turn, and Taft suddenly left for that politically volcanic island without acting on these

---

[3] Root to Roosevelt, Oct. 12, 1906; quoted in *Panama Star and Herald*, Oct. 20, 1906.

[4] Taft to Magoon, cable, Sept. 1, 1906 (P.C. Rec. Bur., File 28-I-62) (MS).

[5] Magoon to Taft, Sept. 8, 1906 (*ibid.*).

[6] Stevens to Magoon, Sept. 11, 1906 (*ibid.*).

[7] Stevens to Shonts, cable, Sept. 12, 1906 (*ibid.*).

The Steam Shovel, Culebra Cut, 1913

One of the four great instruments of excavation used by the United States in
building the Panama Canal

Courtesy of The Panama Canal

THE RAPID UNLOADER

One of the four great instruments of excavation used by the United States in
building the Panama Canal. Train of flatcars with Lidgerwood plow,
Tavernilla Dumps, 1906

Courtesy of The Panama Canal

THE SPREADER, COROZAL DUMPS, 1907
One of the four great instruments of excavation used by the United States in
building the Panama Canal

THE TRACKSHIFTER, 1906

One of the four great instruments of excavation used by the United States in
building the Panama Canal

urgent requests. Nor did he act upon the proposed reorganization of the Commission, which he wished held over until his return.

The weeks passed, but still there was no decision by the President. Governor Magoon departed, leaving Stevens in full charge on the Isthmus. Stevens kept the cables busy with messages, trying to find out plans but could not. He cabled Shonts, suggesting that Mr. Root would make a good adviser on the November party.[8]

Meanwhile Shonts, dealing directly with the President, obtained Roosevelt's approval of the plans on October 8, afterward advising Stevens of the President's approval of plans for both the reorganization and the visit. Stevens was gratified and cabled back: "Began to think everybody dead." He still had to find out how many would be in the party, as Shonts had failed to mention that incidental.

Stevens was perturbed also about the pending reorganization. He feared adverse action by Taft after his return from Cuba, because of "certain influence" there, for Magoon was in Cuba at the time. However, he advised no "concessions," recommended that the "vacant office you do not mention,"[9] which could have meant nothing but the governorship, should be filled by the chairman or chief engineer for the sake of future harmony. He apparently saw the time ahead when his own service might be terminated and warned that material changes in the reorganization would be regarded as freeing him of "all obligations." What did he have in mind? Was he thinking of resigning from his post then? Was he becoming disgruntled?

At last Shonts cabled that the President would sail for the Isthmus about November 8. The Navy prepared special quarters on the battleship "Louisiana" for the Presidential party. Almost at the last minute it was discovered that there were no President's flags on the Isthmus for the great event, and Stevens had to cable for some to be sent by the next steamer.

[8] Stevens to Shonts, cable, Oct. 13, 1906 (*ibid.*).
[9] Stevens to Shonts, cable, Oct. 15, 1906 (*ibid.*).

Shonts again conferred with Roosevelt and Root on reorganization. The President agreed to all essential proposals put up by the Chairman and Stevens and agreed to settle the organization matter during his visit to the Canal Zone.[10]

Preparations on the Isthmus gained momentum, and Stevens took full charge of arrangements for the expected arrival of the President at Cristóbal on November 15. Mayors of Canal Zone towns received instructions to clean up, prepare flag displays, and make arches of bamboo or palms. Stevens requested the Commanding Officer of the Marine garrison, Major C. C. Long, to prepare a saluting battery. There was no saluting battery in the Canal Zone, and the Major had to borrow a battery and ammunition from Panamá. Platforms erected at La Boca (now Balboa) for Mr. Root's visit were shifted to a dock at Cristóbal. Division Engineer F. B. Maltby and Chief of Material and Supplies W. G. Tubby were appointed to decorate the dock at Cristóbal for the reception at the end of the visit. Executive Secretary Reed was to arrange police protection and handle the crowds.

Stevens invited President and Mrs. Amador to accompany him and Mrs. Stevens to Colón to spend the night before the visit at the Tubby home. General Manager Bierd was directed to place the track from Dock 11 in first-class condition, with the additional precaution that just prior to the movement of the President's train "every switch from this track out thru the yards to the main line be spiked."[11]

Last-minute changes in plan were proposed and had to be handled. The list of persons to be received at Cristóbal had to be revised. The Fire Department wanted to put on a display. Invitations had to be sent for a reception at the Tivoli for the President.

The Republic of Panamá declared the day of arrival a national holiday; the Alcalde of Panamá City, San José F. de la Ossa, proclaimed a day of "joy and exalted enthusiasm" and

[10] Shonts to Stevens, cable, Oct. 22, 1906 (P.C. Rec. Bur., File 28-I-62) (U.S.).
[11] Stevens to W. G. Bierd, Nov. 6, 1906 (*ibid.*).

called for suspension of all local differences during the welcome of the President, warning that "all thinkers, sociologists and philosophers of the universe have their eyes upon us in penetrating scrutiny."[12] All arrangements were complete, and the programs were distributed.

Unexpectedly early, a battleship was sighted emerging from a rain squall off flag-decorated Colón on Wednesday, November 14. It was the "Louisiana," displaying the President's flag. The guns from Dock 11 gave a twenty-one-gun salute. The telegraph wires vibrated with the long-awaited news that the President had arrived at 1:00 p.m. Receptionists from all points rushed to the Atlantic terminal.

ROOSEVELT'S THREE DAYS ON THE ISTHMUS

The first formality was a courtesy call by President and Señora Amador to welcome the Roosevelts, which did not take long. The Presidential party remained on board ship through the fourteenth, as Roosevelt did not wish to upset plans all set for the next day. He required some rest, for the three days ahead would be strenuous even for a man of his extraordinary vigor.

The next morning the program started early. It called for a reception on Dock 11 at 7:30 a.m. President Amador, Shonts, Stevens, and Bierd arrived on time. Suddenly, from the shore end came the President at a vigorous pace to greet them. "Good morning, gentlemen, I have already had two hours' work this morning."[13] He had been rowed ashore two hours before and had taken a stroll on the waterfront. The reception was brief.

Near by, at the foot of the pier, were some saddle horses. The best-trained one was led to the President, but he observed a more fractious-looking mount, seized the reins of its bridle, and mounted. Wearing a southwester with its broad rim resting on his shoulders, he rode through the town in the lead of his escort,

---

[12] J. F. de la Ossa, *Proclamation of November 14, 1906 (ibid.)*.
[13] S. M. Hitt, Memorandum to the author, March 8, 1941.

with horse hoofs splattering mud far and wide, listened to the songs of the school children, and made a short address near the railroad depot—all in time to board the special train leaving Colón at 8:10 A.M.

The trip across the Isthmus was made slowly, with the train stopping at small stations for Roosevelt to view the school children. Whenever he left the train he was in the van of his party. When the train stopped at Las Cascadas, a group of natives gathered around the observation platform. He went out to greet them, reached over and helped one to the platform, talked a few minutes in Spanish, and was acclaimed.

Not until 11:00 A.M. did the train arrive at the provisional station that had been erected near Tivoli Crossing in Ancon. The two presidents separated, Amador returning to the Presidencia in Panamá and Roosevelt to the Tivoli between lines of enthusiastic observers. But before going to his quarters, Roosevelt asked to see Ancon Hospital. Led by Chief of Police Shanton on his charger, the President toured the hospital grounds.[14] He then went to La Boca (now Balboa), where he boarded the tug "Bolivar," steamed down the Rio Grande to the Bay, around Naos, Perico, and Flamenco Islands, observing the approaches to the future Canal as De Lesseps had done many years before.

When the "Bolivar" returned to La Boca after the trip, Roosevelt, instead of going to the Tivoli for a prepared lunch, suddenly decided to dine with employees at La Boca Hotel and descended upon them in his "usual democratic" manner. He liked the food; he questioned the men about its quality and heard their complaints. He went into the kitchen, where he wanted to know every detail, and then returned to his headquarters at the Tivoli for a short rest.[15]

Since early morning there had been hard intermittent rains, but there was no change in the program. By 3:00 P.M. large crowds were gathered along the line of march and at the Cathe-

[14] *Panama Star and Herald,* Dec. 17, 1906.
[15] *Ibid.,* Nov. 26, 1906.

dral Plaza, where the ceremonies were to take place. Central Avenue was decorated with arches, flags, and lanterns. Flags of the United States and Panamá were draped about the Cathedral and banners from buildings. The Plaza was "ablaze with color and designs"[16] expressing welcome to the guest. The front platform of the Cathedral, chosen as the place for the ceremonies, was covered by a canopy of bright color and bordered by decorative palms.

The rain abated into a light drizzle, and balconies soon filled with the expectant and happy. The procession was late, and it was not until about 4:00 P.M. that the expression *"Ya viene"* could be heard from the populace as they caught glimpses of their new hero, who had displaced De Lesseps as the great patron of the Panama Canal.

The long procession was headed by the carriages of the two presidents, escorted by a detachment of 100 Panamanian police dressed like the "Rough Riders," the regiment in the Spanish-American War with which the name of Roosevelt was so closely associated. Waves of enthusiasm surged through the crowds as the President passed. Roosevelt, standing in his carriage, acknowledged the gracious accolades until he ascended the Cathedral steps.

There President Amador made the address of welcome, expressing fullest appreciation of Roosevelt's part in the struggle for a waterway across the Isthmus. He lauded the great work of the "indefatigable Stevens," and characterized Colonel Gorgas as the "guardian of the health and life of the soldiers of toil."[17] He acclaimed Roosevelt as the Commander in Chief of an American-Panamanian alliance in the great struggle of progress.

When applause stopped, Roosevelt replied that this was the first time a President of the United States had stepped on foreign soil since the time of Washington. He confirmed the views presented by Doctor Amador of partnership in the "giant engineer-

[16] *Ibid.*, Nov. 19, 1906.
[17] *Ibid.*

ing feat of the ages" and prophesied a great future for the Isthmus. He also warned that revolution would mean the end of the Republic, but he promised the United States would never interfere with Panamá.

His "striking masculine pose, bold visage and straightforward address"[18] won the crowd completely. He turned toward Dr. Amador, and the two presidents shook hands while the ardent applause of the drenched spectators marked the passing of another historic event in Isthmian life.

In the evening there was a dinner at the Presidencia and fireworks. Later in the evening the party was entertained in the parlors of the Commercial Club in a tropical setting of palms, evergreens, and colors. The two presidents and the ladies entered the hall through an avenue of guests, to the strains of patriotic music. Roosevelt broke ranks and circled the room until halted by a group of enthusiastic young Panamanians. Young José Lefevre addressed the President, portraying Panamá as a land where school children were the only standing army. Roosevelt, touched by the sentiment, was quick to express his pleasure to see the "army of which any country may be proud—that of the next generation,"[19] and bowed to the cheers.

The next day, in a pouring tropical rain, the President got an early start at 6:30 A.M., dressed in a light white suit, khaki leggings, a Panama hat, and raincoat.

The train stopped first at Pedro Miguel, where he visited the lock site. He climbed into a steam shovel, asked questions about the machine, and observed its operation. He saw a track-shifter relocating tracks on a spoil dump. He talked affably to the men. One asked for more pay, and Roosevelt asked him if the President should not have more. The man replied, "Oh, we'll vote for that,"[20] and the trip continued.

The special train stopped by a dump to watch the unloading of a dirt train with a Lidgerwood unloader. A large plow was

[18] *Panama Star and Herald*, Nov. 19, 1906.
[19] *Ibid.*   [20] *Ibid.*, Nov. 26, 1906.

pulled through the entire length of the train by a cable from a steam-operated drum on a car at the opposite end. When the exhibition was over, the load was on one side and Roosevelt was covered with mud.

He visited Negro quarters at Rio Grande, asked questions about their living conditions and treatment, and listened to their complaints, especially about commissary prices. Roosevelt appeared determined not to be led around but rather to seek exact information and to break through the barriers that always surround high officials.

In Culebra Cut he saw steam shovels in action, power drilling and blasting, dirt trains on their way to near-by dumps, and other dirt trains on the way to dump their loads for railroad embankments and large dams. Banners spread on steam shovels reflected the spirit of the men: "We'll help you dig it" and "We're going to put it through."

A mule-drawn carriage took the President from Culebra Station to the Chief Engineer's home for lunch and a change of clothing. On the way, men watched from windows of the Administration Building but could not see through the carriage curtains, drawn because of rain. When the carriage returned, it stopped in front of the steps of the Administration Building. Roosevelt pulled back the curtains, alighted in the rain, and rushed two steps at a time into the building, followed by Stevens and his party. From this building on the hill he could see the Culebra Cut extending southward between Gold Hill and Contractors Hill, and he could see the activity of cutting through the continental divide—all in a panorama of jungle-covered hills of extraordinary beauty.

Employees gathered in the drafting room and lined up to meet the President. Roosevelt shook hands with each one, making some personal remark suggested by his name, button, or other feature; bade them good-bye and turned toward the door. Cries of "Speech! Speech!" came, but Roosevelt shook his head and said he had too much to do. The men persisted, formed around him, blocked the doorway, and almost forced him back. In response to their high spirits and friendliness he changed his mind,[21] nodded vigorously, showed his famous teeth, returned into the room and addressed them while Chief Engineer Stevens sat on a window sill with a twinkle in his eye. Roosevelt told them they were earning a right to the country's gratitude, like soldiers in a great war. He noted the pride of achievement in evidence on the Isthmus and appealed to the men to identify themselves with the digging of the Canal so that their own work would confer the "patent of nobility"[22] upon them. But those young North Americans did not think of themselves as heroes and took his sentiments simply as well-meant political flattery.

After leaving Culebra he went as far as Gorgona and made intermediate stops, asking questions on the way. He inspected shops and foundries at Bas Obispo, always brushing ceremony aside and setting a swift pace for his followers and winning admiration from the crowds that no rain could keep from gathering whenever he passed. As he advanced along the Cut, steam shovels blew their shrill whistles with a variety of pitches and people waved their hats and cheered.

During that day he had walked ties, jumped ditches, and climbed hills. When the party arrived at the Tivoli at about 5:00 P.M., Roosevelt announced he was feeling "fine, and ready to start out tomorrow morning at the same time."[23]

The next morning the President started early on his third day, again dressed in hiking clothes. The party included many officials and leaders. At Paraiso a landslide forced his train to enter Culebra Cut, which had been heavily inundated by the rains. Many of the scenes of the day before were repeated. While he was passing between Gold and Contractors Hills, drillers gave cheers and then set off a dynamite salute of twenty-one blasts in honor of the Commander in Chief of the Army of the Panama Canal.

[21] S. M. Hitt, Memorandum to the author, March 8, 1941.
[22] *Panama Star and Herald,* Nov. 19, 1906.
[23] *Ibid.,* Nov. 26, 1906.

At Empire he inspected gold-priced bachelor quarters for gold-salaried employees, saw where an undermined track between Obispo and Matachin had sent a locomotive into the swollen Chagres, and was greeted by school children at Gatun. Here, with Chief Engineer Stevens and Division Engineer Maltby, he climbed the hills of Gatun to see the young town of Gatun near by, to watch shovels working at the side of the future locks and dam, and to gaze upon the vast jungle which some day would be covered by the water of Gatun Lake, as Stevens explained the features from large maps. He had to acknowledge cheers and make another speech, repeating many statements expressed at other places; he then speeded on toward Cristóbal, stopping by Mount Hope to inspect the water reservoir. There he saw the launch "Poultney Bigelow" placidly resting on the waters of the reservoir that had been condemned by that able but indiscreet writer.

That evening at Cristóbal the farewell reception was held on Dock 11 by the employees, and Roosevelt had to make another address. He emphasized the importance of the Canal undertaking and how gratifying it was that he could tell the people back home that he could guarantee success. He again stressed the similarity of digging the Canal to a great war and praised the workers for their spirit everywhere shown.

Suddenly, a voice from the rear yelled: "How about Mr. Bigelow?" The President replied, "Oh, you refer to the boat on the reservoir?" and then proceeded to give the vanquished Poultney Bigelow another indirect castigation.

He expressed to them the wish that one of his own boys were old enough to work on the Canal. He promised to provide a medal for those who for a certain time had been "engaged in this war." Concluding, he said: "You are doing a work the like of which has not been seen in the ages, a work that shall last through the ages to come, and I pledge you as President of the United States, and speaking for the people of the United States, every ounce of support and help and assistance that it is in my power to give you, so that we together, you backed by the people of the United States, may speedily bring this greatest of works to a triumphant conclusion."[24]

After the reception he boarded the "Louisiana" and departed, leaving the Isthmus in a state of animated enthusiasm not felt since the visits of Ferdinand de Lesseps.

RESULTS OF ROOSEVELT'S VISIT

All of Roosevelt's work was not sight-seeing, gathering of information, or receiving impressions. He also made important decisions, one being his approval of the reorganization that Stevens had drafted and his intimation to Mr. Stevens that he would be appointed as chairman. On his last day on the Isthmus he signed an Executive Order of November 17, 1906, reorganizing the Commission, the wording of which even surpassed the hopes of Stevens in its tendency toward centralization.[25]

It provided for quarterly meetings on the Isthmus and abolished the Executive Committee. It organized the work into departments under the chairman. The title of Governor of the Canal Zone was abolished and his duties were assigned to the general counsel. Sanitation was separated from government and made into a new department. Material and Supplies were placed under the chief engineer. In the absence of the chairman from the Isthmus, the chief engineer was to have full power within the Canal Zone.

With this authority vested in him, Shonts on November 19 appointed the following heads of departments: Stevens as chief engineer, R. R. Rogers as general counsel, Colonel Gorgas as chief sanitary officer, D. W. Ross as general purchasing officer, E. S. Benson as general auditor, E. J. Williams as disbursing officer, and Jackson Smith as manager of labor, quarters, and

[24] President Theodore Roosevelt, *Special Message* . . . . *to Congress Concerning the Panama Canal* . . . ., Dec. 17, 1906; Appendix 1 (Society of the Chagres, *Yearbook 1911*, pp. 17–23).

[25] I.C.C., *Annual Report for the Year Ending Dec. 1, 1906*, p. 16; pp. 151–53: Exhibit K (U.S.).

subsistence.[26] Three days after the President's departure the Commission gave its approval to these appointments.[27]

On the same day Chairman Shonts interpreted the new order to the heads of departments, saying that its essence was "concentration of power in a single head." He appealed to them to avoid the "rock of self-exploitation,"[28] and warned that the decisions of Stevens would govern in his own absence.

By the end of the month the process of centralization was completed and the Chairman had left the Isthmus. The reorganization could only mean that Stevens had become supreme in the Canal Zone. Thus at last the centralized organization developed by the French had been forced upon the government as a necessity. It was essentially the type of organization that Governor Davis had urged in 1904.

After President Roosevelt returned to Washington he sent an illustrated special message to Congress, reporting on his trip. That was another precedent-smashing act, which brought forth a volume of criticism; but Congressmen proceeded to order many copies for their constituents who liked photographs.

The account of his inspection was detailed, including even his inspection of "between twenty and thirty water closets," one of which displeased him so much that he required Colonel Gorgas to submit a statement. He reported that preparatory work was completed and real construction would start January 1. He lauded the work done on the Isthmus and the resistance that had been made to the pressure from the ill-informed for all kinds of experiments. He slashed at critics of the Canal and reported their complaints as groundless. He singled out Stevens for special mention, lauded his "admirable results" and hoped for their continuance in the future.

He described the work in Culebra Cut and on locks and dams but announced that a special engineering board would visit the Isthmus the following April to check their location. He

[26] I.C.C., *Circular*, Nov. 20, 1906 (P.C. Rec. Bur., File 2-C-13) (MS).
[27] I.C.C., *Minutes*, 116th meeting, Nov. 30, 1906, p. 42 (U.S.).
[28] *Panama Star and Herald*, Nov. 26, 1906.

announced the plan to build by contract as proposed by Stevens and classed the Commission with its seven heads as a "clumsy executive instrument." He looked forward to the time when steam-shovel crews would emulate the competition in excavation results that existed among Navy gun crews at battle practices.

The message stopped the barrage of critical writings and placed detractors on the defensive. It aroused widespread interest throughout the United States and assisted Stevens in his struggle with problems of construction and labor. Roosevelt presented to Congress a picture of confidence when he stated: "Of the success of the enterprise I am as well convinced as one can be of any enterprise that is human."[29]

The President's trip to the Canal created so much confidence that the Commission arranged to send a relief map of the completed Canal to the Jamestown Tercentennial Exposition in 1907,[30] where it would be viewed by thousands from all over the world.

[29] President Theodore Roosevelt, *Special Message* .... *to Congress Concerning the Panama Canal* . . . ., Dec. 17, 1906, p. 28 (U.S.).

[30] *Engineering Record*, Oct. 12, 1907, LVI, 412.

CHAPTER XII

THE CONTRACT CRISIS AND RESIGNATION
OF STEVENS

*The people talk about the success of the army engineer at Panama, but
it was fortunate that Mr. Stevens preceded us. The real problem of digging
the canal has been the disposal of the spoil and no army engineer in America could have laid out the transportation scheme as Mr. Stevens did. We
are building on the foundation he laid, and the world can not give him too
much credit.—*GEORGE W. GOETHALS.[1]

*Under Mr. Stevens the work of digging began, and the work of making
the detailed plans with reference to the construction.—*WILLIAM H. TAFT.[2]

STEVENS PROPOSES THE CONTRACT PLAN

As soon as Stevens' preparatory work was well under way,
the question of constructing the Canal by contract or by day
labor under direct supervision came to the front. The idea of
contracts, however, was neither novel nor new. The French had
used that method. The large railroads of the United States,
when building the transcontinental lines, used the contract
method. Contractors of the country had followings of experienced construction employees—foremen, superintendents, and
engineers. Advocates for contractors claimed that, by using
them, all these experienced men would be available for work on
the Canal.

Shonts was an experienced railroad man. He wanted the
work done by contract. Stevens had built railroads with contractors and had worked for contractors. He was sympathetic,
but practical and realistic. He wanted bidding to be based on
"intelligent specifications"[3] before he could decide.

With preparatory work rapidly nearing completion and
with decision as to type of canal close at hand, decision as to

---

[1] Quoted in Pepperman, *Who Built the Panama Canal?*, p. 4.

[2] Taft's Statement, Jan. 16, 1908 (Hearings No. 19, p. 1) (U.S.).

[3] Stevens' Statement, Jan. 16, 1906 (Hearings No. 18, I, 49 (U.S.).

243

method of work became urgent. Was it to be by contract or by the government? Shonts was so determined to build by contract that he even stated early in 1906 that should "we not be permitted to build the canal in that way we will step aside and let somebody else take it in hand."[4]

At first, building by the government had no powerful advocates, although, when appearing before the Senate Committee on Interoceanic Canals in March 1906, ex-Chief Engineer Wallace had mentioned the letting of contracts under supervision of the Corps of Engineers as a possible method of completion. But this was not popular at the time.

Stevens, carrying on the work on the Isthmus between his trips to Washington, continued to be hampered by political influence as well as "red tape." Critical articles in newspapers read by men 2,000 miles from home assumed an exaggerated importance and nullified his efforts. The men on the Isthmus would say of him: "He is a nice fellow and we like him, but hell, he may not be here six weeks." This was difficult for a man looking only for results in an area about which public opinion had been distorted by all sorts of specious and disingenuous propaganda.

When explaining his needs to Congress in May 1906, Stevens emphasized retention of sanitation and quarters under the government. He suggested dividing the work into several parts, rather than turning it over to one contractor. Stevens knew that contractors were not familiar with work on the Isthmus and that they did not have proper equipment. These factors, he explained, would require them to include all classes of contingencies in their estimates and cause delays in assembling the plant and starting the work. Stevens already had ordered a plant of the best equipment so that it would be ready for the contractors. He wanted to save time and obtain reasonable bids. Although he presented the case for construction by contract, he indicated dissenting views. He did not think anything would be gained by

[4] Shonts, *Speech . . . . before Commercial Club, Cincinnati, Ohio,* Jan. 20, 1906, p. 15.

contract if he were allowed to proceed with a "thoroughly un-hampered business administration."[5]

Roosevelt, probably under the influence of Shonts, who remained close at hand in Washington, was attracted by the idea of rapid construction and completion by contract. In late June he called Stevens to the White House and told him he was "extremely anxious" to have the Canal under construction by contract by November 1906.

In line with this directive, Stevens got busy. He consulted with Walston H. Brown, "able, pushing and financially competent," and wrote Shonts a strong letter, forwarding a memorandum on a plan for an association of ten or fifteen first-rate railroad and general contractors. He wanted them to have a capital of $25,000,000 and to be able to give a $10,000,000 bond for construction of the Canal. This would include dredging of the sea-level portions; construction of locks, dams, and regulating works; excavation from Gatun to Pacific locks, including Culebra Cut; and relocation of the Panama Railroad and the breakwaters. He placed the plan on a percentage-profit basis, with deductions for overrunning agreed estimates and bonuses for each month saved. The Commission should retain control of government and sanitation, material and supplies, municipal engineering and waterworks, building construction, labor and quarters, and the repair of machinery.

Stevens had considered the contract plan for months. He had used this method before on a large scale and knew its dangers. His forwarding letter contained a note of warning: he was "strongly opposed to endeavoring, by advertisement or otherwise, to let the entire work to any one firm,"[6] as that would take too much power from the Commission, make combinations to control prices possible, and might result in disasters, cause delays, and postpone the completion of the Canal.

He emphasized to Shonts the necessity for keeping control

[5] Stevens' Statement, May 28, 1906 (Hearings No. 6, pp. 109–10) (U.S.).
[6] Stevens to Shonts, July 27, 1906 (P.C. Rec. Bur., File 9-A-4) (MS).

in their own hands and under direction of the Commission engineers. He warned the chairman that because of the character and magnitude of the interests involved in constructing the Canal, "in justice to ourselves"[7] it could be carried out in no other way. Stevens wrote the same to Roosevelt, mentioning his letter to Shonts and expressing hope to have the matter cleared by mid-October.

When Shonts received Stevens' plan, he was well satisfied. He enthusiastically endorsed it as the "simplest and most effective" plan suggested for building the Canal that was not based on the government getting "something for nothing."[8] He promised to submit the plan to both Roosevelt and Taft, but asked Stevens to be ready to come north to assist in the awarding of bids.

By August, Shonts had referred the contract plan to the President and was able to cable Stevens, who was anxious about the outcome, the welcome news: "President approves all plans."[9] The framework of the contracts was the idea of Stevens. Their award was in the hands of others, who had promised to consult with him before making awards.

The progress of these events did not escape notice on the Isthmus. Word spread around as to the identity of the real author of the contract plan. It was "conceived, elaborated and prefected in the Chief Engineer's Office on the Zone, where it first saw the light of day."[10]

Nothing in the relations between Shonts and Stevens gives a better picture of the relative values of their contributions to the Canal. Shonts was the chairman of the Commission and was Stevens' official superior—a successful, practical railroad-operating executive, but not an engineer. He did excellent work in the Washington Office at a time of serious crisis, but in fertility and originality of ideas he was only a mirror of Stevens. Any-

[7] Stevens to Shonts, July 27, 1906 (P.C. Rec. Bur., File 9-A-4) (MS).

[8] Shonts to Stevens, Aug. 1, 1906 (*ibid.*).

[9] Shonts to Stevens, cable, Aug. 14, 1906 (*ibid.*).

[10] *Panama Star and Herald*, Oct. 23, 1906.

one who reads deeply into the contract history cannot fail to agree with former Secretary of the Commission J. B. Bishop that Shonts was actually Stevens' "intelligent coadjutor and prompt agent in executing the comprehensive and masterly plans which the fertile and trained mind of Mr. Stevens evolved."[11]

REAL CONSTRUCTION STARTS

While the planners in Washington were fumbling with the contracts and contractors, activities on the Isthmus did not subside. Equipment continued to arrive slowly and was assembled and placed at work with forces that were enlarged by the arrival of every steamer. Excavation yardage steadily increased from July to December 1906, and the plant was ready for large-volume excavation during the coming dry season.

One of the last incidents of that eventful year of 1906 was a flood of the Chagres in December. At Gamboa the river reached a height of 79.9 feet above sea level, which was about 40 feet above the bottom planned for Culebra Cut. The flood showed that a dike would have to be placed across the Cut at Gamboa to protect it from the flood waters of the Chagres and that the old French diversions on each side would have to be placed in service to protect the canal work from that turbulent river.[12]

Living conditions had improved greatly. Building construction increased in 1905 and 1906 and reached its peak in 1907. On January 17, 1907, buildings at Culebra were lighted for the first time by electricity.[13] People no longer had to worry about the wind blowing out oil lights, and housewives enjoyed surcease from washing lamp chimneys.

The streets of Panamá and Colón had been paved, and sewer and water systems were installed in 1905 and 1906.[14] Panamá was the best-paved city in Central America. About 80 per cent of the excavation and transportation plant for the entire under-

[11] J. B. Bishop, The Panama Gateway, p. 162.
[12] Haskins, Canal Zone Pilot, 1908, p. 312.
[13] Panama Star and Herald, Jan. 17, 1907.
[14] Pepperman, op. cit., p. 222, footnote.

taking was on the Isthmus at work, or on order. Dredging was under way in both the Atlantic and Pacific sea-level sections of the Canal. Excavation of both Pedro Miguel and Gatun lock sites was under way. By early 1907 the daily output of all classes of construction was increasing so rapidly that Stevens felt confident—a confidence he later expressed: "The hardest problems were solved, the Rubicon was crossed, the Canal was being built, and everything was set for its completion"[15] by January 1, 1915.

The chaotic days of 1905 had been forgotten. The Isthmus had been transformed into a healthy place. Quarters were abundant for employees and families. Food was plentiful at commissaries all along the Canal line, with prices below those in the United States. The railroad had been rehabilitated and double-tracked and was functioning smoothly in spite of the demands of advancing excavation. Engineering plans were under way for locks and dams. The year 1906 marked the end of what Shonts called the "creative period."

Morale was high under the inspiring leadership of Stevens. Steam shovels were competing for records of excavation. Italian workers gathered in the evenings in their quarters near Ancon and gave stirring renditions of Italian music without accompaniment. Serenades became popular.

But there also were troubles! Spaniards refused to work one day because one had been arrested by a black policeman. They also refused to work under black foremen, and new gangs had to be organized. Stevens had troubles with employees from the United States. He had found out that a few of his own countrymen proved to be the worst class on the Isthmus, and early in his career adopted the efficacious method of handling the problem by sending them off the Isthmus, for which he was very harshly criticized.[16]

Large-scale excavation started in January 1907, with 566,750

[15] Stevens, "The Panama Canal." A.S.C.E., *Transactions*, XCI, 960.
[16] Stevens' Statement, Jan. 16, 1906 (Hearings No. 18, I, 55) (U.S.).

cubic yards from the Culebra Division and a daily average of 31 shovels in Culebra Cut. The yardage for that month would have been much greater had the unloaders he ordered arrived on schedule.

Steam-shovel engineers became the men of the hour, for upon their performance all progress rested. Their pay was high and therefore was accepted as a standard on which other groups wished to base their pay. The steam-shovel men soon felt their services were more valuable than those of the locomotive engineers, who received slightly more pay. They called a meeting and decided to strike for more pay, and appointed a committee to submit demands to the Chief Engineer.

When the delegation arrived at the office at Culebra, Stevens greeted them cordially and asked, "Well, fellows, what do you all have on your mind today?" They told him how hard they had worked and how unjust it was for them not to receive as much as locomotive engineers. Then their spokesman announced: "We have decided to strike for more money than the locomotive engineers receive."

Stevens was not perturbed and replied, "Well, you men know my reputation for standing by my men. You all know damn well that strikes do not get you anywhere. Now, get the hell out of this office and back to work on those shovels."[17]

They returned to work. They did not bother him any more. Instead, they went over his head to the President.

In spite of all these difficulties, excavation from the Culebra Division during February went up again to 639,112 cubic yards; the next month it soared to 815,270. The results were so encouraging that Shonts in Washington was claiming to have brought the Canal from "chaos to contract." Like Stevens, he felt that the engineering problems had been solved, along with sanitation; that the remaining problem was only one of transportation, the object of which was to provide an "endless chain

[17] C. A. McIlvaine, Conversation with the author, March 20, 1941.

of constantly moving trains"[18] to keep steam shovels working at maximum capacity.

As the year 1907 opened, work showed the result of Stevens' unremitting campaign against the inefficiency of the cumbersome Commission. He had evolved a centralized power on the Isthmus to replace the three separate activities of engineering, government, and sanitation. The organization was functioning smoothly. The one aim of the mass of the employees was to "get the Canal dug."

CRISIS AND RESIGNATION OF STEVENS

The contract negotiations revealed a fundamental difference between the views of Stevens and Shonts. Stevens felt strongly that bids for Canal contracts should not be advertised. Shonts, a less experienced man, did not feel so strongly, and when Mr. Taft expressed his desire for "an element of competition"[19] Shonts acquiesced, suggesting competition on the basis of percentage alone. He advised Stevens that he and R. R. Rogers were revising the draft and would send Stevens a copy as soon as completed.

A week later Shonts was ready and arose from a sick-bed to send Stevens a draft copy of the invitation for proposals. He related that Administration friends in Congress—Speaker Cannon and Senator Spooner—had warned him that the "novelty" of Stevens' first proposals might have political repercussions and that he felt that both he and Stevens were then going through the "critical state of our official existence with this work."[20] Congress, he stated, had decided the type of canal, but it was up to them to build the "most perfect" canal with the greatest efficiency and economy. He emphasized that Stevens would have to be in Washington when the awards were made.

Two days later he forwarded to Secretary Taft a letter setting forth reasons why the contract method of construction seemed ad-

[18] Shonts' Statement, Feb. 9, 1907 (Hearings No. 7, p. 894) (U.S.).
[19] Shonts to Stevens, Aug. 22, 1906 (P.C. Rec. Bur., File 2-C-13) (MS).
[20] Shonts to Stevens, Aug. 27, 1906 (*ibid.*, File 9–A–4).

visable and recommending that the entire work be awarded to an association of contractors on a percentage basis, as proposed by Stevens.[21]

When Stevens heard that his plans were approved, he was pleased; but he did not want to go to Washington, as he had already lost too much time from his work. He also regretted the decision to advertise for bids, and predicted it would become a "conglomeration of bids and powwow that will cause the whole proposition to result in smoke."[22] But Shonts assured him by cable that the association would be of expert firms.

In September the situation became clearer. Shonts apparently had to bow to political pressure, for he wrote Stevens that he thought his plan ideal and that the President would have stood for it but for Taft's desire for advertising. He did not think it would become a "conglomeration of bids" but wanted Stevens to assist in deciding on the bidders. Under the pressure of this appeal Stevens had no other course than to approve, with a request for speed in getting things started.

Shonts held many conferences with contractors. At first they were antagonistic and bitter, but finally, with the exception of William B. Parsons, they usually agreed that Stevens' plan was right. Shonts wrote that Parsons was against them, wanting a contract on the same basis as the New York subway and also a thirty-year lease to operate the canal.[23] One contractor submitted a proposition to obtain advance annual distribution of the final bonus. Shonts, instead of rejecting the proposal, passed it on to Stevens for decision, who promptly replied that it was "misleading and dangerous." He wrote Shonts that he knew contractors from bitter experience and that in dealing with them "one has to be as wise as a serpent, and apparently as harmless as a dove."[24] A little later he wrote Shonts he feared they would

[21] Shonts to Secretary of War, Aug. 29, 1906 (*ibid.*) (MS). I.C.C., *Annual Report for 1906*, pp. 128–31; Exhibit I (U.S.).

[22] Stevens to Shonts, Aug. 30, 1906 (P.C. Rec. Bur., File 9-A-4) (MS).

[23] Shonts to Stevens, Sept. 18, 1906 (*ibid.*).

[24] Stevens to Shonts, Sept. 25, 1906 (*ibid.*).

get into "endless complications and entanglements."[25] Stevens also thought that the introduction of Secretary Root's influence in changing the contract form had emasculated the plan to such an extent that in attempting to carry out the work there would be "endless friction and conflicts of authority."[26]

Notwithstanding the many differences which had arisen between the Chief Engineer and the Chairman, the proposals for bids were advertised on October 9, 1906, substantially as tentatively agreed upon in a previous informal conference with the Commission. These embodied directions to the bidders and the form of contract, and set January 12, 1907, as the date for opening all bids received.[27] During the long wait, progress on the Isthmus was so rapid that Stevens was praised as solving the problem without any contractors. The need for contract work was disappearing.

When bids were opened on January 12, only four were there: George Pierce and Company, Frankfort, Maine, 7.19 per cent; William J. Oliver and Anson M. Bangs, New York City, 6.75 per cent; MacArthur-Gillespie Company, Chicago, Illinois, 12.50 per cent; and North American Dredging Company, San Francisco, California, 28 per cent. Shonts cabled Stevens for advice as to the "best thing to do."[28] Stevens did not answer the question. He replied that the lowest was too high, and he wanted to know the "record and capacity"[29] of each firm before deciding.

In the midst of this, Shonts received an offer to head a great transportation merger in New York City and decided to resign. He reminded the President of his promise of April 1905 to release him when excavation of the Culebra Cut was under way.

Roosevelt did not bear the resentment toward Shonts that he did toward Wallace and on January 22, 1907, accepted Shonts's

[25] Stevens to Shonts, Oct. 2, 1906 (P.C. Rec. Bur., File 9-A-4) (MS).

[26] Stevens, "The Panama Canal," op. cit., p. 956.

[27] I.C.C., Annual Report for 1906, p. 15; pp. 132–50: Exhibit J, Oct. 9 (U.S.). I.C.C., Minutes, 119th meeting, Jan. 21, 1907, pp. 4–20 (U.S.).

[28] Shonts to Isthmian, cable, Jan. 15–16, 1907 (P.C. Rec. Bur., File 9-A-4) (MS).

[29] Stevens to Isthmian, Jan. 16, 1907 (ibid.).

resignation, effective March 4, "with extreme reluctance" and acknowledging his "energy, administrative capacity, fertility of resource and judgment."[30] The resignation of Shonts was a personal regret to his many friends. In spite of the President's polite acceptance, rumors began. Friends reported he had become disgusted with "Washington red tape and Washington political interference."[31] Probably it would be nearer the truth to say it was due to his relations with Stevens. The Chief Engineer's star was in the ascendant. Harmony no longer existed between them.

Stevens had been notified by Secretary Bishop on January 24 about Shonts's resignation, and he cabled at once to Roosevelt: "Request no action until matter thoroughly discussed."[32]

What was on Stevens' mind to inspire such a message? Roosevelt did not know and replied that he did not understand the cable but agreed to take no action until he heard from Stevens.[33]

The Isthmus was electrified by the resignation of Shonts. Coming after so many praises of him from Roosevelt, it was a great surprise. Who was to be his successor became the question of the hour. The press was critical. From the beginning of construction, it commented, removals and resignations had been the order of the day, and Culebra Cut was not the only problem for the United States. However, Stevens was regarded as the "controlling director"[34] of everything done on the Isthmus and became their man of destiny.

Reporters rushed to him with the news and found him sitting on an embankment at Tavernilla, more interested in a sidetrack than in the resignation of Shonts and his own probable appointment as chairman. Stevens did not relax his efforts for the Canal

---

[30] Roosevelt to Shonts, Jan. 22, 1907; quoted in Pepperman, *op. cit.*, pp. 16–17.

[31] *Panama Star and Herald*, Feb. 7, 1907.

[32] Stevens to Roosevelt, cable, Jan. 24, 1907; quoted in J. B. and F. Bishop, *Goethals, Genius of the Panama Canal: a Biography*, p. 137.

[33] Roosevelt to Stevens, cable, Jan. 25, 1907 (*ibid.*, p. 137).

[34] *Panama Star and Herald*, Jan. 27, 1907.

but continued his extensive inspection walks along the line of work. Everywhere he was hailed as Shonts's successor.

Shonts's first act after receipt of the bids was to confer with Roosevelt and Taft, without consulting Stevens as he had promised. They agreed that awarding the contract to the 6.75 per cent bidder, Oliver and Bangs, was warranted.[35] Ten days later it was definitely decided to allow W. J. Oliver ten days to qualify with new associates in a $5,000,000 corporation, but Bangs was eliminated.

On the Isthmus the contract proposition was watched closely, and Stevens again cabled Shonts that he believed it would be a mistake to award the contract to Oliver, who, he considered, was not qualified by nature, experience, or achievement.[36] He strongly objected and explained that the changing of associates was the same as allowing a new bid. Besides, Oliver had gained an intense ill will of the best employees by his published interviews. To Mr. Taft also the Chief Engineer sent a cable, stating it would be a mistake to award the contract to Oliver.[37]

Stevens became thoroughly alarmed. Both the President and the Secretary of War were on the verge of awarding the building of the Canal to contractors they did not know. Stevens had long felt he was slated for the highest position but had been seriously hampered by interference and "red tape." Naturally, he longed to return to the railroads, where his creative abilities would not be fettered, but he had not made up his mind. He did remark, however, that he could make $30,000 a year much more easily in the States than on the Isthmus.

When Roosevelt and Taft decided to award the contract to a concern whose capacity he questioned, without consulting him as had been promised, he saw the futility of his efforts to protect the interests of the Canal. He therefore decided that only drastic action could save the situation from a chaos he feared would

---

[35] Shonts to Stevens, Jan. 18–19, 1907 (P.C. Rec. Bur., File 9-A-4) (MS).

[36] Stevens to Isthmian, cable, Jan. 29, 1907 (*ibid.*).

[37] Stevens to Secretary of War, cable, Jan. 29, 1907 (*ibid.*).

THEODORE ROOSEVELT
From the medal designed by Victor D. Brenner, 1908 (see p. 298)

GATUN DAM CONSTRUCTION, SOUTH TOE, AUGUST 27, 1908
Looking west from lock site

reach the proportions of that in 1905 and endanger completion of the Canal.

On January 30 he wrote directly to Roosevelt a six-page letter expressing his desire to leave the Canal and return to the railroads. The letter was not received at the White House, however, until February 12. In the meantime Stevens continued his efforts to avoid the abyss toward which the political leaders were taking the Canal. To his close associates he revealed his disgust and irritation at Washington officialdom.

When Taft received Stevens' cable asserting that award to Oliver would be a mistake, he requested Stevens to amplify his cable with reasons.[38] That was what Stevens wanted, and in a confidential cable he replied with emphasis that the great object of the contract was to assemble large numbers of the best specialists for each class of work and that ability and fitness were worth more than money. He explained that the bid under consideration was simply a proposition by one man not fitted by "nature, experience or achievement," and that changing of associates was the equivalent of a new bid.

He asserted that Oliver's published interviews had created intense feeling on the Isthmus and would produce a state of affairs that could not be controlled but would require a reorganization as great as that of eighteen months before, with serious setbacks. His message cut deep when he stated that, as a business proposition, the "contract should never have been advertised" and that for securing best results the specifications should make the contractors simply agents of the Commission.

Then he included a note of confidence—that work was going well, with over half a million yards from Culebra Cut in January and with a steady increase in the future "certain." He advised taking time in order to make the best arrangements and not to make the award to Oliver.[39]

When Taft received this broadside, he wanted further enlight-

[38] Taft to Stevens, cable, Jan. 29, 1907 (ibid.).

[39] Stevens to Secretary of War, cable, Jan. 30, 1907 (ibid.).

enment on Oliver's published interviews, which he had not seen. Stevens again had to explain in a long cable that nearly every paper from the States contained reports of interviews which stated that the party would come down at once with large numbers of steam-shovel men to make the dirt fly; that men would be "properly housed and fed," a statement Stevens felt as a "direct implication"; also that Oliver favored bringing thousands of Negro convicts from the South. To this Stevens added his observation that "a Napoleon is not needed here, but such an organization as outlined in my letter of July 27 to Chairman,"[40] which he asked the Secretary to look up.

Read with a knowledge of conditions on the Isthmus, this summary by Stevens of Oliver's contract plan is revealing; for no man at all familiar with the problems on the Isthmus could have made so many errors as Stevens reported were made by this ambitious contractor.

But Taft was persistent. He cabled Stevens that Oliver proposed to have John B. MacDonald, a New York subway contractor, John Pierce, a masonry contractor of Maine, and the Milan Dredging Company of Baltimore as associates and that Oliver had stated the reported press interviews were unfounded. In the meantime, however, he held acceptance of Oliver's bid in abeyance.[41]

Stevens did not reply with his customary promptness but waited until the sixth, when he cabled Taft that he did not know Pierce, that the dredging company was no strength to the combination, although "MacDonald was well known but means Belmont and that means Parsons, a bitter opponent of project."[42] He informed Taft that the Oliver interviews were in direct quotation and, if untrue, Oliver was unfortunate. Apparently more disheartened, he concluded that the entire contract situation had "drifted" into a proposition different from that proposed by him

---

[40] Stevens to Taft, cable, Jan. 31, 1907 (P.C. Rec. Bur., File 9-A-4) (MS).

[41] Taft to Stevens, cable, Feb. 3–4, 1907 (*ibid.*).

[42] Stevens to Taft, cable, Feb. 6, 1907 (*ibid.*).

on July 27. He felt it was "entirely wrong" and if concluded would be a "one-man proposition," to which he was opposed.

Even this did not change the insistent Secretary, and Taft again cabled Stevens the names of other men in the combination, of which the total backing was $1,500,000. The names included W. J. Oliver, F. C. Stevens, John Pierce, John B. MacDonald, R. A. C. Smith, and five others. He wanted to know about them from the Chief Engineer.[43]

Stevens now felt the complete futility of all his efforts and answered only with a short message that he knew nothing about the parties, as they were "not prominent enough to be generally known."[44] Moreover, he thought they were included to meet technical requirements but were "technically failing" in capital, and he had no reason to change his mind. Taft was also at the end of his resources to influence Stevens.

Roosevelt now intervened and sent Stevens a confidential cable, naming the associates of Oliver and requesting his knowledge. He thought it "far fetched" to think MacDonald would be influenced by Parsons and expressed his astonishment that Stevens should think the contract matter "entirely wrong," since it had been drawn up in the first place to accord with Stevens' views and later agreed to in his presence with Shonts, Taft, Root, and R. R. Rogers on December 12. Then the President ominously added, "I would not be willing now to alter this policy entered into with such deliberation, save for grave reasons which can be stated publicly, and verified."[45] Notwithstanding his unwillingness, Roosevelt was in a dilemma and appealed to Stevens: "I need your assistance in carrying the policy through and I wish full comment from you" on the bid and bidders. This was certainly a strange way to act when, in the early days of the contract negotiations, the points expressed were that contractors should be of demonstrated ability and capacity and that Stevens should pass upon the awards!

[43] Taft to Stevens, cable, Feb. 6–7, 1907 (*ibid.*).
[44] Stevens to Secretary of War, cable, Feb. 8, 1907 (*ibid.*).
[45] Roosevelt to Stevens, confidential cable, Feb. 8, 1907 (*ibid.*).

Roosevelt's cable was refreshing to Stevens. He replied that
it was the "first comprehensive advice" he had received on the
contract matter, as previous information indicated simply a one-
man project. He listed the points differing from his original
plan—the capital was one-fifth, the bond required was one-half,
current payment was to be on percentages, and the contractor
was to supply all labor. He stated that he had objected to the
last two provisions in the December 12 meeting but was overruled and that his silence was misconstrued as "explicit approval." He explained that his desire was to make contractors
agents of the Commission and that he did not know the personnel
well enough to advise but considered the proposition simply as
a new bid.

Then he added, "You should receive personal letter tomorrow which may clarify situation."[46] It was his resignation.

On February 12 Stevens' letter of January 30 arrived at the
White House. It was an unusual document, in which he expressed his appreciation of Roosevelt's approval of his work on
the Isthmus, explained that he had not sought the Canal position,
and stated that he had sought the Philippine appointment and
that he had accepted the Canal post against his better judgment.
He related that at first he thought the Canal work would be a
"purely business proposition" but instead had found it necessary
to engage in a "continuous battle with enemies in the rear." He
claimed that he had been continuously under attack by people
"I would not wipe my boots on in the United States." He felt
he had been losing more than $100,000 annually while at Pan-
ama and that the honor of building the Canal did not appeal to
him. He claimed he could return to positions, some of which
"I would prefer to hold, if you will pardon my candor, than the
Presidency of the United States." He alleged that the Commission had not been given a "fair trial" but reported that he had
a good organization and was confident of a "speedy completion
of the Canal." He requested Roosevelt's "calm and dispassion-

[46] Stevens to Roosevelt, Feb. 9, 1907 (P.C. Rec. Bur., File 9-A-4) (MS).

ate" consideration. On the Isthmus nothing was known concerning Stevens' action.

ROOSEVELT SELECTS A SUCCESSOR TO STEVENS

Roosevelt acted immediately and sent this letter to Secretary Taft, stating, "Stevens must get out at once." He indicated that, even if Stevens should change his mind as he had done before, he would not reconsider the matter because of the "tone of the letter." Roosevelt wanted to avoid any conflict with Stevens and desired to handle the crisis on the basis of "meeting his wishes."[47]

Secretary Taft consulted with General Alexander Mackenzie, Chief of Engineers, who recommended Major Goethals as the "fittest man" from the Corps of Engineers for appointment as chief engineer on the Canal. Taft wanted to be ready, should the President decide to change the policy in appointing members of the Commission.

Roosevelt had had two civilian chief engineers on the Canal, and now the second was leaving just as the work was getting into high gear. The Canal could not be built with chief engineers leaving every year. He considered the Canal his greatest work, which he ranked with the Louisiana Territory Purchase of 1803. But the end of his second term as President was approaching, and the days of preparation and organization were over. Progress and organization of the undertaking were such as to permit its being placed in permanent hands that would see the work through, and he decided, "I propose now to put it in charge of men who will stay on the job till I get tired of having them there, or till I say they may abandon it. I shall turn it over to the army."[48]

At the conference the next day Roosevelt and Taft discussed the matter and agreed that a change should be made. Roosevelt asked Taft for a recommendation of someone from the Corps

[47] Roosevelt to Taft, Feb. 12, 1907 (Taft Papers: Taft-Roosevelt, Box III) (MS).

[48] J. B. Bishop, *The Panama Gateway*, p. 176.

of Engineers, and Taft urged Goethals for Chief Engineer of the Panama Canal.

Within 48 hours after receipt of Stevens' letter on February 12, Roosevelt cabled him that he acquiesced in his desire to be relieved as soon as a successor could be appointed and could become familiar with the work.[49] He wrote fully, promising to send someone to take his place, probably an army engineer, but wanted Stevens to continue until after his successor arrived and had a chance to take over the work. He feared damage would be caused by an early departure of Stevens and wanted the work to "continue without a break."

On the same day he sent to the Senate his nominations for recess appointments of members of the Isthmian Canal Commission. Included were the names of two new members: W. C. Gorgas as chief health officer and Jackson Smith as manager of labor, quarters, and subsistence. Both already were nominees of Stevens and carried over into the new regime. When all the facts are examined, the entire episode looks strange. Stevens had just succeeded in having his own plan of organization adopted. He had the confidence of Roosevelt, and there is little doubt that he would have been left in supreme control had he not desired to leave the Isthmus.

Six days after receiving Stevens' letter, Roosevelt sent for Goethals. That evening the Goethals family were entertaining an old friend, Colonel Gustav J. Fieberger, when a White House messenger arrived with a note from the President wanting to know if Goethals could come to see him the next morning. Major Goethals immediately called Secretary William Loeb by telephone to acknowledge, and Mr. Loeb told him not to wait but to come the same evening at 10:30. Goethals left his guest, donned his uniform, and rushed to the White House, where he was ushered in to meet the President.

Roosevelt told Goethals of the events that made a change

---

[49] Roosevelt to Stevens, cable, Feb. 14, 1907: quoted in J. B. and F. Bishop, *op. cit.*, p. 140.

necessary at Panamá. He expressed regret at Stevens' resignation and explained that he wanted to secure continuity of leadership without periodic changes. He told Goethals that he wished to reorganize the Commission by combining the offices of chairman and chief engineer in order to eliminate the friction which had existed at times between these two officials. He regretted his inability to secure a change in the law requiring a seven-man Commission, so it was necessary to work under the existing law; but his efforts were unsuccessful. His one purpose was to build the Canal, and he finally determined to "assume powers which the law did not give but which it did not forbid him to exercise."[50] Thus, on that evening of February 18, 1907, at the White House, Goethals was assigned to duty with the Panama Canal.

What was the previous record of Goethals? Graduating from West Point in 1880, he was assigned to the Corps of Engineers. As a young engineer he had served with General Nelson A. Miles in the Northwest, worked on the Ohio River on surveys and construction of dams and locks, served as instructor at West Point in civil and military engineering, and as engineer in charge of the Tennessee River, which included the Muscle Shoals Canal and locks, served in the Spanish-American War as a colonel, and finally reached the General Staff. There he served on the Fortification Board and at the War College. He had built an excellent record but could look forward to little more, when suddenly he was appointed to the Panama Canal.

By the last of February Roosevelt was ready. On the twenty-sixth he wrote Chairman Shonts regarding the contract situation in an analysis that shows the strong hand of Stevens, even to its phraseology. He explained that Stevens, who devised the contract form, had advised against the award, that he had received a letter from Stevens requesting to be relieved, that this withdrawal removed the chief reason for awarding the contract, as Stevens had been expected to supervise the work. He recommended that the Commission reject all bids received, none of them being a

[50] Goethals; quoted in J. B. and F. Bishop, *op. cit.*, p. 144.

satisfactory fulfillment of the proposed contract. Formal notice
to this effect was taken by the Commission on February 27.[51]

The withdrawal of Stevens gave Roosevelt a way out of his
dilemma. He had no choice except to say "I have accepted his
resignation." He therefore requested the Commission to appoint Major Goethals, an army engineer, as chief engineer on
the Canal in order to secure administrative continuity. He
avowed it was not intended to "disturb in any way the present
organization on the Isthmus, which is very satisfactory, nor to
interfere with the admirable work" then being done by Assistant
Chief Engineer Ripley and other heads of departments. He had
confidence that the organization would continue to do well. He
stated that two other "competent members" of the Engineer
Corps would accompany Goethals—Majors D. D. Gaillard and
W. L. Sibert. The Commission, at its one-hundred-and-twenty-
first meeting on February 27, 1907, resolved that Goethals be
appointed chief engineer vice John F. Stevens.[52]

Secretary Taft entered the picture in these last days of Stevens' regime by sending him a cable stating that the President
relied upon him to use every endeavor to assist in the substitution of Goethals with "as little friction and as little loss of efficiency in the organization which you have created" as was possible and that Stevens should remain in charge as long as he
and Goethals should desire.[53]

When the news spread about the rejection of the contract and
the Chief Engineer's resignation was published the next day in
Panamá it was a "bolt from the blue." Stevens' name had become a household word on the Isthmus and throughout the
United States. Great results had been expected from him because of the fine construction organization he had created and
the smoothness with which everything was running. Press reporters telephoned his secretary for confirmation, but the re-

[51] Roosevelt to Chairman Shonts, Feb. 26, 1907 (P.C. Rec. Bur., File 9-A-4)
(MS). I.C.C., *Minutes*, 121st meeting, Feb. 27, 1907, pp. 33–34 (U.S.).
[52] I.C.C., *ibid.*, p. 34.
[53] Taft to Stevens, cable, Feb. 1907 (P.C. Rec. Bur., File 9-A-4) (MS).

port was denied. Not satisfied, they telegraphed Stevens himself at Culebra, and he replied that any information would have to come from Washington.[54]

So complete was the surprise of the workers that they were stunned. Even Culebra Cut became "quiet as a grave yard." An old employee lamented: "Culebra's Cut to the heart; we are cut through and through."[55] When interviewed, Stevens refused to talk, but stated that the President's position entitled him to be the "first to speak." When callers became too insistent, he answered, "Don't talk, dig."[56]

Employees spontaneously started a petition requesting Stevens to retract. Four thousand men signed. Executive Secretary Reed issued a notice to all heads of divisions that a petition was being circulated to show the "loyalty and admiration of the men who have worked almost two years under his direction."[57] Reed knew what had gone on behind the scenes and that this effort of the employees would be futile, but he could not stop the movement. The petition read: "Please withdraw your resignation and remain in charge of our work. We will show our appreciation and loyalty by working for you even harder than we have up to this time."[58]

In a few days all the petitions were turned in, with over 10,000 signatures. Some of the men did not like the implication that they had not worked hard, for they felt they could not have worked any harder; so many changed the phraseology on their copies. About that particular angle Stevens himself had something to say many years later: "I did not loaf very much myself in the old days when I was on the Isthmus—and one regret that I still have is that I didn't work everybody harder."[59]

The men also took up a collection for three presents for Stevens that were suitable to be passed along to his sons—a gold

[54] *Panama Star and Herald*, Feb. 28, 1907.
[55] *Ibid.*, March 1, 1907.   [56] *Ibid.*
[57] H. D. Reed to heads of divisions, March 2, 1907 (P.C. Rec. Bur., File Personnel, Stevens) (MS).
[58] Petition to Stevens from workers (*ibid.*).
[59] Stevens to McIlvaine, March 2, 1936 (*ibid.*).

watch, a diamond ring, and a silver table set which included a tray bearing an engraving of the completed Canal. So highly was he esteemed that almost everyone wished to contribute.

There was universal disappointment on the Isthmus that an Army man should be appointed to relieve Stevens. Workers feared the possibility of regimentation; they wondered if they would have to answer roll calls and salute superiors and were advised to extend their military vocabulary.[60] In the United States the reaction was more objective, Goethals being approved as a "man without prejudice" and as an exceptional executive.

It was predicted that Goethals would demand from his staff "implicit obedience to his orders and absolute frankness in their reports"[61] which, if met, would make him an ideal leader. But of more importance, it was remarked that he knew government routine. That had been one of the rocks which helped to end Stevens' fine career on the Canal.

As soon as the workers had a chance to talk matters over there was a great deal of conjecture as to why Stevens had resigned. One story declared that he had submitted an ultimatum to the President, threatening resignation, but that Roosevelt had called the bluff by accepting. In answer to that, Stevens has stated that he did not attempt to bluff Roosevelt. Secretary Taft stated it was the "nervous strain that made him insist on leaving the work early in 1907."[62] Goethals thought he had "broken down with the responsibilities and an evident desire to look after too many of the details himself."[63] Another reason suggested was that he had refused a pay increase to the steam-shovel men!

Stevens never revealed why he resigned, remaining silent to his grave. His only statement was that the reasons were "private and of no particular interest to the public"[64] and that there had been not the slightest friction with the President.

[60] *Panama Star and Herald*, March 3, 1907.
[61] *Engineering Record*, March 2, 1907, LV, 225.
[62] Taft's Statement, Jan. 16, 1908 (Hearings No. 19, p. 1) (U.S.).
[63] Goethals; quoted in J. B. and F. Bishop, *op. cit.*, p. 151.
[64] Stevens, "The Panama Canal," A.S.C.E. *Transactions*, XCI (Dec., 1927), 961.

When all the events are reconstructed, the reasons appear clear. His removal afforded a way out of the contract impasse of the Administration, which had been created by men not familiar with the pitfalls of business. His elimination appears to have been a voluntary sacrifice on the altar of political expediency.

In spite of the short time that Stevens was chief engineer he was able to rescue the Canal from chaos and defeat; to arrive at the great decision for a high-level lock-type canal plan, with a large summit-level terminal lake on the Atlantic, and secure its adoption; to solve the problem of the Culebra Cut; and to form an efficient organization for constructing the Canal. The testimony of those who witnessed his work on the Canal and the perspective of many years of marine operations establish John F. Stevens as the greatest constructive builder of the Panama Canal.

STEVENS TURNS THE TASK OVER TO GOETHALS

One of Roosevelt's first acts in this crisis was to appoint Stevens as chairman, by an Executive Order of March 4, thus making him both chairman and chief engineer. This act, completing the transfer of power to the Isthmus, was the combination that Roosevelt wanted in order to remove friction; it had been recommended earlier by Stevens. This fine recognition of Stevens' work went a long way in easing the transfer of power from Stevens to Goethals. As the last significant step in the formation of the organization for Canal construction, it made Stevens the first dictator on the Canal Zone.

It was not until March 12 that Major Goethals, accompanied by Gaillard, arrived at Cristóbal. They were warmly greeted by Chairman Stevens, Jackson Smith, W. G. Tubby, Executive Secretary Reed, and the press. Immediately, Goethals was asked what changes he intended to make. He replied quickly that no changes whatsoever would be made in the "splendid organization"[65] built up by Mr. Stevens and that the work would be continued as it was without interference.

[65] *Panama Star and Herald*, March 13, 1907.

On crossing the Isthmus, Goethals was impressed with the progress of two years. He observed that Stevens had done "an immense amount of work"[66] and things looked much better than in 1905. After his first lunch at the Tivoli he became the house guest of the Gorgas family in the hospital grounds.

Stevens lost no time in expediting the process of transferring authority. He took Goethals and Gaillard to Culebra and explained all features of the work.[67] After several days of close observation Goethals wrote: "The magnitude of the work grows and grows on me; it seems to get bigger all the time, but Mr. Stevens has perfected such an organization so far as the R.R. part of the proposition is concerned, that there is nothing left for us to do but just have the organization continue in the good work it has done and is doing."[68]

As he went out on the line and saw what had been accomplished he could not understand why Stevens had resigned. He appreciated the work of the man whom he was to succeed—the man who had really accomplished things but who would "never get any credit, or, if he gets any, will not get enough. . . . . "[69]

He found the transportation part far advanced but thought the lock part was far behind because of an unfortunate selection of men. He recognized that Stevens' contributions were in fields in which army engineers were untrained. He did not dread the work on locks and dams, and he must have sensed the situation between employees and Congress when he stated, "the hard part of the work is not going to be the Engineering end."[70] Also he observed the spirit of the men as he explored the various projects and talked with them. Of their esteem and affection for Mr. Stevens he said: "I never have seen so much affection displayed for any man, and if I can so carry things on as to build up a

[66] Goethals; quoted in J. B. and F. Bishop, op. cit., p. 150.
[67] Panama Star and Herald, March 16, 1907.
[68] Goethals; quoted in J. B. and F. Bishop, op. cit., p. 151.
[69] Ibid., p. 152.
[70] Ibid., p. 153.

similar feeling when I get through, it will be the proudest work of my life."[71]

Goethals' first task was to gain the confidence and respect of the men who were suspicious and hostile. To them he had to show that he was determined to carry on the work of Stevens. As an army officer he was experienced in handling men and knew how to win them. On his rounds he sometimes saw old soldiers who had served under him in earlier years. He always sought them out in the crowd and greeted them.

The visiting Congressmen who had come down in the same ship with Goethals had to be entertained. A smoker was arranged on Saturday night, March 16, at the Corozal Club. Goethals was invited and attended. Stevens did not come, as it was to be the welcome to the new chairman, who was also the chief engineer.

The toastmaster, Mr. John P. Kyte, made a few remarks to the Congressmen, casting some slurs upon the Army. He requested them not to think employees "loco" if they should see men drop their tools and come to a salute, as it was simply a case of preparation for the next Canal regime. This "irritated and angered" Goethals.[72]

Congressman S. E. Payne addressed the workers, explaining how much the loss of Stevens was felt, but that they had a man in Goethals who would carry on "as Stevens has organized and started it." The crowd was pro-Stevens. Every time his name was spoken there were prolonged cheers; when Goethals' name was mentioned there was silence. Even so, the crowd wanted to hear from the new chief, and he had to rise and speak in that antagonistic atmosphere.

Goethals told them about his visit to the Isthmus in 1905 with Secretary Taft and how hopeless the prospect of the Canal seemed but how surprised he was to have seen the progress since then. In his clear resonant voice he continued: "I fully realize

[71] From speech by J. R. Freeman; quoted in *Panama Star and Herald*, Feb. 18, 1927, p. 4.   [72] Goethals; quoted in J. B. and F. Bishop, *op. cit.*, p. 155.

that Mr. Stevens has perfected an organization which, if maintained, will carry this canal through to completion. [Prolonged applause.] I want to say here that it is my intention to keep that organization as he has established it. [Applause.]

"I have understood that there was some little feeling on account of militarism, but I want to state here that I do not expect a salute from any man on the job. [Applause.]"

He explained that when he was a company commander in the Army every man understood he could see him at any time about a grievance and that he would see the Canal employees in the same way and would welcome suggestions. "You will not have to come to the office; you may speak to me anywhere along the work, and I will gladly listen to you. I will set no time to see you; you may come to the office at any time and I will gladly listen.

"While we are on this subject of militarism I will say that I expect to be the chief; the division engineers and the heads of departments are going to be the colonels; the foremen are going to be the captains, and the men who do the labor are going to be the privates. You have your colonels with you, and they will remain; you have your captains with you, and they will remain. There will be no more militarism in the future than there has been in the past.

"I am no longer a commander in the United States Army. I now consider that I am commanding the Army of Panama, and that the enemy we are going to combat is the Culebra Cut and the locks and dams at both ends of the canal, and any man here on the work who does his duty will never have any cause to complain of militarism. [Prolonged applause.]"[73]

He had won his audience and convinced them of his sincerity. When one of his former soldiers read the speech, he exclaimed, "That sounds just like him!"[74]

By March 21 Stevens and Goethals agreed they would be

[73] *Panama Star and Herald,* March 19, 1907.
[74] *Ibid.,* March 22, 1907.

ready to make the transfer of authority on April 1, and the Secretary of War was notified.[75]

There was plenty of criticism as people looked around, trying to place the blame for taking Stevens away. They blamed it on party politics, on incompetent commissions, on a vacillating Congress, and on the transcontinental railroads. An editorial in Panamá reviewed Stevens' brilliant career on the Isthmus, stating that he had brought results by "untiring effort and conscientious work," that Chairman Shonts had been given all the credit when he resigned, and that Stevens' great ambition was to "dig the canal alone and unhampered," for which he received the accusation that he was suffering from "enlarged cranium and unsettled nerves." But the real view of those on the Isthmus was: "We, here on the ground, and every American worker on the Isthmus, will say that the credit very justly belongs to John F. Stevens."[76]

Chairman Stevens called a meeting of the Commission for March 27, which was attended by Goethals, Gaillard, Sibert, Admiral Rousseau, Gorgas, and Jackson Smith. Stevens submitted his resignation, effective April 1, 1907, and Goethals' previous appointment as chief engineer was confirmed and made effective to relieve him on the same date. It was Stevens' only meeting with the Commission as its chairman, and there was much business; but he succeeded in obtaining approval for the Isthmian Canal Commission Band, with paid members and a full-time salaried director and librarian.[77] After the meeting he completed the plans for turning over his official duties to Goethals. In the evening he attended a dinner in his honor at the United States Legation, where the crowd sang his favorite songs.[78]

On March 30, Secretary of War Taft arrived at Colón aboard

[75] Stevens to Secretary of War, March 21, 1907 (P.C. Rec. Bur., File 2-C-4) (MS).

[76] Panama Star and Herald, March 22, 1907.

[77] I.C.C., Minutes, 122d meeting, March 27, 1907, pp. 42–44 (U.S.).

[78] Ibid., p. 49. Panama Star and Herald, March 29, 1907.

the "Mayflower," with consulting engineers Noble, Stearns, and J. R. Freeman, and a group of Congressmen. Stevens greeted them early and accompanied the party ashore, whereupon they proceeded in the rain to Panamá City without ceremony. During this transit Taft viewed Gatun and visited Culebra with Stevens, who gave detailed explanations of the work but was always willing for subordinates to speak. At Culebra he proudly introduced D. W. Bolich, the division engineer, as "the man who is digging the Culebra Cut."[79]

At midnight of Saturday, March 31, 1907, John F. Stevens terminated his service with the Canal, and upon the shoulders of Goethals fell the heavy weight of that responsibility.

FAREWELL TO STEVENS

Even after Goethals took charge, Stevens went around with Secretary Taft. When inspecting Culebra on April 1, Stevens held back to let Goethals explain to the Secretary, but Goethals insisted on Stevens talking. Stevens then called upon Mr. Joseph Little, superintendent of excavation, to tell the Secretary about the steam-shovel work.[80]

His last days on the Isthmus were happy and free of official responsibility. The University Club, to which Stevens had been admitted as an honorary member because he was not a college graduate, held a reception for him on April 3, with guests from all along the Canal. Secretary Taft gave out a statement praising Stevens and predicting that his organization would continue under Goethals.

Stevens planned to leave the Isthmus on April 7, and employees arranged a farewell reception to be held on Pier 11 at Cristóbal. Special trains came, crowded with guests from all along the line, many remaining overnight to see him depart the next day. Goethals, displaying the same regard that Stevens had exhibited toward him at Cristóbal, did not attend.

[79] *Panama Star and Herald*, March 31, 1907.
[80] *Ibid.*, April 3, 1907.

GENERAL GEORGE WASHINGTON GOETHALS, 1858–1928
Chief Engineer, Panama Canal, 1907–1914
Governor, The Panama Canal, 1914–1916

Again Pier 11 was decorated with flags, lights, palms, bunting, and greens at a place that had been the scene of so many ovations to notables—the builders of the Panama Railroad, Ferdinand de Lesseps and the French canal builders, and more lately Theodore Roosevelt. On the receiving stand were his friends, Jackson Smith, Colonel Gorgas, Assistant Chief Engineer Ripley, Alfred Noble, F. P. Stearns, J. R. Freeman, H. D. Reed, Captain Shanton, and their ladies.

At 9:30 that evening Stevens appeared, accompanied by a group of close friends—the Bierds, the Tubbys, and the Maltbys. The Isthmian Canal Commission Band, which he had sponsored, played "The Conquering Hero Comes," and the crowd spontaneously made an aisle for their hero's entrance to the stand.

It fell to Mr. Bierd to be the spokesman for the employees. He said it was unnecessary to explain the reasons for this demonstration of such regard and affection, but he did want Mr. Stevens to know the full measure of esteem in which he was held. He reviewed the work of the two years. Though admitting Mr. Stevens was no "easy taskmaster," Bierd said he had won their respect and affection because they were convinced he was a man "able at all times to overcome all the problems involved; to keep together all the details making for the success of the whole work, and whose decisions always impressed his subordinates with the belief that they had been made for what he believed to be right."

Stevens was generous and gave credit to Wallace for the organization he had inherited and which he had modified. He revealed that two years before he was almost as overwhelmed as the President by the vast volume of preparatory work required. He added that "until Colonel Gorgas had lifted the dark cloud which the unsanitary conditions placed over the work" he was doubtful of success. But when that cloud was lifted he knew the men with him would complete the Canal and that it would be opened for traffic by January 1, 1915.

He appealed to the men as a friend to take their "little differences and complaints" not to Washington, but to Chief Engineer Goethals, for whom he asked the same loyalty they had shown to him.[81]

Bierd then told Stevens about the three presents the men had subscribed and presented two bound volumes of 10,000 signatures asking him to stay. Stevens, visibly moved by the demonstration, turned to board a vessel in the bay for the night.

It was almost midnight, and the tropical sky was clear as he walked alone toward the tug "Gatun" that was waiting. He was met by a young tugmaster to whom he said, with tears in his eyes, "Captain, I am ready."[82] Overpowered by the demonstration and the realization of its significance, he knew it marked the end of an episode in his life; and with its passing went forever his high hope of becoming the builder of the Panama Canal.

The next day was Sunday. The S.S. "Panama," full dressed in honor of her distinguished passenger, waited at her dock. Hours before sailing, the largest crowd since the United States occupaton, including many who had remained in Cristóbal overnight, gathered at the pier to see Stevens sail away. Officials paid their last respects and left the ship. At noon the "Panama" left her dock and headed toward the Caribbean, amid the cheers of the crowd and the whistles of the ships in the bay. The band sounded "Auld Lang Syne" while Stevens, standing at the rail with his young son, looked on, "pale and sad."[83]

[81] *Panama Star and Herald*, April 9, 1907.
[82] Pilot A. T. Luther. Conversation with author, Sept. 9, 1941, quoting Stevens.
[83] *Panama Star and Herald*, April 9, 1907.

Chapter XIII

THE ARMY OF PANAMA UNDER GOETHALS

*I felt well assured that the work which had been so near my heart, had been given into competent hands, as the future proved in every way to be the case.—*John F. Stevens.[1]

*Colonel Goethals proved to be the man of all others to do the job. It would be impossible to overstate what he has done.—*Theodore Roosevelt.[2]

*Mr. Stevens probably will never get credit for the work he has done.—*Joseph G. Cannon, Speaker of the House of Representatives.[3]

GOETHALS CONTINUES THE ORGANIZATION FROM STEVENS

To have been the successor of Stevens at the height of his tremendous popularity would have been difficult under the best of circumstances. Goethals was appointed at a time of crisis—during an almost complete change in the Commission and in the midst of labor agitation. These were difficulties to test any man.

The organization Goethals inherited aroused his sincere admiration. The transportation system was complete. About eighty per cent of the plant for the entire undertaking was on hand. Excavation in Culebra and hauling to the dumps were proceeding at a record pace. Four steam shovels were excavating at Gatun Lock site. Dredges for both the Atlantic and the Pacific sea-level sections of the Canal were on hand or under contract. Surveys for the Canal and for the railroad relocation were almost completed. Large machine shops at Gorgona were operating. At Empire and Paraiso, shops were under construction. Gatun Dam site had been cleared except for the roots of trees.

Goethals' general impression was that the work at Culebra and the transportation system were perfected but that little had been done on the locks and dams except design work and clearing of sites. It was apparent even then that the completion date depended on Gatun Dam rather than on Culebra Cut.

[1] J. F. Stevens, "The Panama Canal," A.S.C.E., *Transactions*, XCI, 961.
[2] *Theodore Roosevelt, An Autobiography*, p. 543.
[3] Quoted in *Panama Star and Herald*, April 20, 1907.

Commissaries were being operated for employees all along the line. The recently equipped Panama Railroad steamers, the new cold-storage plant at Cristóbal, and the new refrigerator cars on the railroad made possible cold-storage service from New York to all stations on the Isthmus.

The Tivoli Hotel at Ancon was operating. Fifteen small hotels along the line were supplying meals to gold employees at 30 cents a meal. Mess halls were serving food to Spanish and Italian laborers at 40 cents a day, including wine. West Indians were served at kitchens for 30 cents a day. Quarters for about 75 per cent of the gold employees were completed.

Health conditions were excellent and the Health Department well organized. There was no yellow fever and very little malaria,[4] although the total Canal force on June 30, 1907, numbered 29,446. On all sides there was progress and work, in contrast to the hysteria and chaos of 1905. It is not strange that Goethals was impressed with the monumental achievements of Stevens, who had accomplished so much, which he now inherited. But there was still much to do.

Secretary Taft had come down with consulting engineers, who were checking rock foundations for locks. He had been sent by the President to investigate complaints of the steam-shovel men, who had gone direct to the White House after Stevens had refused their demands.

Mr. Taft's first official act was designed to strengthen Goethals' position as chairman. He signed an Executive Order of April 2, 1907, vesting authority of the Governor in the chairman.[5] Thus Goethals found himself legally chairman, chief engineer, and Governor—the Czar of the Canal Zone. But troubled waters were ahead. The Commission was still charged with responsibility for building the Canal and was therefore a potential source of trouble. Goethals' position was by no means secure.

[4] Goethals' Statement, Jan. 14, 1908 (Hearings No. 11, pp. 3–4) (U.S.).

[5] Executive Order of April 2, 1907, signed by Taft by direction (P.C. Rec. Bur., File 2-C-13) (MS).

Goethals made his arrival round of dinners and receptions in the evenings. During the day he took Secretary Taft on inspections and soon felt they were becoming too "chummy."[6] At the office the steam-shovel men, locomotive engineers, and conductors descended upon Goethals with threats to resign if not granted a pay increase. He refused them but arranged for them to see the Secretary of War.

Taft cordially welcomed the men and inquired if they had read a statement to Mr. Shonts in their behalf by a Mr. Dolan, an official of a steam-shovel concern. He received a deluge of words. They did not know Mr. Dolan. He was not their representative. They were in a class by themselves, and wanted a revision of pay, upward, of course, and desired him to decide right then and there. They thought he had come for that purpose.

Taft was firm and refused to consider their statements but suggested they study the papers he had brought along and write him their reaction. The steam-shovel committee did not like this proposal and stated that no one could change their determination to ask for more money and that wages in the United States were no basis for comparison, as they thought five years on the Isthmus would unfit them for work in the States. They wanted more money; they would resign in a body if this were not granted. They wanted to see the President. Taft was not browbeaten, as they recognized. He refused them and took matters under consideration for future decision. He listened to similar representatives from the railroad groups and did not decide their cause either.[7] Instead, he returned to Washington to consult with the President about labor troubles on the Isthmus.

Goethals started his custom of daily inspections. After early breakfast he would walk down the hill to the Culebra Station to board a northbound or southbound train, or to take his special car, painted yellow and known as the "yellow peril." He always seemed to turn up at the most unexpected times, but returned to

[6] Goethals to George R. Goethals, April 4, 1907; quoted in J. B. and F. Bishop, *Goethals, Genius of the Panama Canal: a Biography*, p. 160.

[7] *Panama Star and Herald*, April 7, 1907.

his office in the afternoon and worked until ten or eleven at night to get out enough work to keep the forces busy the next day.

It was while working like this that he became impressed with the vastness of building the Panama Canal. For a while he feared it was going to be too much for him. As time passed, however, his perspective changed, and "gradually this phase was replaced by the realization that it was not at all big, but only a mass of irritating details."[8] The Administration Building at Culebra became the "old mill" for grinding out the multitudinous details required by the Canal plan.

The first four clubhouses—Empire, Culebra, Gorgona, and Cristóbal—were nearing completion when Stevens left. He had hoped to inaugurate them before leaving but could not. However, he did not forget. The first clubhouse was inaugurated at Gorgona under the auspices of the Y.M.C.A., with A. Bruce Minear as General Secretary. It was a two-story building with large verandas and a spacious lobby. There were smoking rooms, a gymnasium, a 600-volume library, and a soda fountain—all for the inaugural crowd to view as they milled around looking over their new social center. To an appreciative crowd the General Secretary read a letter from John F. Stevens and told how Stevens had said before leaving the Isthmus that the Clubs would become the "monuments to which he could look back with most pride."[9] They were, indeed, monuments; for from that day the clubhouses of the Panama Canal have remained the great centers of community life among the employees—their one great escape from the boredom and monotony of life in the tropics.

Goethals examined his organization shortly after taking charge. As desired by the President, the new members of the Commission had to live on the Isthmus and work as heads of departments. Of the new engineers, it was Sibert who had the widest construction experience. Rousseau had been Chief of the Bureau of Yards and Docks of the Navy. Goethals, himself,

---

[8] Goethals; quoted in J. B. and F. Bishop, *op. cit.*, p. 235.
[9] *Panama Star and Herald*, May 27, 1907.

has left an interesting insight on reasons for assignments: "Sibert's experience on locks and dams makes his assignment to that work very necessary. Rousseau, the navy man, is a crackerjack on buildings, machine shops, etc. . . . . so Gaillard had to take the Cut."[10] This organization had been discussed with Stevens before he left.

When the organization was completed, each commissioner was assigned to a department. Sibert was placed in charge of Lock and Dam Construction; Gaillard, of Excavation and Dredging; Rousseau, in charge of Municipal Engineering, Motive Power and Machinery, and Building Construction; Colonel Gorgas, as Chief Sanitary Officer; and Jackson Smith, in charge of Labor, Quarters and Subsistence. Joseph Ripley, who had been assistant chief engineer under Stevens and in charge of Lock and Dam Construction, was designated as special designing engineer. Major H. F. Hodges was appointed general purchasing officer, in charge of the Washington office. The organization of the construction divisions remained as it had been under Stevens.

Naturally, when army engineers were placed in control, there was considerable apprehension felt by the civilian engineers. But this gradually disappeared as the men became acquainted with the new leaders. Mr. Ripley was not satisfied with the new arrangement and resigned in resentment. Nevertheless, the new Commission took on the aspect of being in "continuous session."[11]

Mr. Taft had had time now to return to Washington and take up the demands of the steam-shovel men with the President. They realized the possibility of trouble. They also knew the steam-shovel men had no real grievance but instead were in the highest-paid group on the Isthmus and hence were accepted as a basis for making other pay rates. The Government could not afford to yield under pressure to their demands for an increase from $210 to $300 per month, for at that time in United States history it would have been a costly precedent.

[10] Goethals; quoted in J. B. and F. Bishop, *op. cit.*, p. 167.

[11] J. B. and F. Bishop, *op. cit.*, p. 167.

It was not until Sunday, May 5, 1907, that the action of the Secretary of War was published. Taft wanted both locomotive and steam-shovel engineers to receive the same pay. He authorized an increase to transportation crews and seniority of 5 per cent for the first year, with 3 per cent for each succeeding year, to steam-shovel, transportation, and mechanical-trades men.[12] This was a compromise. "It was a sop thrown to the steam-shovel men."[13]

Like many compromises, it did not work. The steam-shovel men struck, and almost overnight the number of steam shovels operating was reduced from sixty-eight to thirteen. The strike became a more gripping subject of conversation on the Isthmus than digging Culebra Cut or controlling the Chagres. Many strikers left for the United States, and the excavation of Culebra spiraled downward to a low of 624,586 cubic yards in June. This was a severe setback.

Goethals recruited new crews. As they became proficient, yardage came up slowly but surely. Later, many strikers tried to return but found they had lost their seniority, as that was conditional on continuous service. They had to start over again. This was Goethals' first serious crisis. It was not a victory, but he learned how to deal with strikers.

The next important decision for Goethals was the contract matter, held over from the Stevens regime. Contractors had continued their pressure on the Secretary of War in Washington. Goethals referred the problem to the Engineering Committee of Gaillard, Sibert, and Rousseau, and they reported adversely.[14] Goethals was then fortified in his official position.

He wrote Secretary Taft explaining how the work natur-

[12] Goethals, Address, March 6, 1915 (Society of the Chagres, *Yearbook 1915*, pp. 162–63).

[13] Goethals' Statement, Nov. 11, 1907 (Hearings No. 1, p. 113) (U.S.).

[14] I.C.C., Engineering Committee, *Report*, June 24, 1907 (P.C. Rec. Bur., File 9-A-4). The history of the contract episode is summarized briefly (1) by J. F. Stevens in Bennett's *History of the Panama Canal*, p. 321, and (2) in the *Index to Reports of Engineers, U.S. Army, 1866–1912*, Vol. II, Part V, "The Panama Canal," pp. 2441–42 (House Doc. 470, 63d Cong., 2d sess.).

ally divided itself into dry excavation by steam shovels at Culebra, dredging of the sea-level portions, construction of locks, dams, regulating works, terminals, and the relocation of the railroad. He emphasized that Culebra was already in progress with hired labor, and that 80 per cent of the plant was on hand or under contract for the entire excavation of the Canal. He pointed out, however, that lock gates and operating machinery could be constructed better by contract. Moreover, conditions then were different than when the contract was first proposed. The project was under way with a large force and an efficient organization. He concluded that the work could be done "better, cheaper and more quickly by building the Canal by the Government."[15] His report definitely ended all chance of building the Canal by contract, even if it did not stop the efforts of the contractors.

By that summer in 1907 the Canal Zone had taken on more nearly the appearance of a normal North American settlement. Families had arrived in increasing numbers and set up homes in villages surrounded by jungle. There were schools for the children, work for the men, but little diversion for the women. There was need for some social organizers, and they appeared.

Two ladies visited the Isthmus in the summer of 1907—Gertrude Beeks and Helen Varick Boswell. Miss Beeks was a social investigator who could get closer to the workers than the officials could. Each worker talked frankly with her without fearing to be known as a "kicker."[16] She inspected the Canal, the towns, and living quarters. She checked on hot and cold water, tub baths and shower baths, insects and screens, kitchens and toilets and submitted a long list of items to her National Civic Federation, covering almost every kind of complaint. When the report eventually came back to the Canal Zone it was found that most of the criticisms no longer applied.[17]

15 Goethals to Taft, July 30, 1907 (P.C. Rec. Bur., File 9-A-4) (U.S.). Sibert and Stevens, *Construction of the Panama Canal*, pp. 322–24.

16 J. J. Meehan, "The Early Days" (Society of the Chagres. *Yearbook 1913*, pp. 145–46).

17 *Canal Record*, Oct. 16, 1907, I, 53–55 (U.S.).

Miss Boswell represented the Federation of Women's Clubs. She visited the towns along the line, talked to the women, explained her desire to organize social clubs, and outlined plans for organization. Within a few weeks clubs were being organized in all the larger towns, and these clubs united in a local Federation of Women's Clubs[18]—an organization that continued until near the end of construction days.

Until September 1907 the Commission had published no regular bulletin of information, and workers had complained about it to Miss Beeks. She suggested to Colonel Goethals that he start a newspaper to inform the men about decisions and progress of the work. Thereupon, with the approval of the Isthmian Canal Commission, he engaged a young newsman to start the *Canal Record,* a weekly paper to be issued free to employees. Goethals declared it was not a clipping bureau for United States papers, nor an organ for aggrandizing the reputation of commissioners, but solely a factual bulletin about the Canal for distribution to employees, Members of Congress, and United States papers.[19] It gave accurate information and by so doing tended to stop much propaganda and inaccurate or misleading articles that had plagued the Canal.

The *Record's* editorial policy forbade publication of anything in praise of any official. Even the very name of Goethals was mentioned only twice in the index to seven volumes, once in Volume 2 with a note to "*See* Chairman and Chief Engineer," and once in Volume 7, listing his appointment as First Governor in 1914. With an example like that set by the chairman, Secretary Bishop had no trouble in carrying out that policy to the end.

By late summer the effect of the strike was subsiding. Goethals cabled the President that 1,274,404 cubic yards were excavated in August—a better record than ever reached before by the United States. Roosevelt sent his congratulations for break-

18 *Canal Record,* Oct. 2, 1907, I, 3 (U.S.).

19 I.C.C., *Minutes,* 133d meeting, Aug. 31, 1907, pp. 7–8 (U.S.). Goethals' Statement, Jan. 17, 1908 (Hearings No. 19, pp. 71–72) (U.S.).

ing the previous record of excavation, stating, "I am as surprised as I am pleased that you should have surpassed it."[20] When this interchange of messages was published in the *Canal Record*, it made a tremendous impression and stimulated work. The entire country took notice, and Goethals was acclaimed as the hero of construction.[21]

Goethals came to power at a significant time. Preparation of Gatun Dam site started in April 1907 with one shovel and work on the dam toes in July. Excavation of the Atlantic sea-level channel was started in the dry through Mindi Hills with steam shovels—made possible by excluding the water with a dike at the French Canal. Excavation at the Pacific locks and construction of the relocated Panama Railroad also started about July.

Work on dams and locks took shape rapidly in late summer at both terminals. Masonry work was expected to start on Gatun Locks in eighteen months. The plant would have to be ordered in 1907. Two shovels were working on Gatun spillway. Trestles were under construction for dumping rock for the toes of the dam. The Chagres was diverted, and pipe-line dredges were expected to start pumping material to the dam in January 1908.

Construction had developed "faster than contemplated." Previously, Culebra had been accepted as the feature of canal construction governing the date of completion; then it was the work at Gatun; and this, in turn, was dependent on removing the old Panama Railroad from the dam site to its new location. Goethals cabled these facts to Secretary Taft, requesting $8,000,-000 to "push" the work. He asked to be informed as soon as possible in order to reduce work if not approved. The message had its desired effect. The President approved, and work was not delayed.[22]

[20] Roosevelt to Goethals, Sept. 5, 1907, *Canal Record*, Sept. 11, 1907, I, 9 (U.S.).

[21] *Panama Star and Herald*, Sept. 11, 1907.

[22] Acting Secretary of War to Goethals, Aug. 26–27, 1907, *Canal Record*, Sept. 11, 1907, I, 9 (U.S.).

After the seat of power was moved to the Isthmus, another innovation was adopted by Congress when the House Committee on Appropriations arrived at the Isthmus on November 7, 1907, to conduct hearings for the 1909 estimates. They received a cordial welcome by the entire Isthmian Canal Commission and, after inspecting conditions at Cristóbal, were taken on a tour of Gatun Locks and Dam, the dumps at Tavernilla, thence on a trip through the Cut, over the Pacific locks and dams, to Ancon Hospital and, as usual, to Taboga. The next evening a minstrel show at the Culebra Club was given in their honor—the first public entertainment in the Canal Zone.[23]

The Congressmen were very inquisitive. They were critical of the wages and privileges of Canal workers, to whom living quarters were assigned in conformity with their salary level. They visited every type of house. When they were in the chairman's house at Culebra, they wanted to go upstairs to see how Goethals lived. Goethals was angered. One Congressman asked if, on his own $7,500 salary, he would receive a house of proportionate size. Goethals replied that if he were on the Isthmus he would not receive "anything near $7,500 a year."[24]

On the way to the Administration Building in Culebra to hold hearings in the forenoon, the Congressmen saw all porch electric lights on in full daylight. This happened because current was turned on at that time for fans at hotels. They were critical of this useless expenditure and abuse of privileges and brought up the rent question, which was kept under discussion until employees were charged rent.

At the hearings, Congressman James A. Tawney, chairman, explained the unusual procedure of coming to the Isthmus. Goethals, placed on the defensive, outlined his organization— the Colón Dredging Division, from the Atlantic to Gatun; the Gatun Lock Division, which included the Porto Bello quarries;

[23] *Canal Record*, Nov. 13, 1907, I, 83 (U.S.).

[24] Goethals, Address, March 6, 1915 (Society of the Chagres, *Yearbook 1915*, p. 167).

the Chagres River Division, from Gatun to Bas Obispo; the
Culebra Division, from Obispo to Pedro Miguel; the La Boca
Division, which included Pedro Miguel and La Boca Locks; and
the La Boca Dredging Division to the Pacific, including dams.
He also gave a review of the work for the year.

Asked how the resulting reductions in personnel would be
handled if salary appropriations were cut, he replied that it
would be preferable to do it by legislation rather than leave it
to him "to discover the way of doing it."[25] Asked if he thought
it necessary to continue the advantages employees were receiving, he replied: "I do not. Personally, I think they are getting
too much."[26] He told them the steam-shovel men were getting
too much and that they formed the basis for agitation among
others. A member suggested that the men might strike if reduced. Goethals countered: "All right; suppose they do. We
will get additional men. We had that trouble in May. We will
have some trouble so long as these steam-shovel men are on the
Isthmus. There may be men who will go, but we will not have
any strikes."[27]

Other Commissioners followed Goethals and went into the
details of specific projects, but he always remained at their side
ready to assist or intervene. Major Sibert was asked if there
were any differences of opinion as to the stability of Gatun Dam.
He replied, "I think not."[28] Goethals interrupted and stated,
"I can say that there is not." The Committee talked strongly to
Colonel Gorgas about the large number of hospitals. They
wanted more centralization, with transfer of patients from the
line to the terminal hospitals by train and the elimination of
unnecessary hospitals.

Though the Congressmen were critical while on the Isthmus,
when they returned to Washington they reported conditions at
Panama were in "excellent shape."[29]

[25] Goethals' Statement, Nov. 11, 1907 (Hearings No. 1, p. 96) (U.S.).
[26] *Ibid.*, p. 97.   [27] *Ibid.*, p. 98.
[28] Sibert's Statement, Nov. 11, 1907 (*ibid.*, p. 167).
[29] *Panama Star and Herald*, Dec. 5, 1907.

The President also desired centralization for the general Canal organization. He had requested Congress to place the work under one man but had been refused. He did not want Congress, by legislation, to interfere with the Canal Zone Government. Nor did he want Commissioners causing trouble. Gorgas and Sibert were at loggerheads with Goethals and were reported as having joined forces to eliminate him.

When Goethals went to Washington in January 1908, he carried a draft of a proposed Executive Order, prepared with the assistance of the general counsel, R. R. Rogers. It gave greater strength to the order drafted by Stevens, by increasing the power of the chairman in appointing heads of departments and in adjusting duties among the members. It required the members of the Commission to reside on the Isthmus.

When Goethals delivered the draft, he requested of Mr. Taft: "Tell the President that while that's what we'd like, it isn't in accordance with the law." When Roosevelt heard this he made a characteristic reply: "I don't give a damn for the law; I want the Canal built!"[30] and signed the order on January 6, 1908. This Executive Order completed the process of centralizing power in the hands of the chairman and chief engineer. It effectively placed one man in charge of the work, in spite of the refusal of Congress to legislate, and practically relegated the Commission to a position of impotence.

In December 1907 excavation in Culebra Cut reached 1,025,-485 cubic yards. As the new year started, progress steadily increased on all projects. Plans were under way for transporting rock by barge from the quarry at Porto Bello and sand from Nombre de Dios for the Gatun work. Rock for the Pacific locks was to come from the quarry on Ancon Hill and sand by barge from Chamé.

The Cucuracha slide, which had caused the French so much trouble, started moving again and threatened the steam shovels.

[30] Goethals to Mark Sullivan, April 12, 1926; quoted in J. B. and F. Bishop, *Goethals, Genius of the Panama Canal: a Biography*, p. 193.

Goethals expected more slides later on but planned on removing them as they occurred during construction. He prepared the plant for building Gatun locks and Pacific locks and added to the excavation and transportation equipment as needed.

Living conditions continued to improve in spite of slight inconveniences. When the sinking of the Panama Railroad tracks in Black Swamp occurred, train service was interrupted. The Canal line south of the accident had no ice. In Panamá the price of ice increased 100 per cent. When the Isthmus became short of coffee, the merchants ran up their prices. Goethals remonstrated to Congress about the Panamanian merchants, stating that "whenever they can get us in a tight place they squeeze us."[31] Nevertheless, the commissaries improved. In late April 1908 the Cristóbal bakery was ready to deliver "pies, pastry and rolls"[32] and soon afterward even such luxuries as ice cream to messes along the railroad.

The excavation in Culebra continued upward, with yardage for the early months of 1908 around 1,250,000 cubic yards. Steam-shovel operations and transportation improved. Workers from many quarters of the globe gave a cosmopolitan color. The ceaseless activity in Culebra Cut made it the most spectacular part of the Canal work.

The operation of shovels at that time has been interestingly described: "The man who ran the steam shovel, who had charge of the engine and manœuvred it, was an Irishman. The man on the crane, who attended to the dumping, was an American. The two stokers at the engine behind were Jamaican negroes, and the six members of the 'move up' crew, the men who leveled the ground where the shovel stood and placed the tracks so that it could move forward and keep its nose to the bank, were Sikhs from the north of India, who wore white turbans on their heads and worked like automatons."[33]

[31] Goethals' Statement, Jan. 17, 1908 (Hearings No. 19, p. 82) (U.S.).
[32] *Canal Record*, April 15, 1908, I, 257 (U.S.).
[33] S. G. Blythe, "Life in Spigotty Land," (*Saturday Evening Post*, March 21, 1908, p. 6).

With over fifty shovels working in the Cut, with projects getting under way all along the line, and with the railroad actually becoming an "endless chain" hauling away spoil, there was no longer any doubt of the future, for the plant was there and directed by trained hands. It is no wonder that one who viewed those scenes could exclaim: "It is all over but the shouting, gentlemen, barring a few years of work. The Canal will be dug!"[34]

THE FINAL ORGANIZATION FOR CONSTRUCTION IS ADOPTED

The visit of the Appropriations Committee to Culebra in November 1907 started Goethals thinking seriously about effecting economies. He had found the old organization "objectionable" because he could not keep in close touch with it as he desired. He said: "I felt a tendency on the part of some department heads to make the department bigger than the whole,"[35] and he concluded the only thing to do was to reorganize. He had the authority in the Executive Order of January 6, 1908. The only question in his mind was when to act.

When trouble developed on the dams at Sosa Hill, work was stopped by Goethals pending investigation. The resulting relocation of Sosa Locks at Miraflores appeared a convenient opportunity to start reorganizing. Goethals created a new unit—the Pacific Division, Lock and Dam Construction. He appointed Sydney B. Williamson, a civilian friend of long standing, as division engineer. Did this mean that Goethals planned on breaking up Major Sibert's department?

In the next move the dredging and excavation from Miraflores to the sea was placed under the veteran W. G. Comber. Another indication of the impending reorganization was the designation of H. F. Hodges, the general purchasing officer in Washington, to be in charge of the design of lock gates in addition to his purchasing duties.[36]

[34] *Canal Record,* April 1, 1908, I, 245 (U.S.).
[35] Goethals' Statement, Feb. 15, 1909 (Hearings No. 8, p. 4) (U.S.).
[36] Goethals' *Circular,* Feb. 21, 1908 (P.C. Rec. Bur., File 2-C-13) (MS).

Courtesy of The Panama Canal

CULEBRA CUT, SHOWING SLIDE, NOVEMBER 25, 1909

GATUN LOCK CHAMBERS UNDER CONSTRUCTION, MARCH 1, 1910

Looking south from east wall, upper Gatun Lock

In the meantime able Jackson Smith, head of Labor, Quarters and Subsistence, became the object of attack by labor organizations in the United States, and Secretary Taft came to the Isthmus to relieve him. Smith had made fundamental contributions at a time of the greatest crisis; but in spite of this, conditions were such that he had to resign. In his letter of resignation to the President he referred to his three years during the organization of the Canal under "difficulties of a number and nature not again to be encountered"[37] as the best evidence of the interest he had. Roosevelt acknowledged that the efficiency of his department would make his successor's task an easy one and the importance of his work was known to all familiar with Canal history.

With Jackson Smith out of office the way was open to appoint Hodges to the Commission. Goethals explained his plans to Secretary Taft, and in May Goethals decided to complete his reorganization of construction forces. He wanted to divide the functions of Labor, Quarters and Subsistence. The most sensitive problem was the Sanitary Department. No changes there were planned except to turn over grass cutting to the Quartermaster and sanitary-ditch digging to the construction forces. The sanitary engineers would then outline the work desired, rather than be constructors as in the past.

Goethals explained his plan to Gorgas, who was "sure it wouldn't work"[38] but agreed to try it for six months. Relations between Goethals and Gorgas became more tense, till they were hardly on speaking terms.

As could have been foreseen, in mid-June Goethals announced the abolition of the Department of Lock and Dam Construction, effective July 1, and the formation of a new Atlantic Division embracing all territory north of Tavernilla, to be under Major

[37] Jackson Smith to President, June 1, 1908; quoted in *Canal Record*, July 1, 1908, I, 349 (U.S.).

[38] Goethals to Mark Sullivan, April 12, 1926; quoted in J. B. and F. Bishop, *op. cit.*, p. 173.

Sibert as division engineer.[39] This was a change designed to have far-reaching consequences in the final form of the Canal on the Pacific.

Ten days later another *Circular* abolished the Department of Excavation and Dredging and formed a Central Division under Major Gaillard, with Mr. L. K. Rourke as assistant division engineer. A third *Circular*, forming the Pacific Division under Sydney B. Williamson, was issued. Thus was completed the final reorganization into major construction divisions—the Atlantic, the Central, and the Pacific.

Other changes followed as rapidly as they could be planned and circulars prepared. The Department of Motive Power and Machinery, Municipal Engineering, and Building Construction was distributed among the three great construction divisions.

In the Central Division, Rourke represented the civilian element. He had had an interesting career. After graduating from Massachusetts Institute of Technology in 1895 he worked on the Boston and Maine Railroad. Later, he went to the Isthmus and became supervisor of tracks on the Panama Railroad. He resigned from this position to become roadmaster of the Guayaquil and Quito Railroad in Ecuador, where he was promoted to superintendent. After that he traveled widely in Mexico, the United States, and Chile. All together he had spent six years in the tropics and was acclimated. He knew West Indian labor and how to work it.

Rourke entered the Canal service in December 1905 and worked his way up from superintendent of tracks. When dumps were started, he became superintendent of tracks and dumps and later division engineer of the Culebra Division when D. W. Bolich resigned in May 1908. He was a red-faced Irishman, who knew his work. He gained the confidence of the men in Culebra Cut by working along with them at the time of the organization of its construction forces under Stevens. Rourke was fitted by

[39] Official *Circular No. 183;* quoted in *Canal Record,* June 24, 1908, I, 342 (U.S.).

nature, ability, and background of experience on the Isthmus for his task. He was the real organizer of the Culebra Division for mass excavation.[40] When Goethals' reorganization of July 1908 came, Rourke was the logical choice as assistant division engineer of the Central Division under Major Gaillard. How well he succeeded we shall see later.

The old Labor, Quarters and Subsistence Department was split up. A Quartermaster Department was formed under Major C. A. Devol. Personnel records were transferred to the Chairman's Office. All sanitary construction went to the great construction divisions, and superficial ditching, cleaning, and grass cutting to the Quartermaster Department.

But still more changes came. Colonel H. F. Hodges, who was appointed to the Commission on July 16, 1908, was made assistant chief engineer, and Admiral Rousseau became assistant to the chief engineer. Goethals then organized his Chief Engineer's Office into four divisions: first, Design under Hodges; second, a Division of Building, Power and Machinery under Rousseau; third, a General Survey Division; and fourth, a Personnel Division.

With the *Canal Record* publishing excavation figures each week, the organization was ideal for development of rivalry between divisions, between steam shovels, and between men. On the Atlantic side, army engineers were in complete control; on the Pacific, civilians; in the Central Division, a combination of civilians and military. The final boundaries of the great construction divisions were natural, the Central extending between the south end of Gatun Locks to the north end of Pedro Miguel; the Atlantic, everything to the north; and the Pacific Division, everything southward.

Goethals used the reorganization as an opportunity to adjust the personnel. He urged the heads of divisions and departments to scrutinize their forces for regrading or discharge of those who

[40] J. B. Bishop, *The Panama Gateway*, p. 192 .

did not measure up to standard.[41] He also had ideas about training young officers on the Canal. His plan was to secure the services of a small group each year for assignment to positions in competition with civilians at the bottom, where they could work their way up the ladder from rodman to levelman, transitman, and finally to chief of survey party. He wanted young army engineers to obtain actual experience and to be promoted on the basis of results. The first group, consisting of Second Lieutenant Glen E. Edgerton, George R. Goethals, and James G. Steese, arrived in 1908 and started off on this basis, but very shortly the War Department training program interfered. Goethals had to give up the plan, which he felt would have benefited the young officers most. Instead of assigning them to definite positions in which they would be held responsible on the same basis as civilians, he had to rotate them among the departments as students.

The reorganization of the Medical Department proved beneficial. It reduced hospital expenses and enabled a reduction in the number of doctors and nurses. The question arose whether the basis for reduction of nurses should be on length of service or on efficiency. Goethals decided for efficiency. Rating lists of nurses were prepared by doctors and head nurses and turned over to Colonel Gorgas for consolidation. The last ten nurses were dropped. There was also a reduction in clerks in this department; and no longer when Goethals inspected clearings would he find two different gangs, under separate foremen, cutting grass in the same location.

In Congress there was some desire to re-create the political office of Governor of the Canal Zone. One Congressman asked why Goethals, as chairman, should be superior in authority. Goethals replied: "I do not see how we are going to operate here unless some one is vested with authority to step in and decide questions." The Congressman continued to press Goethals on the point. He was asked about the possibility of conflict with his duties if there were some other co-ordinator. He answered: "It

---

[41] Goethals' Memorandum, July 23, 1908 (P.C. Rec. Bur., File 2-C-13) (MS).

did prior to my coming, and I presume it would while I remain here."[42] In line with the general idea of centralized power, Goethals opposed introduction of trial by juries on the Isthmus. He expressed himself as being a "firm believer on this job in summary justice. Juries can be obtained, but not without interference with the work."[43] Summary justice kept order more effectively.

Nothing showed up the administrative capacity of Goethals to better advantage during his career on the Canal than his reorganization. Geographically, the reorganization was a consolidation of Stevens' construction districts. It was a natural evolution from the previous organization and was just about what was needed at the time. It practically gave the Canal three construction chief engineers—Sibert, Gaillard, and Williamson. It freed Goethals from many irritations and enabled him to give his time to other things. For example, when the head of Civil Administration, ex-Senator Blackburn, was absent on leave, Goethals assumed his duties to gain a better understanding of the Canal Zone Government.

Goethals was not an easy taskmaster. He held his division engineers accountable for results and did not interfere. As he stated, "I do not impose the employment of any man on any division engineer. I let them select their forces, and hold them strictly responsible."[44] The men quickly learned that he was fair and just. He was familiar with government routine and knew how to secure results in spite of it. He proved himself a past master in handling Congressional committees by dealing with them with disconcerting directness. He was an able executive and a great administrator.

CHANGES IN THE CANAL DURING CONSTRUCTION

Through the first years of the Canal work by the United States there were many changes. The planners had not foreseen all.

[42] Goethals' Statement, Jan. 7, 1909 (Hearings No. 12, p. 140) (U.S.).
[43] Ibid., p. 139.
[44] Goethals' Statement, Jan. 22, 1908 (Senate Committe Hearing No. 19, p. 158).

The general plan for the lock canal, as adopted by Congress, contained sites for two locks on the Pacific, one at Pedro Miguel, and another near Sosa Hill. This arrangement gave a spacious intermediate-level lake for the Pacific terminal. Work originally started on the dams under Stevens, who did not like the scheme because the Sosa location was too close to the coast and subject to gunfire from ships in the bay. He had explored the area and taken borings. He had chosen Agua Dulce, a location to the south of Miraflores, but this change had not been adopted. He had also suggested combining the Pacific locks into one structure, as a desirable change to improve the Canal plan, but he had not had the marine experience to justify the plan with power.

Meanwhile, under Goethals, construction had gone ahead on dams for Sosa Lake. One night a trestle toppled and the fill sank eight feet. When a train passed the next morning, the track sank six feet. Goethals stopped work immediately. Then he started an extended investigation, with test borings from La Boca to Pedro Miguel, to find a suitable foundation.

He also appointed a board to investigate the lock locations. They studied four projects—first, a one-lift lock at Pedro Miguel and a two-lift lock at La Boca; second, a two-lift lock at Pedro Miguel and a one-lift at Miraflores; third, a one-lift at Pedro Miguel and a two-lift at Miraflores; and fourth, a single-lift lock at each of the three sites. They considered all combinations, except the one most desired by John F. Stevens, William Gerig, and later by Sibert. They recommended the third project—one lift at Pedro Miguel and two lifts at Miraflores.

Goethals considered combining all the locks at Miraflores but found it would require a large concrete fill for a foundation, which would have been prohibitive. He reported to the President on December 9, 1907, in favor of one flight at Pedro Miguel and two at Miraflores—an arrangement which would enable continued use of the Panama Railroad terminals at La Boca. The Sosa Lake plan would have forced the abandonment of La Boca terminals. The President approved on the twentieth, to the great satisfaction of the engineers who were struggling with the problem.

Goethals, then in Washington, wrote the news to Major Gaillard, who was then acting chairman and chief engineer on the Isthmus. He stated it would seem a change in organization and directed him to place Mr. Williamson in charge of Pacific Locks and Dams.[45] Later, when appearing before a committee in Congress, he was asked who originated the idea of changing the location of Sosa Locks. He replied with his usual frankness: "The first mention of the change was from Mr. John F. Stevens."[46]

Another important change was in the dimensions of locks. The Canal plan called for locks 95 feet wide. President Roosevelt, in his message of December 3, 1907, expressed the belief that the locks should be 120 feet wide.[47] The Navy General Board requested the width be increased to 110 feet to take the largest battleship then planned, which was about 100-foot beam. Goethals doubted whether the Navy would build vessels requiring a "lock of a greater width than 100 feet."[48] But the Commission recommended the change requested by the Navy, and the President approved it on January 15, 1908. There were others who thought the 110-foot locks were too narrow. A few years later, when visiting the Kiel Canal in 1912, Goethals was told by Kaiser Wilhelm that the Panama Canal locks should have been wider. But then it was too late.

One other change by Goethals was the construction of a breakwater from La Boca to Naos Island. Strong silt-bearing currents swept westward across the outer harbor, silting the channel to a dangerous extent. When the dump at La Boca was started, the idea of extending it in the form of a breakwater to Naos Island was natural. In spite of the large tidal range on the Pacific, water near the island was always sufficiently deep, regardless

[45] Goethals to Gaillard, Dec. 22, 1907 (P.C. Rec. Bur., File Personnel, Williamson) (MS).

[46] Goethals' Statement, Jan. 7, 1909 (Hearings No. 12, p. 122) (U.S.).

[47] *Messages and Papers of the Presidents*, XVI, 7101 (U.S.).

[48] Goethals' Statement, Jan. 18, 1908 (Hearings No. 19, pp. 140–41) (U.S.).

of the state of the tide. In La Boca the vessels could be handled only at high tide. The plan to connect the railroad with deep water at Naos Island was old in the history of Panamá. Such a provision had been included in the concessionary contract for the Panama Railroad of 1867.

Later came a change in the west breakwater at Colón, which was relocated to run from Toro Point eastward across Limon Bay to the channel instead of paralleling the channel as originally intended by the first Commission. This change made it practicable to complete the breakwater protection of the harbor by constructing an east breakwater.

The adopted lock-canal plan called for a bottom width of 200 feet in Culebra Cut. With its rocky sides capable of gouging holes in the hulls of vessels, it was necessary to widen the Cut as a measure of safety to prevent sinkings, particularly for larger-sized ships. Goethals recommended 300 feet, which the President approved on October 23, 1908.[49] These changes made the estimates for the cost of the Canal soar, and Goethals then estimated $250,000,000 as the probable total cost.

Gatun Dam for a long time had been the subject of an extended controversy. After work had started, a newsman visiting the Isthmus wrote about an underground lake at Gatun Dam site—a story that received wide credence.

Later, on November 21, 1908, after a period of heavy rain, a part of the rock in the upstream toe of the dam slid. It was an event of absolutely no significance—one slide of many not worth notice. Unfortunately, another enterprising reporter crossed the Isthmus in a train at the time. While viewing the sights of Gatun, he observed floodwater and the dent made by the slide. He saw a chance to make a headline and cabled to the States a story that Gatun Dam was destroyed by dropping into an underground lake.[50] The result was a national sensation made possible

---

[49] Roosevelt, "Memo to Secretary of War," Oct. 23, 1908; quoted in *Canal Record*, Feb. 10, 1909, II, 185 (U.S.).

[50] *Canal Record*, March 31, 1909, II, 244 (U.S.).

by a credulous public. Gatun Dam became a political issue, and the Canal again came under attack.

Engineering News on December 24 came to the support of the Canal in a strong editorial, emphasizing the stability of the dam. In its next week's issue, John F. Stevens rushed to the rescue with an open letter supporting Goethals and condemning the outbreak of sensational journalism. He admitted that when the dam was designed, 25 feet had been added to the height, and both toes of the dam had been unduly enlarged as a "concession to prejudice" but said that he had intended to reduce the cross section of the dam later during construction. He felt that the motive for the attack was deep and that the object was the abandonment of the entire Panama undertaking, to enable the resurrection of the Nicaragua Canal by its powerful backers. He emphasized that the choice of the route had been made and that the work was planned and under rapid execution. He appealed for all the "encouragement and moral help possible"[51] to Colonel Goethals and predicted that eventually the engineering world would be proud of the result.

Congress entered the fight and sent a committee to the Isthmus to investigate the Canal—a type of investigation that would have placed most men on the defensive. The members were inquisitive about the dam, but Goethals was ready and replied with simplicity and directness. Finally, when asked if he had consulted fully and freely with his associates, he replied, "Always —not only with the division engineers, but lower down. I will consult a foreman about his particular class of work. It helps the foreman and it helps me."[52]

Roosevelt, recognizing the effect of these scare stories on the public mind, sent President-elect Taft to the Isthmus with a board of eminent engineers to investigate. They studied the Gatun Dam with special reference to its earthy material—the central point of discussion; and they examined other questioned

---

[51] *Engineering News*, Dec. 24, 1908, p. 717; and Dec. 31, p. 751.
[52] Goethals' Statement, Jan. 7, 1909 (Hearings No. 12, p. 127) (U.S.).

features of the Canal. On February 16, 1909, the Board reported that there was no doubt as to the "safe, tight, and durable character" of the dam.[53] They recommended a twenty-foot reduction in its height and confirmed the decision for the lock-type canal.

Roosevelt forwarded the report to Congress, asserting "it would be an inexcusable folly to change from the proposed lock to a sea-level canal" as proposed by the detractors; and that any future attack on either locks or dams would be "in reality merely attack upon the policy of building any canal at all."[54]

Meanwhile, when Taft returned to New Orleans, he appealed for support of the Canal and for stopping the "fire in the rear"[55] that was so destructive to the Canal builders.

The idea of combining the Pacific locks did not die. Sibert had revived the subject and had submitted a definite plan.[56] He wanted an anchorage space above the locks in what is now Miraflores Lake, so that ships emerging from the Cut at Pedro Miguel could anchor safely—a plan that would have improved the operation of the Canal. His plan was referred to Colonel Hodges, who wrote in opposition to the combination, for he considered a "division of lifts,"[57] as adopted, to be safer. Goethals sided with Hodges' views, because he considered him the best lockman in the United States. Goethals and Sibert had already cooled toward each other, and Gorgas thus had a companion who was not on friendly terms with the chairman.

Congress became interested. The proposal was examined by a board which had recommended the combination of the Pacific locks. But Goethals thought the combination would "seriously

[53] President Theodore Roosevelt, *Isthmian Canal*. Message . . . . transmitting report of Board of Engineers . . . . to accompany . . . . Taft to the Isthmus, 1909 (U.S.).

[54] *Ibid.*, p. 1.

[55] Taft's Speech, Feb. 12, 1909; quoted in *Canal Record*, Feb. 24, 1909, II, 204 (U.S.).

[56] W. L. Sibert to D. D. Gaillard, Jan. 31, 1908 (P.C. Rec. Bur., File 9-A-11) (MS).

[57] Hodges to Chief Engineer, Nov. 17, 1908 (P.C. Rec. Bur., File 9-D-17) (MS).

delay" opening the Canal. He wanted to hasten completion; but, as the plant for the two locks had been ordered, a change would have caused a long delay. After carefully considering all the factors, he explained that the "suggestion of the Board"[58] could not be adopted when it was proposed, although the report was made to the President.

Thus were made the fundamental errors in the design of the Panama Canal—the failure to create a summit-level anchorage between Culebra Cut and the Pacific locks and the failure to build the Pacific locks in single structures.

Adopting that plan, even if it had meant a delay, would have been fully justified. Correcting that error in design remained a problem for the future.

It should be explained, however, that at the time the Panama Canal was still the subject of bitter attacks. Propagandists would have seized upon any change in plan as a weakness, to alarm the public. Perhaps there was no other course; but nowhere do we find that the reasons for making the change were submitted with sufficient force and clarity to convince authorities of its importance. There was no background of marine-operating experience from which to draw, and there was much to overcome. Now there is over a quarter of a century of operating experience that was not possessed by the builders. It is easy, therefore, to point out this mistake after so many years of operation and to determine the solution that will supply the best canal for transiting vessels.

WORK PROGRESSES ON ALL FRONTS

Goethals' reorganization of July 1908 was the signal for sustained progress on all projects. The weekly publication of the *Canal Record* placed every organization on a competitive basis. The Canal Medals, promised by Roosevelt in November 1906, had arrived and had become a powerful incentive for effort,

[58] Goethals to J. R. Freeman, June 18, 1909 (*ibid.*). Sibert and Stevens, *Construction of the Panama Canal*, pp. 139–44.

highly prized by the employees. On one side the Medal bore a portrait of President Roosevelt, completed by Victor D. Brenner, and on the other side a view of the finished Culebra Cut with vessels passing through the artificial rocky gorge between Gold Hill and Contractors Hill. Inscribed "For two years' continuous service on the Panama Canal"[59] and "Presented by the President of the United States," with the employee's name inscribed beneath the shield of Panama, these became implements for progress as the spirit of the workers crystallized into one idea: "Get the Canal dug!"

Morale was higher than ever before, for gold employees had become stabilized. The social life on the Isthmus was taking form. At Ancon, the Tivoli Hotel became its center. At Colón, it was the old Washington House built prior to 1861; there, planked steaks were served on lignum vitae cut from 50-year-old Panama Railroad ties.[60]

Transportation became the keynote of the day. With maximum train movements of 574 a day and a daily average of 458, the Isthmus was a place that astounded the whole transportation world.

With the organization of construction forces completed, the plan for work and supplies took form. Spoil from Culebra was carried to dumps on the main line at Tavernilla; on the railroad relocation, to dumps at Gatun Dam, at La Boca, at the Naos Island breakwater, and to a few intermediate dumps. Rock from the Porto Bello quarries and sand from Nombre de Dios for Gatun work were towed in barges by stout tugboats up the old French channel to their stowages. On the Pacific, rock for the locks came from Ancon quarry, and sand was towed from Chamé to La Boca. Cement was brought by the Panama Railroad steamers "Ancon" and "Cristóbal" from the United States. When the President in his Message to Congress on December 8, 1908, stated that the Canal was being constructed with "speed, effi-

---

[59] *Canal Record*, Nov. 25, 1908, II, 97 (U.S.).
[60] *Ibid.*, Oct. 21, 1908, I, 59 (U.S.).

ciency and entire devotion to duty,"[61] he had a real basis for his words.

The concrete work was a great problem. Plants for Gatun locks and spillway, for Pedro Miguel and Miraflores locks were ordered and set up on the locations. Employees were hired, and auxiliary rail lines run. The first concrete on the Canal was poured in Gatun spillway on March 17, 1909. Concrete work was started at Gatun locks on August 24, 1909, at Pedro Miguel on September 1, 1909, and at Miraflores in February 1910. Towing locomotives were ordered, and contracts were placed for manufacture of lock gates, the last required to be in place on January 1, 1914—a date that was expected to be anticipated. Goethals had to push concrete work, planning completion of locks by June 1, 1913, for an official opening of the Canal on January 1, 1915.

One of the strangest incidents of lock construction was the struggle between lock contractors and Colonel Gorgas' sanitation workers, who were spraying oil over every possible pool of water. In earlier days they had placed oil even in the holy water of the Cathedral. When they saw pools of water on top of fresh concrete they poured oil on that also, to the dismay of the engineers.[62]

Goethals and Sibert got into another controversy. Owing to the long tow from Nombre de Dios, sand for construction on the Atlantic side cost about $1.75 a cubic yard. At the Pacific locks it was less expensive. Goethals wanted the Atlantic Division to shift to the Pacific supply for sand and appointed another board, which did not recommend as he desired. He said they preferred to retain "everything under their own control."[63]

Later, sand and rock costs at Gatun came up for more detailed discussion during hearings in Congress. There Goethals stated it was a mistake not to have shifted sources for these materials

[61] *Messages and Papers of the Presidents*, XVI, 7231 (U.S.).

[62] J. G. Steese, Conversation with author, June 12, 1941.

[63] Goethals' Statement, Nov. 17, 1909 (Hearings No. 2, pp. 8–9) (U.S.).

to Ancon and Chamé, as he had suggested. He thought the sand could have been delivered cheaper from Chamé. Sibert had thought otherwise and asked at what price. Goethals countered: "It is given in the annual report of last year." Sibert had explained that Ancon Quarry was not thought of at first for that purpose, but Sosa Hill; and he asked if a plan were ready, to which Goethals answered: "No, but I allowed six months" to provide one. Sibert then asked to see the calculations.

A Congressman suggested to Goethals that he understood he was a "young czar" and everything had to go his way on the Canal, that he would have made the change had he had the power. Thereupon Goethals replied: "I can issue instructions with a view to bringing about results, but I am not in a position to take hold of the details and attend to their execution so as to secure results."[64]

It should be pointed out that the key to this problem was transportation and that it would have been impossible for the Panama Railroad to haul the sand and rock for the Atlantic locks and Gatun spillway from the Pacific end of the Canal.

The relocation of the railroad had to be finished before the Canal, because the rising waters of the lake would flood long stretches of track. Work on this project was rushed, with a plan to run the railroad through Culebra Cut on the east berm. Engineers wanted the best location for the railroad line, and General Manager H. J. Slifer placed the decision squarely up to Colonel Goethals in a plan showing three locations. One of these ran the main line via Gatun, for which Slifer felt the only reason was purely a "sentimental one."[65] Instead, he recommended that Gatun be placed on a spur and that the main line run from Frijoles direct to Mount Hope.

Goethals chose the "sentimental" location and, without explaining, directed the adoption of the plan running the main line via Gatun as the "final location of the railroad line."[66]

[64] Goethals' Statement, Nov. 18, 1912 (Hearings No. 4, pp. 69–70) (U.S.).
[65] H. J. Slifer to Goethals, July 9, 1908 (P.C. Rec. Bur., File 45-G-7) (MS).
[66] Goethals to H. J. Slifer, July 20, 1908 (*ibid.*).

Relocating the railroad was a monumental work, involving large cuts and great fills. The result far surpassed the first road completed in 1855. During its relocation, the lignum vitae ties placed in 1855 were taken up unrotted and used again and the locomotives were changed from coal to oil. When slides revealed the dangers of having the line on the Canal berm, the line was rerouted around Gold Hill with a summit elevation of 271 feet, as a "temporary" measure.

On the sea-level sections of the Canal, dredges operated. At La Boca a new channel was being dredged to the west of Naos Island, paralleling the breakwater. While working by the old railroad dock, one dredge removed "rock and silt, copper, sugar, shoes, nails, boiler tubing, hemp and wire cables, canned goods, railroad rails,"[67] that had been dropped during cargo handling. Others picked up pieces of eight and cannon balls three centuries old.

On this channel old French equipment was still working. An old French dredgeman, who had worked at the Pacific entrance for over twenty years, was crushed between two clapet dredges and was taken to the Ancon Hospital critically ill. Two days later the resident engineer visited the injured man, who greeted him with the words nearest his heart:

"How many yards? .... And the *Gopher*—what did she do?"

"She holds the record by over 3,000 yards," was the reply.[68]

This soothed the injured man. The *Gopher* was a French dredge on which he had been master for years. It was a spirit like this that moved the earth at the Pacific terminal.

On February 1, 1909, the first five miles of the Panama Canal was completed. Two Pacific Mail steamers, full-dressed, entered La Boca Harbor amid whistles from the ships. In a few days the old French channel was closed by the Naos breakwater. Today that channel is almost unknown. Yachtsmen of the world, who now use it as an anchorage basin, do not know they are located in

[67] *Canal Record*, Nov. 11, 1908, II, 81 (U.S.).
[68] *Ibid.*, April 7, 1909, II, 250 (U.S.).

what was the first Pacific entrance channel. They do not know the struggles it took to create even that very small part of the Canal.

On the Atlantic side, part of the sea-level section was being excavated with dredges. Another part, protected by a dike, was being excavated in the dry by steam shovels.

Of all the construction operations during this period, Culebra Cut remained the most dramatic—the greatest attraction of construction days, covering about nine miles of intense activity with numerous steam shovels operating on terraces. Its magnitude impressed visitors profoundly. The danger of slides was always a sword of Damocles over the heads of the engineers; and because of these slides, Culebra Cut remained to the end the great problem of the Canal.

The most impressive sight of the Canal was the view from the bottom of the artificial gorge between Gold Hill and Contractors Hill. To both north and south one could see "a swarming mass of men and rushing railway trains, monster-like machines, all working with ceaseless activity, all animated seemingly by human intelligence, without confusion or conflict anywhere."[69] Empty trains entered the Cut on an upgrade to the summit and there backed downgrade to steam shovels, where they were loaded and then hauled away to a dump. There Lidgerwood unloaders quickly removed the spoil from the flatcars, spreaders leveled the discharged earth, and trackshifters adjusted the location of tracks, keeping pace with the bank as it extended.

Steam-shovel crews worked eight hours, from 7 to 11 A.M. and 1 to 5 P.M. After their day's work, engineers took locomotives to the hostling yards for check and repair. The night assumed an atmosphere of action as service trains ran through the Cut to supply steam shovels and trackshifters with coal and water. In the morning at 6:30 about sixty locomotives would pull out of their yards, coupled to trains of twenty to thirty cars, to start another day's work in what was an endless chain of dumpcars from the Cut to the dumps.

[69] J. B. Bishop, *op. cit.*, p. 195.

Courtesy of The Panama Canal

GATUN LOCKS AND DAM, JUNE 7, 1912

Showing south approach wall before the water rose

First Aircraft to Fly across the Isthmus, April 27, 1913

Piloted by Robert G. Fowler

The protection of that work against interruption was a necessity, for the floodwaters of the Chagres at Gamboa rose high enough to enter the excavated Cut. To prevent what would have been a catastrophe, the Cut was protected from the river by a dike at Gamboa 78 feet above sea level.

By August 1909, at Bas Obispo the Culebra Cut was down to the full depth of forty feet above the sea. At the continental divide it was at 120 feet above sea level, with an excavation rate of 1,200,000 cubic yards a month and 42,332,400 yards remaining to be removed. The problem had been solved.

It was rumored that relations between Gaillard and Rourke were not smooth. Rourke had become widely known as the organizer of the excavation in Culebra Cut. He received an offer as Superintendent of Streets in Boston and resigned, leaving the Isthmus on May 31, 1910. Goethals wrote him, reviewing the positions he had held on the Canal and stating that Rourke had accomplished effective results in each assignment, had won the good will of the men, and had secured their best efforts. "The work in the Culebra Cut has been directly under your charge, and to you the credit is mainly due for the satisfactory and rapid progress which has been made. The termination of your service is a distinct loss to the Commission."[70]

In 1910 the work on the Chagres section of the Central Division was suspended, and men were shifted to augment the railroad relocation work. Forty-two shovels were working in Culebra Cut, but the number would have to be reduced as the Cut deepened and narrowed. By November 1911, over 70,942,244 cubic yards had been excavated, and only 18,501,761 were estimated as remaining. Completion of excavation was expected in January 1913.

GOETHALS PUSHES TOWARD COMPLETION

Goethals' great task was to co-ordinate the projects so they would be completed in the desired sequence. He had to appear

[70] Goethals to Rourke, May 9, 1910 (P.C. Rec. Bur., File Personnel, Rourke) (MS).

before committees of Congress each year to obtain funds. At the start of each year's hearings he always gave a summary of the Canal organization, the work in progress, and the degree of completion. Then he took up new questions.

In 1909 work was progressing at all points, with fifty-four shovels in Culebra and the high point of the Cut one hundred feet above the bottom. Goethals lamented the constant changes in labor. "We get the roamers. The men who have good positions in the States will not come down."[71] He wanted the men to stay at least two years. The Commission tried to coax them with club-houses which served also as churches. Chaplains were employed and assigned to the Sanitary Department. Their duties were "to visit the sick, write letters for them, give them spiritual consolation, and attend at the graves when they die."[72]

Two events of considerable local interest occurred in 1909. The Peruvian Minister to Panamá, following the precedent of naming Cristóbal and Colón for the discoverer of the New World, suggested to Colonel Goethals that the Pacific terminal bear the name of the discoverer of the Pacific. The suggestion was adopted, and the name of the Pacific port was changed from La Boca to Balboa by direction of the President.[73]

Ex-President Amador of Panamá died on May 2, 1909, only a few months after the end of his term of office. The next day all Canal work stopped for five minutes at 4 P.M., the time of the funeral. The Secretary of War, then on the Isthmus, wrote, expressing sympathy to the Panamá Government and announced that the fortifications of the Pacific would be named Fort Amador,[74] after the Founder of the Republic of Panamá.

In spite of distractions, Goethals pushed toward completion. Construction of the Gatun Dam began on the east sector between Lock Hill and Spillway Hill. This arrangement forced the Chagres to the westward of Spillway Hill, through the old French

[71] Goethals' Statement, Feb. 15, 1909 (Hearings No. 8, p. 45) (U.S.).
[72] *Ibid.*, p. 27.
[73] *Canal Record*, May 5, 1909, II, 281 (U.S.).
[74] *Ibid.*, II, 282.

West Diversion which was left open to prevent its waters from
backing up the river valley. Not until April 1910 were the dam
and spillway ready to be closed. Hundreds of carloads of spoil
were dumped into the West Diversion, and at 5 P.M. on April 25,
1910, the flow of the Chagres past Gatun ceased. Gatun Lake, at
first no larger than a millpond, began to form.[75] Rapidly the im-
pounded water backed up. In June it surrounded Lion Hill, the
first town to be abandoned; its twenty-four houses had already
been transported to New Frijoles on the relocated railroad.[76]

Wide publicity was given to the dangers of the rising lake,
but the natives refused to believe it would rise high enough to
cover their homes. They would not leave, and police had to be
sent to evacuate them in time. In one case a flood caused a rapid
rise in level. A police launch stopped at a house near Lion Hill
which the water had almost covered and found the old native
with his family resting in a cayuca moored to the roof. The
anxious police inquired: "Don't you know that the lake is going
to cover your house completely?" The old native, not perturbed,
replied: "That is the same old story the French told my dad thirty
years ago."[77]

When Goethals reported conditions for October 31, 1910,
the Atlantic sea-level sector was 57.4 per cent complete; Gatun
Lock concrete work, 42 per cent; Gatun Dam, 53.8 per cent;
Gatun Spillway, 46.3 per cent; Central Division, 67.5 per cent;
Pedro Miguel Locks, 35.2 per cent; Miraflores, 4.7 per cent;
and Pacific sea-level sector, 71.7 per cent.

The railroad relocation was progressing. Goethals planned
to bring up Gatun Lake to 55 feet after January 1912. That
would cover a part of the old railroad connecting Tiger Hill and
Mamei.

Mr. Taft, now President, visited the Isthmus in November
1910. Escorted by Colonel Goethals, he started across the Isth-

[75] *Ibid.*, April 27, 1910, III, 273–74 (U.S.).
[76] *Ibid.*, June 15, 1910, III, 329 (U.S.).
[77] J. G. Steese, Conversation with author, June 16, 1942.

mus on an inspection. Colonel Goethals' gasoline car stopped at
Monte Lirio, then locally known as Mitchellville, where Goethals
was always given iced tea or lemonade by the stationmaster,
Mike Mitchell, with whom he had become quite friendly. Goethals proudly introduced his railroad friend to the rotund and
perspiring President, who accepted the refreshing jungle hos-
pitality.

"They tell me you are quite a big shot around here," remarked Mr. Taft to his host.

"You bet your big, fat stern I am," Mitchell replied un-
abashed.[78]

Goethals squirmed and bit his lips, but the hearty Taft gave a
powerful guffaw at this break in tropical monotony, swallowed
his tea, and continued his journey refreshed.

Taft, as the successor of Roosevelt, had a busy schedule on
the Isthmus. He inspected Gatun Locks and Dam, Culebra Cut,
and the Pacific Locks. He received labor delegations, attended
banquets, and made speeches. He described the Canal as a
smoothly working "machine with Colonel Goethals in control of
the lever."[79]

He addressed the workers at Paraiso, contrasting the conditions he saw before him with those he saw in 1904 on his first
trip. Culebra Cut in 1904 was only "a notch" in the range, and
only a small trench showed where the French intended the Canal
to be. The conditions in 1910, he said, had aroused the "in-
tensest interest, the greatest enthusiasm, and the profoundest admiration for Colonel Goethals"[80] and for all who had contributed
to make this result possible. He departed from the Isthmus,
leaving the labor problem to Goethals to handle. Goethals, having handled one strike in 1907, had learned some lessons.

The crisis came during Goethals' absence in Washington,
about February 1911. A locomotive engineer, who was drunk

[78] J. G. Steese, Conversation with author, June 16, 1942.
[79] *Canal Record*, Nov. 23, 1910, IV, 97–98 (U.S.).
[80] Society of the Chagres, *Yearbook 1911*, pp. 29–32.

on duty, had passed a signal and crashed into the rear of a freight train, killing a man. The engineer was sentenced to one year's imprisonment for involuntary manslaughter. The locomotive and steam-shovel engineers did not like this. A group of about fifty engineers went to the home of Colonel Hodges in Culebra and demanded unconditional release, under a threat to strike. Hodges, who was acting chairman and chief engineer, refused and advised waiting for the return of Goethals. The engineers then submitted an ultimatum.

Goethals returned, learned of the situation, filed the ultimatum without taking action, and waited for developments. He was ready. His position of power was firmly established, and he could act unhampered.

The time limit approached. The engineers, worried by the inaction, appointed a spokesman to call the chairman. In the evening the spokesman telephoned Goethals at his home and demanded to know what he was going to do about that ultimatum, soon to expire.

Goethals listened and then replied: "I have three things to say. First, I am not in the habit of being dictated to over the telephone. Second, I am not going to grant it; and last, anyone not at work at seven in the morning will be sent off the Isthmus on the next boat."[81] That ended the incident. The men were at work ahead of time the next day.

Canal work reached its peak in 1911. The fame of the builders was mounting. When Goethals appeared before a Congressional committee, he was applauded for the first time and given a eulogy by the chairman. Percentages of completion mounted also. Steel lock gates would be completed in January 1913, and Goethals wanted the locks completed by October 1912 to be ready to receive the gates. He expected the Culebra Cut to be finished by September 1913. He wanted to pass ships through the Canal in 1913 but held to January 1, 1915, as the opening date, for he wanted time to organize the operating forces and to

[81] J. G. Steese, Conversation with author, March 7, 1943.

test the machinery. He expected a demand from the Navy to transit the Canal and wanted it handled well.[82]

Durng this trip to the United States, recognition of Goethals' work increased rapidly. He spoke before both Houses of Congress, the Supreme Court, and Cabinet members. He lectured at the National Geographic Society and at universities and had to decline many invitations.

When he again appeared before a Congressional committee in June 1911, Goethals received a greeting of unusual warmth. The chairman stated that the Committee was entitled to the "credit for building the canal," for it had a "proprietary interest" in Goethals and great pride in his work.

Goethals emphasized the approaching completion and the need for permanent organization. He expected to begin disbanding in June 1912 and said, "we can see the end." He reported further increases in completion percentages for the excavation in Culebra Cut and that everything was going according to plan. One Congressman remarked that he had heard Gold Hill was not safe. Goethals silenced him by replying: "You can hear almost anything on the Isthmus." He explained that he wanted the organization decided within a year, to facilitate an easy transition from construction to operation and to enable return of all foreign labor to its "native heath."

What should be the first vessel to go through the Canal? The chairman of the Committee stated that he wanted a naval vessel. Goethals did not like this, and replied, "The first thing I want to put through is a Panama Railroad ship."[83] He also wanted the question of tolls settled.

The year 1911 not only was the peak year of the construction work but gave evidence of a stable population. The Society of the Chagres was organized, its memberships limited to white employees who had earned the Roosevelt medal and two bars prior to opening of the Canal. A medal was awarded for two years'

[82] Goethals' Statement, Feb. 11, 1911 (Hearings No. 13, pp. 6–7) (U.S.).

[83] Goethals' Statement, June 7, 1911 (Hearings No. 14, pp. 6–13) (U.S.).

continuous service on the Canal and a bar for each additional two years.

The Washington Hotel at Colón was started to replace the old Washington House. Because there was no Congressional authority or appropriation for its construction, the hotel was built by the Panama Railroad Company, of which Goethals was president.

Later, when asked in Congress if he had inquired into the right of the Panama Railroad to build the hotel under the laws of New York, Goethals replied with his usual directness: "No, sir; I got an order from the President of the United States to build that hotel and I built it."[84] There was no more discussion on that point.

Two sixteenth-century anchors were discovered at Cruces, where they had been left by the Spanish. A young Army officer produced a scheme to transport them to West Point to adorn the entrance to the library and started their removal. A few weeks later Colonel Goethals received a cable from the Secretary of War: "The President directs that this be not done."[85] Today these anchors grace the lawn of the Atlantic Terminal Building in Cristóbal instead of the entrance to the West Point Library.

In line with the original plan of Stevens and the desires of the President, the Commission as an organization was gradually relegated to an innocuous position. Its record for the Walker and Shonts Commissions filled two thick volumes covering one hundred twenty-two meetings in about three years; for the Goethals Commission, it filled one thin volume covering forty-three meetings in a period of about seven years. At first under Goethals it functioned as usual, but controversies developed. The power of the Commission was terminated by Roosevelt's Order of January 6, 1908. In that year only ten meetings were held, and the number each year was reduced still further as work progressed.

When work was at its peak, Goethals was asked whether the

[84] Goethals' Statement, Nov. 18, 1912 (Hearings No. 4, p. 22) (U.S.).
[85] *Canal Record*, May 31, 1911, IV, 314 (U.S.).

Commission held regular meetings. He answered: "No, sir; it meets whenever I conclude that I have business enough to occupy them for the afternoon." He held three meetings in 1910 and in 1911, mainly for the purpose of issuing licenses for saloons. The days of debates in the Commission were over, for there was no opportunity to engage in one. Goethals consulted directly with his advisers and came to his own conclusions. He was open-minded, however, and often changed his plans of action. He said: "I generally discuss a proposition with those in whose ability and judgment I have confidence, whether commissioners or otherwise, and come to a conclusion after that, and I act."[86]

Decision was made to locate the new permanent Administration Building at Balboa and to place the best buildings around it. Goethals wanted the Administration Building large and planned on giving both the Army and the Navy space in it. He thought better co-ordination would result by having all together under one roof.

The Canal required space for only 210 employees and for the records, which he wished to collect from scattered locations. He had not yet settled in his mind what the title of the head of the Canal should be, but he wanted him to be a member of the Corps of Engineers. His main aims were to "finish within the $375,000,000 estimated as the cost of the Canal in 1908, and to finish on time."[87] He did not intend to allow anybody or anything to interfere with his aims.

Relations of Goethals with Sibert and Gorgas did not improve as time went on. Evidences of conflict frequently came to light at Congressional hearings. When Colonel Sibert suggested one time that the white man needed "more law than the West Indian," Goethals intervened, calling this an "unwarranted slur" on whites, not supported by police records. He was equally frank with Gorgas and attacked his estimates with detailed figures, when on one occasion Gorgas claimed he could get along with-

[86] Goethals' Statement, Oct. 26, 1911 (Hearings No. 20, p. 76) (U.S.).
[87] *Ibid.*, p. 9.

out the work for which his department was being charged over-
head. This gave an unexpected chance to Goethals, who countered that, if Colonel Gorgas could get along without the over-
head services rendered his department with the personnel he
then had, it was evident that Colonel Gorgas' organization was
"too large"[88] and could be reduced.

Much was written about the Canal during construction days.
Colonel Hodges had given the Sanitary Department greater
credit than even Colonel Gorgas was willing to state. In one
article Hodges stated it was the sanitation work, particularly in
extinguishing yellow fever, which had "made the construction
of the canal possible."[89] He felt that a force could not have been
held together under previous sanitary conditions.

This idea came up in Congress. Gorgas was asked if he
thought it would have been possible without the sanitation measures that were taken. Gorgas was not quite specific but stated
that "no matter how great the mortality from yellow fever, we
would have found Americans who, for the sake of adventure
and danger involved, would have been willing"[90] to work on the
Canal. That was the experience of the French, who had had
much illness; but they were always able to recruit more than
enough to take the places of the fallen. The same probably
would have been true of North Americans.

The waters of Gatun Lake gradually advanced, covering
more land and villages each month and making islands out of
mountains and hills. In December 1911 the Pacific Locks concrete work was 87 per cent complete, and Division Engineer
Williamson expected the entire Pacific Division to be completed
by June 1913. There was similar progress at Gatun and in
Culebra. After May 1912 it would be too late to see the work-
ings on the Canal, because so much would be covered by water.
Goethals said that fifteen or twenty years hence he expected a

88 Goethals' Statement, Nov. 21, 1911 (Hearings No. 3, pp. 215–17) (U.S.).
89 H. F. Hodges, "The Panama Canal," E.S.P. *Journal*, July 1909, I, 338.
90 Gorgas' Statement, Oct. 27, 1911 (Hearings No. 20, p. 198) (U.S.).

Congressional investigation to find out "what became of the money which Congress appropriated for the construction of the Panama Canal." His work would be covered by "water and vegetation."[91]

How prophetic! Today vessels glide along the smooth surface of the lake among jungle-green islands, and Gatun Dam forms a part of the natural landscape. They pass between the green banks of Culebra Cut, spotting an occasional alligator basking in the sun on the banks. The impression is one of the permanence of natural existence, rather than of the creation of man. It is impossible to imagine the activity that once existed on the course of that waterway.

At this time there were no Army or Navy forces in the Canal Zone. The only garrison was a small Marine detachment. But planners of the Federal Government were studying the defense of the Canal. An Interdepartmental Fortification Board had visited the Isthmus in 1910 to plan for its defense. Fortifications were discussed, and one member expressed fear of danger from bombing by aircraft, then in its first stages of development. Goethals replied: "I have not the faith in the airship that you have."[92] The Congressman said his faith had been strengthened during the year. When asked how much land would be required for defense purposes, Goethals gave a significant reply, critical of tendencies too frequent in the Government services to expand without definite programs or for specific reasons. He said: "I can only state that when the fortification board was here in 1910 and outlined the land required by the Army and Navy I began to question if after the Army and Navy got through there would be enough land left to provide for construction of the canal."[93]

At the end of the hearing in December 1910, Goethals received the usual acclaim from the chairman. The Committee was proud of the Canal work, supported Goethals' aims, and predicted he would receive the praise of all mankind. There was

[91] Goethals' Statement, Dec. 22, 1911 (Hearings No. 15, I, 429) (U.S.).
[92] Goethals' Statement, Dec. 19, 1911 (*ibid.*, p. 209).
[93] *Ibid.*, p. 210.

a strange note, however, when the chairman stated, "While you are the king of the Isthmus, you are our servant, and most faithful servant."[94]

In 1912 construction was on the descendent; the locks and dams rose, the lake grew larger, and Culebra Cut deepened. On February 15, the old Panama Railroad between Gatun and Gorgona was abandoned, and in May the new Gold Hill section was turned over to the railroad for operation.

By November the rise of Gatun Lake had caused the waters of the Chagres to back up as far as Palo Grande above Gamboa.[95] Floating islands of vegetation came to the surface and had to be towed to the spillway and allowed to flow over. In Culebra there remained only about 8,300,000 cubic yards to remove between Paraiso and La Pita, and progress was steady in spite of the slides.

In the midst of all this, people were talking about a tropical paradise opened up by the lake. Goethals had no illusions of creating a tropical utopia in the Canal Zone and employed an expert to investigate. After two years of experiment in trying to raise fresh vegetables, he decided it was more important "to finish the canal within the estimate than it was to supply fresh vegetables to our employees."[96]

On October 31 Gatun Dam was 90 per cent complete; Gatun Spillway, 92; Central Division, 93; Gatun Locks, 93; Pacific Locks, 94. But slides had continued. Goethals decided to abandon the plan of placing the railroad on the 95-foot berm of the Cut and to retain the Gold Hill line as permanent.

The first break in the construction organization came when Sydney B. Williamson, division engineer of the Pacific Division, resigned to take a new position in London. Goethals took over his work, knowing it would not be for long. He was hoping to place the first vessel through the Canal on September 25, 1914, the anniversary of the discovery of the Pacific by Balboa.

[94] Quoted in Goethals' Statement, Dec. 22, 1911 (*ibid.*, I, 433).
[95] *Canal Record*, Nov. 6, 1912, VI, 89 (U.S.).
[96] Goethals' Statement, March 29, 1912 (Hearings No. 21, p. 8) (U.S.).

Chapter XIV

THE END OF THE LONG STRUGGLE FOR A WATERWAY

The real builder of the Panama Canal was Theodore Roosevelt. The execution of the work was directed by other hands, chosen and empowered by him, but if he had personally lifted every shovelful of earth in its construction he could not be more fully entitled to chief credit than he is for the accomplishment of the task.—George W. Goethals.[1]

It was a going concern that Stevens, in spite of his short term, turned over to the Army, one that functioned efficiently and with lower construction costs in some particulars than were ever achieved again. It is Stevens' canal quite as much as it is Goethals' canal.—William Franklin Sands.[2]

CONSTRUCTION DRAWS TO A CLOSE

Early in the year 1913 the Canal builders knew the end was approaching. Thirty-seven steam shovels were operating in Culebra Cut. Concrete work was still in progress at Gatun Locks and at Miraflores. Gatun Lake was rising and was expected to reach 50 feet above the sea by July and its final height of 85 feet by December.

The Gamboa Dike across the north end of Culebra Cut was 78 feet above the sea and protected it from the rising waters of the Chagres. Because the lake was expected to reach a level of 74 feet about October 10, the dike could not serve much longer. A dike across the Pacific channel south of Miraflores Locks protected the locks from the waters of the Pacific.

Greatest of all the dangers that could imperil the scheduled completion was the Cucuracha slide in Culebra Cut. That was the picture of the Canal when Robert G. Fowler made the first flight over the Isthmus in a hydroplane on April 27, 1913.[3]

[1] Quoted in J. B. and F. Bishop, *Goethals, Genius of the Panama Canal,* p. 144.

[2] W. F. Sands, *Our Jungle Diplomacy,* p. 41.

[3] John O. Collins, "The Year 1913 in Canal History" (Society of the Chagres, *Yearbook 1913,* pp. 117–36).

Early in May it became evident that Culebra Cut would have to be completed by dredging after flooding. The Cut had remained to the last as the great problem of the Canal. To prepare for this work, Goethals placed all dredging equipment and operations under Mr. W. G. Comber, in the Sixth Division of the Chief Engineer's Office, later to become the Dredging Division.

Concrete work at Miraflores Locks was completed on May 17, 1913, and at Gatun Locks on May 31. Pedro Miguel had been completed earlier, and the spillways were nearing completion. Installation of lock gates and machinery was well advanced.

Cucuracha slide proved a difficult task. When it started moving in January 1913, it crossed the Cut until it reached the opposite bank. At first shovels could make no headway, but gradually space was opened for trucks, and this was kept open by constant excavation as the slide advanced.[4]

Elsewhere in the Cut there was no interruption, as steam shovels on bottom grade were approaching each other on the last lap. At 4:30 P.M. on May 20, 1913, amidst steam whistles and cheers of the workers, the meeting of the shovels on bottom grade occurred, opposite "Hodges Hill," Culebra.

During these days of record activity in Culebra Cut the Goethals Commission suffered the first break among its engineering members. Colonel Gaillard, Division Engineer of the Central Division, broke down. His physician advised him to "give up all work, and seek a change of climate and surroundings."[5] He went on leave but was retained as a member of the Commission. A. S. Zinn was appointed to succeed Gaillard as Division Engineer of the Central Division, and the work was continued without interruption.

John C. Collins has left a stirring description of these last days of work in Culebra Cut in August 1913, when about forty steam shovels were working and where "scores of trains were moving back and forth, dynamite blasts and adobe shots came at

---

[4] Goethals, *The Panama Canal*, I, 372.

[5] Gaillard to Chairman, Aug. 2, 1913 (P.C. Rec. Bur., File Personnel, Gaillard) (MS).

unexpected times, dominating the clatter of the work. In day-light one could see, as well as hear, the effort; at night the chug of drills, rattle of coal and repair trains, call of track gangs—in fact, the whole medley of work told to the habituated ear the story of endless, systematic endeavor; and occasionally the flare of a searchlight or the fitful illumination of piles of burning ties unveiled little pictures of labor."[6] As the end approached, everyone was trying to imagine how the Cut would appear after flooding.

This activity continued until September 10. On that day all dry excavation in Culebra ended forever. Pumps which had kept the Cut dry were removed, tracks were removed, worn-out ties were piled and burned, and houses were salvaged.

The first operation of the Panama Canal locks occurred on September 26 at Gatun. Thousands came to see the test and lined the lock walls as Goethals walked nervously up and down. The lake was up to only 65.5 feet, instead of the normal operating level of 85 feet. The operation had been carefully planned and was executed slowly. The day was hot and people were per-spiring.

Water was admitted to the upper chamber and sluiced down by stages to the lowest level. Bullfrogs carried from the lake into lock chambers amused the crowd. The tug "Gatun," with Colo-nel Sibert standing in front of the pilothouse, entered the lower chamber at 4:45 P.M. The gates closed, and the tug was locked up in three steps to the summit level in 1 hour and 51 minutes.[7] The "Gatun" entered the lake—an event heralded around the world as indicating the approaching completion of the Canal. On the Isthmus the feeling inspired among the real Canal build-ers was the humility of responsible achievement.

This lockage was followed by the locking up of the Atlantic dredging fleet on October 9 on its way to Culebra Cut. These lockages also were up to the same standard. Other lockages fol-

---

[6] Collins, *op. cit.*, p. 134.

[7] "Report of First Operation of West Flight of Gatun Locks," Sept. 26, 1913 (P.C. Rec. Bur., File 92-A-5) (MS).

lowed with increasing proficiency as the lock forces gained experience.

The final rise of Gatun Lake had begun when the last spillway gates were closed on June 27 with the level at 48.25 feet. A height of 85 feet was expected by December. On July 1 the water level was at 50 feet. Gorgona was evacuated, and the shops were removed to Balboa. In October heavy rains caused a rapid rise, and the old town of Cruces was abandoned to the encroaching lake waters. Plans for the new town of Balboa were started, and the decision was made to abandon Culebra, Empire, and other towns on the west bank of the Canal which would be isolated when the Cut was flooded.

On October 1, drain pipes in the Gamboa Dike were opened to fill the Cut partially in advance because of the danger from so much water in motion. For ten days dynamite charges were placed in the dike as the level of the lake slowly rose.

The day finally arrived. Three thousand people came to Gamboa to see the union of the oceans. Among them was the French engineer, Philippe Bunau-Varilla, to witness the fruition of his life's dream. In Washington at 2:00 P.M. on October 10, 1913, a new President, Woodrow Wilson, sitting at his desk in the White House, pressed a key. Shortly afterward at Gamboa, tons of rock and smoke were blown into the air from the dike. Water rushed through the opening from the 67.7-foot lake level to the 61.7-foot Cut level, starting a wave in the Cut which reached Cucuracha slide in eighteen minutes. South of Cucuracha the Cut was dry.

Water from the lake had to be passed through the slide to the dry part of the Cut so that dredges could be locked up from the Pacific. Charges were placed in the slide to make a breach. Late the same afternoon they were exploded but were not effective. The only result was to splatter mud on the spectators. Men had to dig a trench in the slide, through which to flood the remaining section of the Cut. On that same day the Central Division was abolished. Only the Atlantic Division remained.

The days of spectacular action were over. Collins has recorded the contrast of dredging in the flooded canal: ". . . . tugs moved silently up and down the canal in answer to the whistled demand of the dredges; the monotonous clank of the ladder dredges echoed between the steep banks at Culebra. Compared with other days, the Cut seemed deserted. In contrast with other nights, it was intensely lonely, save where the many lights of dredges suggested a nook in Fairyland; for the rest, the water reflected the stars coldly, not even the wash of waves along the bank broke the eerie quiet."[8]

Water from the Pacific reached Miraflores Locks when the Miraflores Dike was blown up on August 31. Miraflores Lake was filled gradually. By mid-October it had reached about 37 feet as compared with its normal level of 55 feet. The first lockage through Miraflores Locks was for the tug "Miraflores" with three barges, "Clapet Dredge No. 6," and a launch from the Pacific level to Miraflores Lake. The time of ascent was 1 hour and 1 minute, to the delight of several hundred spectators.

It was not until October 24 that the first lockage at Pedro Miguel occurred, when the tug "Miraflores" and "Dredge No. 85" and others were locked up from the Miraflores Lake to the summit level. The lockage at Pedro Miguel required 42 minutes. These dredges attacked the south side of Cucuracha in conjunction with dredges on the north side, and in December a channel was clear.

Miraflores Lake continued to rise, reaching about 48 feet on December 8. The ladder dredge "Marmot," with small craft, was locked up to the lake, and the vessels continued across to Pedro Miguel and locked into Culebra Cut—the first continuous lockage from the Pacific level to summit level.[9]

As lockages continued at both terminals, the most elaborate records were required. Special reports of each lockage in much detail were made in those early days of lock operations.

---

[8] Collins, *op. cit.*, p. 134.

[9] "Report of Pacific Lockages," Nov. 11, 1913 (P.C. Rec. Bur., File 92-A-5) (MS).

MEETING OF THE STEAM SHOVELS, MAY 20, 1913
Culebra Cut, opposite Hodges Hill

CULEBRA CUT, NEAR GOLD HILL
Showing work on last ledge, August 14, 1913

The first transit of the Canal was not complete until January 7, 1914, when the crane boat "Alexander La Valley," then at Culebra after a trip from the Atlantic, was locked down to the Pacific.

Only a few construction organizations remained. The Atlantic Division was abolished on February 1, just as Gatun Lake reached its 85-foot level. The small construction that still remained came under the Chief Engineer's Office. The process of closing down included even the Federation of Women's Clubs, whose Executive Committee held a final meeting at the Hotel Washington on April 19, 1913, declared the organization disbanded, and burned its records.

Colonel Gaillard did not live to see the completion of Culebra Cut. When the Gamboa Dike was exploded on October 10, he was critically ill. He died in Baltimore on December 5, 1913, of an "infiltrating tumor in the brain."[10] Goethals published a general notice of his death and summarized his career, stating that his work covered the period of most active construction. "He brought to the service trained ability of the first order, untiring zeal, and unswerving devotion to duty. His name is connected inseparably with the great task which was brought to completion under his guidance, and will be held in lasting honor."[11] Later, President Wilson, by Executive Order of April 17, 1915, decreed that Culebra Cut should be known as Gaillard Cut.[12]

THE PERMANENT ORGANIZATION EVOLVES

Although Goethals was busily engaged in building the Canal, we have seen already that he did not wait for completion before thinking of the permanent organization and operation. While construction work was at its peak in 1911, he started seriously toward that objective, for which four years of responsibility had

[10] Col. L. H. Beach, *Report to Adjutant General*, Dec. 8, 1913 (P.C. Rec. Bur., File Personnel, Gaillard) (MS).

[11] *Canal Record*, Dec. 10, 1913, VII, 142 (U.S.).

[12] *Ibid.*, May 12, 1915, VIII, 338 (U.S.).

provided him with extensive background. The first step was to obtain a basic law. To this end he started his plan during Congressional hearings in 1911.

The President was expected to invite the fleets of the world to assemble at Hampton Roads on January 1, 1915, for a trip to San Francisco via the Panama Canal. Goethals wanted all of 1914 for testing machinery and developing an efficient organization. Naturally, he was anxious. "If anything happened so that fleet were delayed in going through, the Panama Canal will be damned,"[13] and he did not want that to occur. Altogether, three great problems had to be settled by Congressional legislation—organization, tolls, and the relation of the Panama Railroad to the Canal.

He was not specific at first as to the form of organization, except on one point—a single head for the Canal, insisting "you cannot operate that canal with a seven-headed commission any more than you could construct it in that way."[14] He wanted everything subordinated to operation and maintenance of the Canal, under the title of Director General or Superintendent for the position he then held. Every man not connected with the Canal should be kept off the Canal Zone.

As the months passed, Goethals' ideas crystallized and his proposals became stronger and more definite. He thought that, under the conditions of health and privileges already established, the employees were overpaid. He could see no reason for higher pay in the Canal Zone than in Puerto Rico or the Philippines and advocated a wage level only 25 per cent above that for the same class of work in the United States. This would effect a reduction in construction wages. In addition, he wanted to make small charges for rent and light, "to make the employees realize that they were not getting something for nothing."[15] When the time for reduction in the number of employees should

[13] Goethals' Statement, June 7, 1911 (Hearings No. 14, p. 10) (U.S.).
[14] *Ibid.*, p. 20.
[15] Goethals' Statement, Oct. 26, 1911 (Hearings No. 20, p. 11) (U.S.).

come, he planned to make appointments on the basis of seniority and at these reduced wages.

For the railroad, he suggested that it was too expensive to maintain its separate corporate existence, that instead it should be organized as an adjunct of the Canal. He favored placing control of both Canal tolls and railroad rates in the hands of the President, who was in a position to call experts to advise.

Throughout the hearings we find Goethals' reiterated assertion that the head of the Canal should be an army engineer, although he conceded that a civil engineer of the Navy was also fitted for the position. Goethals wanted his assistant to be an army engineer, the chief sanitary officer an army doctor, and the chief quarantine officer an officer of the Public Health Service.

At the hearings on October 26, 1911, he submitted a general outline of the organization with its five departments— Operating, Engineering, Quartermaster, Electrical and Mechanical, and Accounting. The Operating Department was to include the operation of docks, pilotage, lockages, and lighting of the Canal. He had no grandiose scheme of harbor development. At Balboa he was building only one pier for existing commerce, according to a development plan which could be extended along "definite lines"[16] in the future as commerce might require.

It was not until the December 1911 Congressional hearings that he voiced the most fundamental ideas. At that time he predicted a commercial population at the terminals, supported by shipping, and recommended maintenance of the commissaries, not only for the Canal but for general use. He suggested locating Balboa on the dump near La Boca and the Atlantic terminal city at Cristóbal. When members of the Committee criticized his plan of making civilian settlements at the terminals as likely to defeat the military purposes of the Canal, Goethals gave one of his great and fundamental statements: "The construction of the canal is not a military proposition; it is a civil and commercial proposi-

[16] *Ibid.*, pp. 12–23, 32.

tion. The fact that I am in the Army does not alter that situation at all. I look upon the operation and maintenance of the canal as a distinctly civil and commercial function, and that the reason for our being here is for the operation and maintenance of the canal, and after its construction this should be a civil function. But we should create such an entity here that in time of war the military necessities of the situation would predominate, and the operation and maintenance of the canal will be subordinate to those military features."[17] This is the fundamental philosophy that now pervades the Panama Canal Act.

Goethals repeated his advice about the high wage scales, which had been so much criticized throughout the United States. His advice meant a large cut in pay for many, but he advocated cutting from the "top down"[18] as the only fair method. His own pay was to be cut from $15,000 to $10,000.

Regarding the study of tolls, Goethals explained that a board had been suggested; but he was against appointment of a board and recommended Professor Emory R. Johnson, the eminent student of canal tolls, to make the study. Goethals' experience had made him feel strongly about boards: "In the Army a board is considered as long, narrow, and wooden, and that has been my experience with boards, as a rule."[19]

Goethals ended this hearing with a strong plea for early enactment of a law to provide a permanent organization and government of the Canal Zone, which was still functioning under the Spooner Act of 1902. As that law applied only during construction, failure to act would mean that after completion there would be no provision for operating the Canal or governing the Canal Zone.

He emphasized that the man in charge should be in "supreme control" of the Canal and of all its adjuncts. He urged the necessity for an organization that could be changed from civil to military status whenever ordered and advocated the use of

[17] Goethals' Statement, Dec. 19, 1911 (Hearings No. 15, I, 215) (U.S.).
[18] Goethals' Statement, Dec. 22, 1911 (*ibid.*, I, 410).
[19] *Ibid.*

officers who had been educated by the Government for assignment as Canal officials in a few key positions. He wanted an
army engineer as head of the Canal but did not want that requirement included in the basic law; he wanted it left to the
discretion of the President. He desired officers of the Navy to
operate the Canal. He considered that officers with the Canal
should be in the same status as officers with troops in the tropics.

In the meantime on the Isthmus, studies of the operating
organization and government for the completed Canal went
ahead. When Goethals appeared at the March 1912 Congressional hearings he again urged early action by Congress. He
continued to oppose populating the Zone. When asked if he
would let it grow up into jungle, he replied, "Yes, sir; it is the
greatest safeguard the Canal can have."[20] When asked how soon
Congress should reach a conclusion regarding the control of the
Canal, he answered with characteristic directness, "It should
have been reached last summer."[21] He was then planning to put
the first ship through in September 1913 and urged "speedy
action" on tolls and "speedier action" on the organization.

Congress was not speedy. The Panama Canal Act[22] was not
passed until late summer and was approved on August 24, 1912.
It embodied most of the ideas recommended by Goethals except
the title of the head of the Canal. Congress adopted the title
of governor for the operating head, to forestall any attempt to
establish a political governor in addition to a director general,
which would have been probable had the latter title been adopted.
The salary of the governor was set at $10,000 per year. Salaries
of employees were limited to not more than 25 per cent above
that paid for similar services in the continental United States.
When the law was announced, the labor organizations came to
Goethals, offering to aid him in having his own salary increased,
but he refused the proffered assistance.

[20] Goethals' Statement, March 29, 1912 (Hearings No. 21, p. 6) (U.S.).

[21] *Ibid.*, p. 14.

[22] The text of this act is reprinted as Appendix VIII in *Panama Canal Traffic
and Tolls*, by Emory R. Johnson (U.S.).

What was the title of the new organization, Congress wanted to know. Later in the year the Chairman of the House Committee on Appropriations asked Goethals: "Is this the Panama Canal or the Isthmian Canal?" Goethals replied: "The Panama Canal,"[23] and as The Panama Canal it has remained.

Goethals at last was free to make a real start. He required heads of departments to submit their departmental organizations in December and examined them. He anticipated there would be interference from other departments of the Federal Government and determined to be ready to meet them. Accordingly, in May 1913 he appointed a committee, consisting of Gaillard as chairman, and Sibert, Gorgas, and Thatcher as members, to form a permanent organization for The Panama Canal and forwarded to them all files on departmental organizations. The committee worked through May, June, July, and part of August at Gaillard's office. When Gaillard broke down, Colonel Sibert acted as chairman until Colonel Hodges was made permanent chairman.[24]

In the midst of this work on organization, Commissioner Thatcher resigned and was succeeded by Richard Lee Metcalfe, of Lincoln, Nebraska—editor of *The Commoner*, founded by Secretary of State Bryan. This was the first appointee by the Wilson Administration to a responsible Canal position.

The new Secretary of War, Lindley M. Garrison, became interested in the permanent organization and in October visited the Isthmus, where he was entertained by Goethals, whom he commended for staying at his post to the end. But Goethals complained to him about the failure of the President to establish a permanent organization. Garrison was impressed and consulted Judge Frank Feuille, whom he asked to draw up a memorandum giving reasons for Goethals' immediate appointment as governor. The Secretary endorsed this and sent it on to President Wilson. When he returned to Washington, he cabled

[23] Goethals' Statement, Nov. 19, 1912 (Hearings No. 4, p. 199) (U.S.).
[24] Goethals to Hodges, Aug. 26, 1913 (P.C. Rec. Bur., File 2-C-124) (MS).

Goethals inquiring whether, if appointed, he would be willing
to remain two years as governor. Goethals replied he would
remain "as long as the President ordered him to stay."[25]

The organization committee finished its work. A proposed
Executive Order for the President's signature was drafted, and
organization diagrams were drawn. Goethals forwarded all
papers to the Secretary of War on November 14, 1913, with a
strong letter emphasizing points brought out in the hearings of
Congress and the commercial nature of the Canal. He stressed
"operation and maintenance," of which he thought "maintenance" the more important. He advocated the assignment of an
army engineer as governor, because army engineers are familiar
with government methods and the preparation and defense of estimates before Congress and because they could secure continuity.

The governor, he explained, would be in charge of the
Department of Operation and Maintenance, which, as indicated
by its name, was naturally divided into two subdivisions—an
operation section and a maintenance section. He urged that an
army engineer be put in charge of maintenance and a naval
officer in charge of operations. He thought the engineer of maintenance should be selected on the basis of succeeding as governor. He included recommendations for navy officers as port
captains, army doctors as chief health officers, and Public Health
Service officers as chief quarantine officers.[26]

Meanwhile, Goethals had received a letter dated October 9
from General Leonard Wood, Chief of Staff of the Army,
stating that the Navy was coming forward with a plan to take
over the Canal. Wood wanted his opinion and reassured Goethals that the idea would not prevail.[27]

Knowing the strong feeling in Congress against military control, on November 15 he replied to General Wood. Explaining
the history of the Canal organizations, particularly the Department of Operation and Maintenance, he subdivided this into two

---

[25] J. B. and F. Bishop, op. cit., pp. 254–55.
[26] Goethals to Garrison, Nov. 14, 1913 (P.C. Rec. Bur., File 2-C-124) (MS).
[27] Wood to Goethals, Oct. 9, 1913 (ibid).

parts, "the maintaining devolving upon an engineer officer of the Army, and the operation upon a naval officer."[28] When General Wood read this letter, he was well fortified to answer questions and to present the views of experienced men to higher authority.

As the new order began to take form on the Canal Zone, buildings were moved to their permanent locations. A site for the chairman's house in the old Ancon cemetery grounds was selected as the new location for the governor's house.[29] There it would have had a grand view of the Administration Building and Balboa Harbor. But for reasons that are not very clear it was placed instead in a developed tract used for a French almshouse—in a less distracting, though more obscure, location.

The Gorgona Clubhouse was relocated at Pedro Miguel and the Empire Clubhouse at Balboa. Official quarters at Culebra were moved to Balboa Heights, instead of constructing new ones. "In 1913 you had an architect; what happened to him?" Goethals was asked. He admitted that that official had resigned on December 4, "because he thinks we do not need an architect. We can not appreciate his artistic ability."[30] When the Fine Arts Commission inspected the Canal, they commended the construction work in general but condemned the lampposts and were horrified at unsightly emergency dams. Goethals did not give them a chance to examine fortifications.

Throughout the struggle for a permanent organization, exterior influences were felt. Some were open and easy to handle, others were indirect and hence difficult to control. The influence that bothered Goethals most was that of the Navy. As early as April 1913, the General Board had examined the Panama Canal as a "great naval asset" and demanded that the operation of the Canal be under naval officers "at all times" and that these officers be directly under the Navy Department. It concluded that

[28] Goethals to Wood, Nov. 15, 1913 (P.C. Rec. Bur., File 2-C-124) (MS).

[29] H. H. Evans, Conversation with author, Jan. 15, 1943.

[30] Goethals' Statement, Nov. 20, 1913 (Hearings No. 5, p. 49) (U.S.). Commission of Fine Arts, *Reports*, 1913 (U.S.).

"active management and control of the finished canal belongs to the naval branch of the Government."[31]

When the Joint Army and Navy Board met on October 9, 1913, Admiral Dewey asked that Colonel Goethals determine the "proper measure" of naval control on the Canal. General Wood, at the request of the Joint Board, informed Goethals of its discussions and suggested to him that the Navy wanted the Canal in "their hands."[32] Wood was anxious; to offset the naval effort, he suggested to Goethals the idea of making the troop commander on the Isthmus governor, as an alternative arrangement preferable to naval control. Goethals did not like that idea either.

Colonel Hodges submitted his opinion on the Navy plan to Goethals in a remarkably judicious memorandum, emphasizing the Canal as a commercial undertaking and opposing the troop commander as governor because that would subordinate the Canal to the War Department. Although advocating control by the Army or Navy in time of war or danger, he felt it would be possible to maintain personnel more capable of "independence of thought and action,"[33] for men of this type would object to control by either the Army or the Navy.

Interferences with plans for the organization even originated within the Commission itself. The new political appointee, Mr. Metcalfe, was not placed on the organization committee when Commissioner Thatcher resigned. That did not stop him from intervening, and he submitted to the Secretary of War a plan for a permanent organization of a three-man Commission consisting of a chief engineer in charge of operations, a governor, and a chief sanitary officer, which would hold monthly meetings under chairmanship of the chief engineer. Metcalfe even suggested placing commissaries under private enterprise and separating the railroad from the Canal.[34] This was simply a reversion to the earlier organization under Shonts.

[31] President of General Board to Secretary of Navy, April 18, 1913 (P.C. Rec. Bur., File 2-C-124) (MS).   [32] Wood to Goethals, Oct. 9, 1913 (*ibid*).
[33] Hodges' Memorandum to Goethals, Oct. 20, 1913 (*ibid.*).
[34] R. L. Metcalfe to Goethals, Oct. 1, 1913 (*ibid.*).

With his long background on the Canal and the assistance of his able advisers, it was not difficult for Goethals to tear the Metcalfe proposal to shreds in his forwarding letter. It was a mutilated document that reached the Secretary of War.

Even the United States Treasury Department added to the confusion. Although disclaiming any "personal desire" for more authority, Secretary W. G. McAdoo wrote the President, recommending that control of all toll collections be given to his department.[35] He had not seen the proposed Executive Order. When that was shown him, he wrote another letter urging that the Public Health Service, a Division of the Treasury Department, take over quarantine administration in the Canal Zone. President Wilson wanted the Secretaries of War and Treasury to agree on these differences, but of course there could be no agreement on matters so fundamental.

Finally, the Secretary of War himself tried to intervene. He tended toward Metcalfe's views. In spite of the provisions of the Panama Canal Act as passed in 1912, he wanted to continue the "integrity" of the Isthmian Canal Commission until formal opening in 1915, so that its members could participate in the celebration. This plan would give them positions in the permanent organization in the meantime. But he was doubtful of the legality of his plan and wrote direct to Judge Frank Feuille, Head of the Department of Law at Ancon, for advice *in extenso*.[36]

Judge Feuille recognized the critical nature of his subject. He went to source materials—debates and hearings in Congress, annual reports, and legislation. He reviewed the history of the Commission through the years and finally wrote Secretary Garrison he was convinced the President was not authorized to operate the Canal until the Commission was abolished.[37] The Secretary of War was stopped. He had no other course in those days of "constitutional legitimacy" than to follow the plan prepared for him.

[35] McAdoo to President, Oct. 17, 1913 (P.C. Rec. Bur., File 2-C-124) (MS).
[36] L. M. Garrison to Frank Feuille, Nov. 1, 1913 (*ibid.*).
[37] Feuille to Garrison, Nov. 11, 1913 (*ibid.*).

The Secretary was rushed with work. He waited until December 4, when he dictated a letter, forwarding the proposed Executive Order with all correspondence to the President and requesting quick action but regretting inability to retain the Commission for "sentimental reasons."[38] He recommended the centralization provided by the order and advised against distribution of work among the departments. He left his office with directions to type and forward the letter to the White House without signature. This attempt at political interference had failed.

It was not until January 27, 1914, that President Wilson, after considering the Canal matter several weeks, signed the Executive Order with practically no changes from that prepared on the Isthmus, to be effective April 1. The President appended a memorandum outlining his desire that the permanent operation of the Canal should come under the Secretary of War and directing that assignments for certain positions be made from officers of the Government—for example, an army engineer as engineer of maintenance, naval line officers as marine superintendents and port captains, naval constructors as superintendents of mechanical division, Public Health Service officers as chief quarantine officers, and army medical officers as chief health officers.[39] President Wilson then nominated Colonel Goethals as the first Governor of The Panama Canal.

Secretary of the Navy Josephus Daniels did not like the distribution of duties and cabled his dissent to Captain Hugh Rodman, who had been designated as marine superintendent (at first called Superintendent of Canal Transportation) and was then on the Isthmus organizing the Marine Division. Daniels wanted shops and dry docks assigned to the operating division.[40] Rodman passed the request to Goethals, recommending the Navy Yard plan of organization under the naval line officer in charge of operations, instead of under maintenance as desired by Goethals. He claimed that this would be better than "having an

[38] Garrison to President Wilson, Dec. 4, 1913 (ibid.).
[39] Wilson's Memorandum, Jan. 27, 1914 (ibid.).
[40] Daniels to Rodman, Feb. 2, 1914 (ibid.).

army engineer"[41] in charge of repair work but disclaimed any intent for separate control by the Navy Department, though he wanted the Navy Yard plan of organization.

Colonel Hodges commented on this plan also and classed it as a "wheel within a wheel"[42] and stated that the trend was toward the very end that Rodman disclaimed. The result was that shops and dry docks were taken out of the Department of Operation and Maintenance and placed in a separate Mechanical Division, whose head reported directly to the governor instead of the engineer of maintenance.

Goethals spent the last few weeks of the Commission's days working on the permanent organization. The plan was to make a gradual transition, with operating men selected from those who had built the Canal. He recommended Hodges for appointment as engineer of maintenance. Sibert received no appointment.

On March 4, 1914, the Senate confirmed Goethals' appointment as Major General as the result of a law forced through Congress by pressure placed on the members. Goethals did not appreciate the way it was done and did not like rewarding officers or the exclusion of civilians, which could only result in class feeling. He said it deprived him of the "so-called reward of any sweetness or gratification."[43]

Goethals called the Isthmian Canal Commission for its one-hundred-and-sixty-fifth and last meeting on March 27, 1914. All members were there except Gorgas. The chairman read the recent Executive Order for the permanent organization, and the Commission adjourned *sine die*. That was the last gasp of the Commission that had been dying since 1906, when Stevens outlined the essential features of the organization under which the Canal was finally completed.

On April 1, 1914, General Goethals was inaugurated as the first Governor of The Panama Canal. Colonel Sibert sailed away the next day after seven years of work under Goethals.

---

[41] Rodman to Goethals, Feb. 3, 1914 (P.C. Rec. Bur., File 2-C-124) (MS).
[42] Hodges to Goethals, Feb. 6, 1914 (*ibid.*).
[43] J. B. and F. Bishop, *op. cit.*, p. 258.

Inaugurating the Canal Zone Government did not involve radical changes of personnel or duties. It was only a changing of titles. Goethals as governor performed the same duties he had when he was chairman and chief engineer. In addition to being supreme in the Canal Zone, he was head of the Department of Operation and Maintenance.

Captain Hugh Rodman, as first Marine Superintendent, was in charge of Canal transit operations. Colonel Hodges was named as the first engineer of maintenance. He continued his duties as assistant chief engineer and became the governor's chief assistant and first in line of succession during the absence of the governor. Later, the marine superintendent, by Executive Order, became second in line of succession.

Other departments carried on with only minor changes in titles or duties. The new position of Executive Secretary was created, roughly corresponding to the Secretary of State of one of the states of the Union, with C. A. McIlvaine as the first executive secretary of The Panama Canal.

In general, the Canal Zone Government was simply a continuation of the strong centralized control of the last Commission years. It was under the same head, with titles changed from Chairman and Chief Engineer of the Isthmus Canal Commission to Governor of The Panama Canal, who was responsible to the President through the Secretary of War.

THE BATTLE OF THE LOCKAGES

The fundamental idea that permeated the entire design of the locks was safety—safety in operating the locks and safety of shipping. There were heavy chains across the locks in front of gates to protect the gates from damage by vessels not under control, guard gates to prevent ships from ramming main gates, and emergency dams to stop the flow of water in the event of failure of the operating gates. In addition, interlocking devices on electrical controls could be operated only when the operating procedure was followed in proper sequence. The unique fea-

ture about the Panama Canal locks was the towing locomotive—
the invention of Edward Schildhauer,[44] of the Canal engineering
staff.

The plan visualized by Goethals in 1911 provided that pilots
should conduct vessels entering Canal waters to the locks and
moor them to an approach wall. Then the lock personnel would
board and take charge until the lock was passed. A man was to
be placed on the bridge and another in the engine room; cables
from locomotives would be made fast and the vessel towed
through the lock without the use of ship's engines.[45] That was a
procedure somewhat similar to entering a dry dock, where great
precision is required.

When Captain Rodman arrived early in 1913, after studying
Suez methods, one of his first acts was to inspect the Canal. He
reported that the Panama Canal was safe and could be easily
navigated and that changes would be few. At the locks he suggested rounding the ends of the approach walls, requested that
ranges be placed on the center line of narrow reaches, wanted
vessels to sound whistles before sharp turns in the Canal, and
condemned the plan of using electric locomotives during the
lockage of vessels. He feared vessels would take sheers in locks
and show that "inanimate objects may sometimes be the most per-
verse," although he conceded the lockages as planned could be
done at a "snail's pace." He wanted control of vessels "absolutely in the hands of the Canal pilots," with masters on the
bridge "ready to give advice."[46] When the rules for navigation
were issued, the pilot was placed in an advisory capacity instead of in complete control of navigation and movement of
vessels in the Canal.

This advance and too hasty condemnation of the towing locomotives naturally was not popular with the engineers and caused
resentment. They said Rodman was thinking of battleships,
while they were thinking of commercial vessels. At any rate,

[44] *Canal Record*, Sept. 27, 1911, V, 37.

[45] Goethals' Statement, Dec. 22, 1911 (Hearings No. 15, I, 427–28) (U.S.).

[46] Rodman to Goethals, Report on Navigation, March 5, 1913 (P.C. Rec. Bur.,
File 87-B-1) (MS).

Rodman's suggestions were not considered cause for making any change in construction, although Goethals did state that he desired the "actual operation of the locks"[47] should be under a naval officer.

In the early lockages of 1913 the most elaborate records were kept on forms so extensive as to be cumbersome. Colonel Goethals gave written permission for each lockage and required special reports. Gradually restrictions were relaxed as the builders felt their way along the unknown paths of Canal operation. In May 1914, authorization for lockage was turned over to the Marine Division. Port captains issued lockage permits to masters for presentation at each lock. Later, special reports were discontinued and only a routine log was retained.

The earliest lock operations were conducted very much as outlined by Goethals in 1911. Vessels landed at the approach walls; lock personnel came on board and conducted the vessel through and then left. This practice, based on barge-canal ideas of the Mississippi River, proved satisfactory for tests with small vessels and continued for months. As a result, men who were mechanics but had no shiphandling experience were locking vessels. Why Goethals was so insistent is hard to understand. There was, of course, his natural desire to assist employees who did not wish to leave the Canal Zone. It appeared as an opportunity for many of the "canal diggers" to remain with the Canal.

Rodman did not like Goethals' lockage plan and voiced violent opposition. He did not want pilots surrendering control of vessels during lockages to anyone, especially to unlicensed, nonnautical men who had had no experience in shiphandling. He stated that the practice would lead to "delay, confusion and danger." Lock tests with small vessels were no criterion for rulings on large seagoing vessels. Placing vessels during locking under landsmen "neither legally nor professionally qualified" was the result of requiring pilots to be relieved by lock personnel during lockages. He wanted to eliminate stopping at the

[47] Goethals' Statement, Jan. 18, 1913 (Hearings No. 16, p. 680) (U.S.).

approach walls and, instead, to keep ships moving while entering lock chambers. He suggested handling vessels under their own power, using the locomotives as "traveling capstans"[48]—his nautical term that probably would have been more acceptable than "towing locomotives."

Goethals referred Rodman's strong protest to a board of three "land lubbers"—three engineers. They did not see the necessity for licenses for lock operators. They referred to the *International Encyclopedia* for the definition of "pilot." They considered that pilots did not know conditions inside the lock chambers, and they did not like Rodman's disparaging epithets. They asserted that the fundamental principle in the design of the locks was complete stoppage on landing at the approach wall. Handling ships with locomotives was unlike handling with "sluggish tugs." It was a matter of "applying quickly and positively from a fixed track, heavy power, the power being at all times under complete and perfect control, increased and decreased at pleasure and not subject to modifying influence of wind and current." They conceded that a lock supervisor would not use the same methods of control as a pilot. Nevertheless, they wanted a "techical man in charge, specialized in his duties, his machinery, his locks, his currents, his wind."[49] Rodman's letter certainly was not diplomatic, nor was it intended to be; but there was a lamentable lack of reality in the engineers' report on shiphandling, which was emphasized by the preciseness of its wording.

When Hodges passed on these papers, he was conciliatory. He pointed out that use of engines was the "most prolific source"[50] of lock accidents and urged that the precaution be continued of tying up to the approach walls before entering locks.

Rodman followed up his letter of May 18 with another still stronger. He wanted lockage operation under one head to avoid "delays and misunderstandings." He thought it unnecessary to

[48] Rodman to Goethals, May 18, 1914 (P.C. Rec. Bur., File 92-A-5).
[49] Lock Superintendent, Report to H. H. Hodges, May 25, 1914 (*ibid.*).
[50] Hodges to Goethals, May 29, 1914 (*ibid.*).

OPENING TRANSIT THROUGH THE PANAMA CANAL, AUGUST 15, 1914

S.S. "Ancon," of the Panama Railroad, approaching Gatun Locks at 8:00 A.M.

On the right, Governor Goethals observing the vessel

OPENING TRANSIT THROUGH THE PANAMA CANAL, AUGUST 15, 1914
S.S. "Ancon" approaching Cucuracha Slide in Culebra Cut

"continually consult, request, or require"[51] co-operation by the locks and recommended that navigation in the locks as well as in the Canal be placed under the marine superintendent. When Goethals had studied the papers, he wrote Rodman a review of the reasons for caution and concluded that the "plan proposed and adopted by Congress"[52] would be carried out unless actual practice should show another to be preferable. Rodman had lost the first round.

The ideas Rodman opposed were included in the first Canal regulations. Ships were to stop at the approach walls, where they would be boarded by lock personnel and be conducted through locks by lock forces. Pilots, instead of being in complete control, had only an advisory capacity. Practices which today would be judged archaic were an inherent part of a natural spirit of caution essential for those starting a great enterprise. They could not afford to take any chances.

During June and July the drilling of lock crews continued. Vessels were locked up to the summit level and returned to sea level, and the owners of the vessels received letters of appreciation for making their vessels available for this contribution toward completing the Canal. Personnel not familiar with ship-handling had difficult experiences.

But before the formal opening Goethals decided to have a rehearsal transit on August 3, using the Panama Railroad ship "Cristóbal." For this first transit by an ocean-going vessel he invited a limited number of employees and engineers who had been associated with the work for a long time. Among them was Philippe Bunau-Varilla, who had come to the Isthmus for the purpose.

The "Cristóbal" backed clear of the docks and swung into the channel toward the Gatun Locks. Bunau-Varilla was standing on the boat deck, gazing upon the scenes of his former days with the French Company and talking to a group. A young Canal

[51] Rodman to Goethals, June 1, 1914 (*ibid.*).
[52] Goethals to Rodman, June 1, 1914 (P.C. Rec. Bur., File 87-B-1) (MS).

engineer, Mr. George M. Wells, handed him a copy of the morning paper. Bunau-Varilla read the banner headline announcing Germany's declaration of war on France and became silent. He knew its full implication.

Stepping clear of the group and crushing the paper in his hand, he pointed toward the entrance to the Canal: "Gentlemen, the two great and consuming ambitions of my life are realized on the same day: the first, to sail through the Panama Canal on the first ocean liner; the second, to see France at war with Germany."[53]

On this transit the lock force, as shiphandlers, did not measure up to Goethals' expectations for handling this ocean-going ship. At Gatun the currents caused by the mixing of salt and fresh water sheered the vessel into a precarious position and a locomotive burned out a motor. At Pedro Miguel one locomotive cable parted. Colonel Goethals, standing on the lock wall, feared the "Cristóbal" would strike the gates before she could be stopped. The lockage at Miraflores was made without incident.

Goethals was thoroughly alarmed. He then realized that lockmasters were not shiphandlers. The day of formal opening of the Canal was approaching, and the operating force was not ready to transit large vessels.

Goethals immediately directed that pilots "take charge of towing and handling ships" in the locks. He decided to have lock pilots, and they started an intensive course of instruction in signals. He had seen evidences of weakness in the lock force that made it impossible for him to accept responsibility with "landlubbers in charge of the ship." He was afraid that the feelings of one of his army engineers had been hurt by his "giving the Navy charge of the ships and towing locomotives."[54]

Captain Rodman now ordered that pilots board vessels before they reached the approach walls and not leave them until they had cleared the locks. He directed that vessels should not moor

[53] G. M. Wells, Letter to the author, Nov. 8, 1944. Bunau-Varilla, *Great Adventure of Panama*, pp. 260–61.

[54] J. B. and F. Bishop, *op. cit.*, p. 263.

to walls. He wanted vessels to pass through the locks without "touching any of the walls."[55] It was the force of necessity that gave Rodman the final victory in the battle of the lockages.

INAUGURATION OF THE PANAMA CANAL

Dredging had continued on Cucuracha slide from the time it had closed the Canal. When the date of formal opening approached, there was a channel 150 feet wide and 35 feet deep—large enough to pass the Panama Railroad ship "Ancon," which had been selected for the inaugural transit from the Atlantic to the Pacific. Although Canal diggers had looked forward for years to the opening of the Canal, they hated to see the end. Some hoped an earthquake would ruin the Canal so it would have to be built all over again. They looked back to the days of the great urge to get the Canal dug; but those days were gone forever.

At last the day of formal opening of the Canal to commerce arrived—August 15, 1914. When the "Ancon" left Cristóbal that morning, its guests included President Belisario Porras of Panamá and his cabinet, the Diplomatic Corps in Panamá headed by Dr. William Jennings Price, Minister of the United States to Panamá and Dean of the Corps; also John Barrett, then Director General of the Pan American Union.

Entering Gatun Locks at 8:00 A.M., the "Ancon" cleared the locks into the lake in an hour and a quarter, glided across Gatun Lake, arriving at Gamboa at 11:15 A.M. to enter Culebra Cut, passed Cucuracha slide safely, and arrived at Pedro Miguel at 12:56 P.M., was locked down to Miraflores Lake and crossed that small body of water to Miraflores Locks, where she was locked down again to sea level. She entered the Pacific sea-level channel at 3:20 P.M., proceeded to the channel entrance, and returned to Balboa about 5:10 P.M.[56] But Goethals was not on board. He had watched the operation from the lock walls.

[55] Rodman to Port Captains, Sept. 8, 1914 (P.C. Rec. Bur., File 92-A-5) (MS).
[56] *Canal Record*, Aug. 19, 1914, VII, 521 (U.S.).

All along the Canal, thousands waited and watched from vantage points as the "Ancon" passed. They thought of the years of work it took to build the Canal. They visualized the years of routine operation ahead. They knew the passage of the "Ancon" marked the end of an epoch in their lives. They knew that they had witnessed the realization of the dream of four centuries.

EPILOGUE

Three decades have passed. The Panama Canal has assumed the appearance that comes with age. The ranks of the Canal builders have thinned. Only a few are left who can appreciate the great efforts that were required to build the Canal and to evolve the organization under which it operates.

As vessels transit the Canal, the old French Canal north of Gatun is passed almost unnoticed. The weather-stained locks bear the marks of antiquity. Gatun Dam blends with the landscape. Gatun Lake hides most of the work of the railroad pioneers and of the French and North American Canal builders. Culebra Cut, with its green banks, presents a luxuriant beauty that harmonizes with the surrounding jungle.

When vessels pass through the Canal, the gazers do not recognize the vegetation-covered French and North American dump terraces near the banks of Culebra Cut, the upper French levels on Gold Hill overgrown with brush, or the few abandoned hulks of French dredges that remain as dim marks of a past era. They do not see the sites of vanished towns—Culebra, Empire, or Gorgona—where a few foundation pillars, protruding above the growth, and occasional palm trees are the sole remaining evidences of their previous existence. But there is the same eternal panorama of the tropics, with its irregular mountains, its shades of green, and its brilliant flowers.

Culebra Cut, when seen from one of its high banks in the cool of the tropical night, is a sight that can never be forgotten. Red and white bank lights pulsate at each turn in the channel. Green range lights, marking the center line of the reaches of the Cut, guide vessels as they slowly pass. There is profound silence and calm, disturbed only by whistle signals of vessels rounding turns in the Cut, the rustle of leaves in the light breeze,

339

or the euphonious nighttime sounds of insects, birds, and animals—the symphony of the jungle.

The long history of the building of the Panama Canal and its operation has been marked by a series of crises in war and peace that at times have endangered its organization or smooth operation. So far these crises have been overcome. But the Canal still has its detractors and supporters. There are also the patriotic who visit the Isthmus for a few hours and, without any background at all, return home to advocate irrelevant schemes for improving the Canal, such as changing to a sea-level canal or transforming the Panama Railroad to standard gauge. At times these problems have been critical. Elements productive of other crises yet remain, and more crises will come.

The Government of the Canal Zone must remain strong. It must remain flexible to the requirements of both war and peace. In war, the military control in defense of the Canal should be paramount. In peace, the Panama Canal as a great enterprise serving the shipping of the world must predominate on the Isthmus.

Building the Panama Canal was not the work of any one man, but of many men, some of whom were pre-eminent. In building the Panama Railroad there were John L. Stephens, the founder, and George M. Totten, the chief engineer.

It was Ferdinand de Lesseps, the French genius and builder of Suez, who had the vision of building the Panama Canal and started that great undertaking but did not have the means to realize his aim. It was Adolphe Godin de Lépinay who, in 1879 at the Paris Congress, contributed the fundamental concept of the high-level canal with a summit-level terminal lake on each side of the mountains, joined by an open channel cut across the continental divide.

Henry L. Abbot, consulting engineer of the New Panama Canal Company, member of its Comité Technique and later of the International Board of Consulting Engineers of 1905 for the United States, was the student of the Chagres whose work was indispensable for securing adoption of the high-level lock-canal plan.

Philippe Bunau-Varilla, while working on the Canal as a young man in the days of the Old Panama Canal Company, saw the destruction of the French effort. He made the vindication of the name of De Lesseps and the resurrection of the Panama Canal the aim of his life. He maneuvered the Panamá Revolution of 1903 to the advantage of the United States and was author of the Hay–Bunau-Varilla Treaty, by which the United States acquired the Canal Zone.

John F. Wallace, as the first chief engineer for the United States, gathered the nucleus of the construction forces, broke the ground, and discovered the hardships and perils of building the Canal.

The first year of United States effort almost met disaster. It was the eminent engineer and railroad builder, John F. Stevens, whose fertile mind rescued the Canal from chaos and defeat. He organized the railroad-transportation system, brought about the great decision to build a high-level lock-type canal with a dam at Gatun, instead of attempting a sea-level canal. He created the fundamental organization under which the Canal was constructed.

George W. Goethals, as the great administrator, had the power and determination to overcome the inertia of routine government procedure and to see the task through to the end, and thereby won fame as the builder of the Panama Canal.

It was William C. Gorgas who, throughout the entire construction period under the United States, as guardian of the Canal builders and the great leader of sanitation, contributed so much to the success of the effort.

Jackson Smith, as organizer of labor, quarters, and subsistence, was largely responsible for assembling the construction forces. William L. Sibert, builder of the Atlantic locks and Gatun Dam, Sydney B. Williamson, builder of the Pacific locks, and L. K. Rourke, organizer of excavation in Culebra Cut, were the chief construction engineers during the United States effort. H. F. Hodges originated many unique electrical innovations in the locks of the Panama Canal. Of all the constructive builders, none contributed more than Sibert and Stevens.

The opening of the Panama Canal to traffic in 1914 symbolized the completion of the greatest engineering work in the history of mankind—a work that brought fame to its builders and continues to be a source of national pride. But the Canal, when opened to traffic, was not complete. The builders knew that the canal project was so vast it could never be completed.

The plan of the Panama Canal had been developed from years of engineering studies. It had not been evolved from marine operating experience. The form for the final canal had not been determined. The great marine operating problems of the Panama Canal had not been clearly recognized. They remained as problems for which only years of marine operations could supply the solution.

THE FUTURE CANAL

The author was stationed on the Isthmus as Captain of the Port of the Pacific Terminal from March 5, 1941, to June 30, 1944. This was the most critical period in the history of the Panama Canal, and it afforded him an exceptional opportunity to observe and study the marine operations of the canal during both peace and war.

His studies conclusively demonstrated that the Panama Canal as completed in 1914 contained a fundamental error in operational design. That error was the location of the Pedro Miguel Locks at the south end of Culebra Cut and the resulting absence of a summit-level anchorage on the Pacific. This arrangement caused the great traffic bottleneck of the Panama Canal to be at Pedro Miguel.

Based upon his studies and repeated operating experience, the author developed and submitted a plan for the fundamental simplification and improvement of the Panama Canal. He pre-

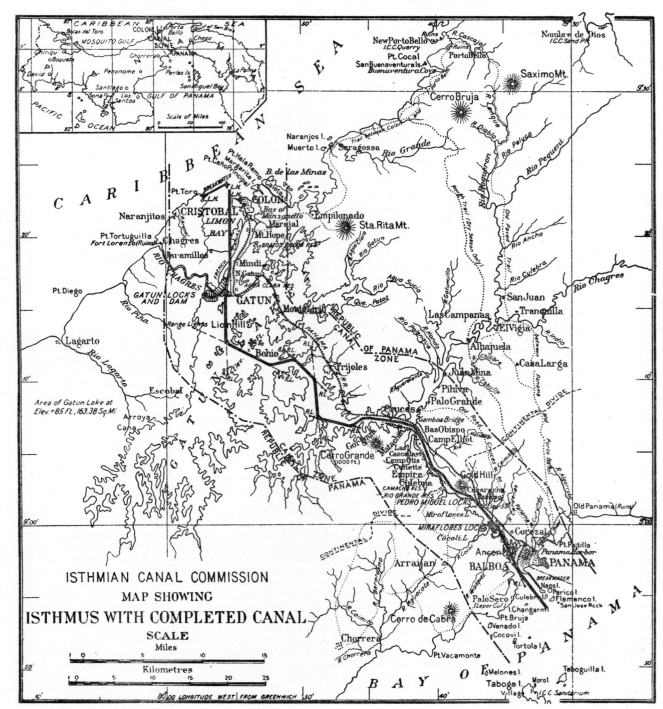

From the *Official Handbook of The Panama Canal*, 4th Edition, 1913.

MAP OF THE ISTHMUS WITH COMPLETED CANAL, 1913

sented his plan publicly on May 20, 1943, before the Panama Section of the American Society of Civil Engineers, in a paper entitled "The Marine Operating Problem of the Panama Canal and the Solution." The plan consists of the removal of the bottleneck lock at Pedro Miguel, the construction of all Pacific locks in single structures near Miraflores, and the creation of a large summit-level terminal lake for an anchorage on the Pacific end of the Canal to match the arrangement at Gatun.

This is the first comprehensive plan for the improvement of the Panama Canal based upon marine operating experience. With the acceptance of its basic principle of the high-level terminal lake on the Pacific as the solution for the great marine operating problems of the Panama Canal, it will be possible at last to build the best canal for transiting ships.

A description of the marine problems of the Panama Canal, with the story of the evolution of this plan and its significance, is planned as a third volume of this series.

APPENDIX

Appendix A

UNITED STATES ISTHMIAN CANAL COMMISSIONS

ISTHMIAN CANAL COMMISSION FOR EXPLORATION, 1899–1901

REAR ADMIRAL JOHN G. WALKER, U.S.N., Retired, *President.*
COLONEL PETER C. HAINS, U.S.A., Retired.
LIEUTENANT COLONEL OSWALD H. ERNST, U.S.A.
SAMUEL PASCO.
ALFRED NOBLE, C.E.
GEORGE S. MORISON.
WILLIAM H. BURR, C.E.
LEWIS H. HAUPT, C.E.
EMORY R. JOHNSON.

ISTHMIAN CANAL COMMISSIONS FOR CONSTRUCTION, 1904–1914

First Isthmian Canal Commission, Appointed March 8, 1904

REAR ADMIRAL JOHN G. WALKER, U.S.N., Retired, *Chairman.*
MAJOR GENERAL GEORGE W. DAVIS, U.S.A., Retired, *Governor of the Canal Zone.*
WILLIAM BARCLAY PARSONS, C.E.
WILLIAM H. BURR, C.E.
BENJAMIN M. HARROD, C.E.
CARL EWALD GRUNSKY, C.E.
FRANK J. HECKER.

Changes

FRANK J. HECKER resigned November 16, 1904.

Second Isthmian Canal Commission, Appointed April 1, 1905

THEODORE P. SHONTS, *Chairman.*
CHARLES R. MAGOON, *Governor of the Canal Zone.*
JOHN F. WALLACE, *Chief Engineer.*
REAR ADMIRAL MORDECAI T. ENDICOTT, U.S.N., Retired.
BRIG. GENERAL PETER C. HAINS, U.S.A., Retired.
COLONEL OSWALD H. ERNST, C.E., U.S.A.
BENJAMIN M. HARROD, C.E.

Changes

JOHN F. WALLACE resigned June 28, 1905.

JOHN F. STEVENS, appointed Chief Engineer, June 30, 1905; member, June 30, 1906; and Chairman, March 4, 1907, to succeed T. P. Shonts.

OSWALD H. ERNST resigned June 30, 1906.

CHARLES E. MAGOON resigned September 25, 1906, without relief.

JACKSON SMITH, appointed February 14, 1907.

WILLIAM C. GORGAS, appointed February 14, 1907.

THEODORE P. SHONTS resigned March 4, 1907; succeeded by John F. Stevens.

GEORGE W. GOETHALS, appointed member March 4, 1907.

DAVID D. GAILLARD, appointed March 16, 1907, to succeed P. C. Hains.

WILLIAM L. SIBERT, appointed March 16, 1907, to succeed M. T. Endicott.

HARRY H. ROUSSEAU, appointed March 16, 1907, to succeed B. M. Harrod.

Third Isthmian Canal Commission, Appointed April 1, 1907; expired March 31, 1914

LIEUTENANT COLONEL GEORGE W. GOETHALS, C.E., U.S.A., *Chairman and Chief Engineer.*

MAJOR DAVID D. GAILLARD, C.E., U.S.A.

MAJOR WILLIAM L. SIBERT, C.E., U.S.A.

HARRY H. ROUSSEAU, C.E., U.S.N.

LIEUTENANT COLONEL WILLIAM C. GORGAS, M.C., U.S.A.

JACKSON SMITH.

JOSEPH C. S. BLACKBURN.

Changes

JACKSON SMITH resigned September 14, 1908.

LIEUTENANT COLONEL H. F. HODGES, appointed September 15, 1908, to succeed Jackson Smith.

J. C. S. BLACKBURN resigned December 4, 1909.

MAURICE H. THATCHER, appointed April 12, 1910, to succeed J. C. S. Blackburn; resigned August 8, 1913.

RICHARD L. METCALFE, appointed August 9, 1913, to succeed Maurice H. Thatcher.

DAVID D. GAILLARD, died December 5, 1913; no successor appointed.

Appendix B

ABBREVIATIONS USED IN FOOTNOTES

The more common abbreviations used are not listed.

A.S.C.E. .... American Society of Civil Engineers.
C.Z. .... Canal Zone.
Cong. .... Congress.
Doc. .... Document.
E.S.P. .... Engineers' Society of Pennsylvania.
Ex. or Exec. .... Executive.
House .... House of Representatives.
I.C.C. .... Isthmian Canal Commission.
Jt. .... Joint.
Misc. .... Miscellaneous.
(MS) .... Group designation for manuscripts consulted in Library of Congress, National Archives, and The Panama Canal Archives, the latter designated as (P.C. Rec. Bur.).
N.G. .... New Granada (now Colombia).
P.C. .... The Panama Canal (official name of government in Canal Zone).
P.C. Rec. Bur. ... Official Archives of the Panama Canal at Balboa Heights, C.Z.
Res. .... Resolution (Congressional).
Sen. .... United States Senate.
sess. .... Session of Congress.
tr. .... Translated.
U.S. .... Group designation for United States official and semiofficial documents.

Appendix C

REFERENCES CONSULTED

NONOFFICIAL PUBLICATIONS

ABBOT, HENRY L., BRIGADIER GENERAL, U.S.A. *Problems of the Panama Canal, Including Climatology of the Isthmus, Physics and Hydrology of the River Chagres, Cut at the Continental Divide, and Discussion of Plans for the Waterway, with History from 1880 to Date.* (2d ed.) New York: Macmillan Company, 1907.

Addresses at the De Lesseps Banquet Given at Delmonico's, March 1, 1880. New York: D. Appleton & Company, 1880. (Pamphlet.)

AMERICAN SOCIETY OF CIVIL ENGINEERS. *Transactions,* New York, XCI (Dec. 1927), pp. 946–67.

Aspinwall Daily Courier, The, Feb. 24, 1855, Vol. I, No. 14. Aspinwall (Navy Bay), N.G. (Available in Panama Canal Library, Balboa Heights, C.Z.)

AUTENRIETH, E. L. *Topographical Map of the Isthmus of Panama.* New York: J. H. Colton, 1851. (Available in Panama Canal Library.)

BAKENHUS, REUBEN E., HARRY S. KNAPP, AND EMORY R. JOHNSON. *The Panama Canal . . . . Its History and Construction, in Its Relation to the Navy, International Law and Commerce.* New York: John Wiley & Sons, 1915. (By men who had worked on the Canal project.)

BARRETT, JOHN. *The Panama Canal, What It Is, What It Means . . . .* Washington, D.C.: Pan American Union, 1913.

BEMIS, SAMUEL F. *The American Secretaries of State and Their Diplomacy.* New York: A. A. Knopf, 1928. 10 volumes.

BENNETT, IRA E. *History of the Panama Canal; Its Construction and Builders.* (Builders' edition.) Washington, D.C.: Historical Publishing Co., 1915.

BIDWELL, CHARLES T. *The Isthmus of Panama.* London: Chapman & Hall, 1865.

BIGELOW, JOHN. *The Panama Canal and the Daughters of Danaus.* New York: Baker & Taylor Co., 1908.

BISHOP, FARNHAM. *Panama, Past and Present.* (Revised edition.) New York: Century Company, 1916.

BISHOP, JOSEPH B. *The Panama Gateway.* New York: Scribner's, 1913.

BISHOP, JOSEPH B., AND FARNHAM BISHOP. *Goethals, Genius of the Panama Canal: a Biography.* New York: Harper, 1930.

BLYTHE, SAMUEL G. "Life in Spigotty Land; the Cohorts of King Yardage," *Saturday Evening Post,* March 21, 1908.

BRESSOLLES, PAUL. *Liquidation de la Compagnie de Panama; Commentaire ... de la Loi du 1er juillet 1893.* Paris: A. Rousseau, 1894.

BROGAN, DENNIS W. *France under the Republic; the Development of Modern France (1870–1939).* New York: Harper, 1940.

BULLARD, ARTHUR (ALBERT EDWARDS, pseudonym). *Panama, the Canal, the Country, and the People.* (Revised edition, with additional chapters.) New York: Macmillan Company, *ca.* 1914.

BUNAU-VARILLA, PHILIPPE. *From Panama to Verdun; My Fight for France.* Philadelphia: Dorrance & Co., *ca.* 1940.

———. *The Great Adventure of Panama.* Garden City, N.Y.: Doubleday, Page & Company, 1920.

———. "How to Build the Panama Canal?" (Lecture before the National Geographic Society in Washington, Nov. 29, 1905.)

———. *Panama: The Creation, Destruction, and Resurrection.* New York: McBride, Nast & Company, 1914.

CHAGRES SOCIETY. *See* Society of the Chagres.

CLAYBOURN, JOHN G. *Dredging on the Panama Canal.* Privately printed, *ca.* 1931. (Paper presented at first meeting of Panama Section of American Society of Civil Engineers, Feb. 27, 1931.)

COLLINS, JOHN O. *The Panama Guide.* Panama: Vibert & Dixon, *ca.* 1912.

———. *Same.* Published at Mount Hope, C.Z., by Isthmian Canal Commission Press.

CONGRÈS INTERNATIONAL D'ÉTUDES DU CANAL INTEROCÉANIQUE ... DU 15 AU 20 MAI, 1879. *Compte Rendu du Séances.* Paris: Imprimerie Émile Martinet, 1879.

DAVIS, GEORGE W. Article quoted in *Canal Record,* Vol. I (Dec. 25, 1907), p. 133.

DE LESSEPS, FERDINAND. "Discussion" (on Interoceanic Canals, with his answers to questions by J. Dirks), in American Society of Civil Engineers, *Transactions,* IX (March 1880), 89–94, 96, 97, 98.

———. *Recollections of Forty Years.* Translated by C. B. Pitman. New York: D. Appleton & Company, 1888. 2v. in 1.

DuVal, Miles P., Jr., Captain, U.S.N. *Cadiz to Cathay.* Stanford University, Calif.: Stanford University Press, 1940.

———. The Marine Operating Problems of the Panama Canal and the Solution. (Paper presented before the Panama Section of the American Society of Civil Engineers, May 20, 1943.)

Engineering News . . . . , New York, LX (July–Dec. 1908). (Editorial, without title, exposing sources and falsity of criticisms on Gatun Dam design, Dec. 24, p. 717); "Letters to the Editor: Mr. John F. Stevens on the Gatun Dam Design" (Dec. 31, p. 751).

Engineering Record, Building Record, and Sanitary Engineer. New York: McGraw Publishing Company, Vols. XLIX–LVI (various dates, 1904–1907).

Goethals, George W. "Address at Annual Banquet . . . . Hotel Tivoli, March 6, 1915." Society of the Chagres, *Yearbook 1915,* pp. 159–72.

———. "The Building of the Panama Canal." Illustrated from paintings by W. B. Van Ingen . . . . and from photographs. *Scribner's Magazine,* Vol. LVII (March–June 1915).

———. *The Panama Canal; an Engineering Treatise.* McGraw-Hill Book Company, 1916. 2 volumes.

———. *Same.* International Engineering Congress, San Francisco, *Transactions,* 1915, Vol. I, Pts. 1–2, "The Panama Canal." *Paper No. 1,* "Introduction," general view of construction in the three divisions of the Canal, with map, pp. 1–30. *Paper No. 10,* "The Dry Excavation of the Panama Canal," pp. 335–86.

Gorgas, Mrs. Marie C. (Doughty), and Burton J. Hendrick. *William Crawford Gorgas, His Life and Work.* Garden City, N.Y.: Doubleday, Page & Company, 1924.

Gorgas, William C. "Health Conditions on the Isthmus," *Engineering Record,* Vol. XLIX (May 14, 1904).

———. "Sanitary Conditions as We Found Them in 1904." Speech, Jan. 20, 1912. Society of the Chagres, *Yearbook 1912,* pp. 37–44.

———. Reports as Chief Sanitary Officer of the Panama Canal, 1906. *See* Isthmian Canal Commission (U.S.), "Population and Deaths" and "Report of Department of Health for January 1906."

Haskin, Frederic J. *The Panama Canal.* Garden City, N.Y.: Doubleday, Page & Company, 1913. (Illustrated from photographs by E. Hallen, official photographer to Isthmian Canal Commission.)

Haskins, William C., *editor. Canal Zone Pilot.* Panama: Star and Herald Company, 1908.

HESS, LOUIS T., COLONEL, MEDICAL CORPS, U.S.A. "Ancon Hospital, Ancon," *Surgery, Gynecology and Obstetrics*, XXXI (October 1920), 424–29.

HODGES, HENRY F., LIEUTENANT COLONEL, CORPS OF ENGINEERS, U.S.A. "The Panama Canal," in Engineers' Society of Pennsylvania, *Journal*, I (July 1909), 311–39.

INTEROCEANIC CANAL CONGRESS, PARIS, May 1879. *See* Congrès International d'Études du Canal Interocéanique.

KIRKPATRICK, RALPH Z. *Reference Book on the Panama Canal.* July 20, 1939. (Mimeographed pamphlet, available in Panama Canal Library, Balboa Heights, C.Z.)

LIDGERWOOD MANUFACTURING COMPANY, Elizabeth, N.J. *Rapid Unloaders for Discharging Dirt, Ballast, Rock or Ore.* Illustrated catalogue, *ca.* 1919).

LINDSAY, C. T. *A Short History of the Panama Railroad.* Address before Caribbean Chapter No. 21, National Sojourners, Colón, June 17, 1936. (Mimeographed pamphlet, available in Panama Canal Library, Balboa Heights, C.Z.)

London Standard, The, Dec. 8, 1880.

London Times, The, Sept. 7, 1888.

MCCAIN, WILLIAM D. *The United States and the Republic of Panama.* Durham, N.C.: Duke University Press, 1937.

MACK, GERSTLE. *The Land Divided.* New York: A. A. Knopf, 1944.

NATIONAL ACADEMY OF SCIENCES, Washington, D.C. "Preliminary Report [Feb. 4, 1916] upon the Possibility of Controlling the Land Slides Adjacent to the Panama Canal," by the Committee Appointed [Nov. 18, 1915] at the Request of the President of the United States, *Proceedings*, II (April 15, 1916), 193–207.

NELSON, WOLFRED. *Five Years at Panama; the Trans-Isthmian Canal.* New York: Belford Company, 1889.

NEVINS, ALLAN. *Hamilton Fish. The Inner History of the Grant Administration*, with an Introduction by John Bassett Moore. New York: Dodd, Mead & Company, 1936.

New York Herald, March 3, 1880, p. 6. [Editorial] "De Lesseps' Visit to the United States."

New York Tribune, Aug. 16, 1876, pp. 1, 5: "An Invasion of Prerogative." (Message to Congress, Aug. 14.)

OTIS, FESSENDEN N. *Isthmus of Panama. History of the Panama Railroad and of the Pacific Mail Steamship Company.* New York: Harper, 1867. (Published originally in 1861 under the title "Illustrated

History of the Panama Railroad"; second edition in 1862.) Text and illustrations on the Panama Railroad and Canal are based on Otis' article entitled "Tropical Journeyings," published under the pseudonym "Oran," in *Harper's New Monthly Magazine,* XVIII (Jan. 1859), 145–69.

PADELFORD, NORMAN J. *The Panama Canal in Peace and War.* New York: Macmillan Company, 1942.

Panama American, March 20, 1936, pp. 1, 8. (Available in Library of Congress.)

PANAMA CANAL, THE. *The Panama Canal, Twenty-fifth Anniversary, August 15, 1939.* Mt. Hope, C.Z.: The Panama Canal Press, 1939.

Panama Canal Record. See Canal Record (U.S.).

Panama Herald. Published by Green & Middleton, Panamá City, N.G. (Various dates, 1851–1853.) Available in *Panama Star and Herald* archives.

PANAMA RAILROAD COMPANY. *Panama Railroad Company, Capital $1,000,000, with Liberty to Increase to $5,000,000.* New York: Van Norton & Ammerman, Printers, 1849.

Panama Star. Panamá City, N.G. (Various dates, 1853–1854.) Available in *Panama Star and Herald* archives.

Panama Star and Herald. Panamá City, Republic of Panamá. (Various dates, 1854–1907, and Feb. 18, 1927.) Available in *Star and Herald* archives.

PEPPERMAN, WALTER L. *Who Built the Panama Canal?* New York: E. P. Dutton & Company, *ca.* 1915.

PIM, BEDFORD C. T., CAPTAIN, R.N. "Remarks on the Panama Canal, October 1884." (A private and confidential document submitted to the Secretary of the United States Navy, Nov. 8, 1884; printed, with the Secretary's permission, in the *Washington National Republican,* Jan. 20, 1885, with other papers by Pim, under the combined title "Nicaragua vs. Panama.")

RICHARDSON, ALBERT D. *Personal History of Ulysses S. Grant.* Hartford, Conn.: American Publishing Company, 1885.

ROBINSON, TRACY. *Panama; a Personal Record of Forty-six Years. 1861–1907.* New York and Panama City: The Star and Herald Company, 1907.

ROOSEVELT, THEODORE. *Theodore Roosevelt; an Autobiography.* New York: Macmillan Company, 1914.

San Francisco Evening Bulletin, July 16, 1887. [Editorial] "The New Panama Canal Loan."

SANDS, WILLIAM F., AND JOSEPH M. LALLEY. *Our Jungle Diplomacy.* Chapel Hill, N.C.: University of North Carolina Press, 1944.

SCHONFIELD, HUGH J. *Ferdinand de Lesseps.* London: Herbert Joseph, Ltd., 1937.

SHELDON, R. C. "A History of Construction, Operation, and Maintenance of the Panama Railroad." 1933. (Thesis presented to Ohio Northern University, Ada. Mimeograph copy available in Panama Canal Library, Balboa Heights, C.Z.)

SHONTS, THEODORE P. *Address by the Chairman of Isthmian Canal Commission, Delivered before the Bankers' Club, Chicago, May 24, 1905.* Pamphlet. Available in Panama Canal Library and in Library of Congress.

———. *Speech by the . . . . Chairman of the Isthmian Canal Commission, before the Commercial Club, Cincinnati, Ohio, on the Evening of Jan. 20, 1906.* Washington, D.C.: Government Printing Office, 1906. Pamphlet. Available in Panama Canal Library and in Library of Congress.

SIBERT, WILLIAM L., AND JOHN F. STEVENS. *The Construction of the Panama Canal.* New York: D. Appleton & Company, 1915.

SIEGFRIED, ANDRÉ. *Suez and Panama.* Translated from the French by H. H. and Doris Hemming. New York: Harcourt, Brace & Company, *ca.* 1940.

SMITH, DARRELL H. "The Panama Canal; Its History, Activities and Organization." Brookings Institution, Washington, D.C. Institute for Government Research. *Service Monographs of the United States Government, No. 44.* Baltimore: The Johns Hopkins Press, 1927.

SOCIETY OF THE CHAGRES. *Yearbook 1911–1917.* From 1911 to 1912 published by Isthmian Canal Commission Press, Quartermaster's Dept., Mount Hope, C.Z.; from 1913 to 1914 published by John O. Collins, Culebra, C.Z.; in 1915, edited by John K. Baxter and F. G. Swanson, Press of W. F. Roberts & Co., Washington, D.C.; from 1916 to 1917, edited by F. G. Swanson, Press of Girard Job Shop, Girard, Kans.

STEVENS, JOHN F. *An Engineer's Recollections.* New York: McGraw-Hill Publishing Company, 1936. (Reprinted from *Engineering News-Record,* between March 21 and Nov. 28, 1935.)

———. "The Panama Canal." Address by the President of the Society at the Annual Convention, Denver, Colo., July 13, 1927. American Society of Civil Engineers, *Transactions,* XCI (Dec. 1927), 946–67.

TOMES, ROBERT. *Panama in 1855: An Account of the Panama Railroad . . . . of the Cities of Panamá and Aspinwall, with Sketches of Life and Character on the Isthmus.* New York: Harper, 1855.

WYSE, LUCIEN N. B. *Le Canal de Panama, l'Isthme américain, explorations ... un plan panoramique du Canal de Panama supposé achevé, un tableau synoptique des divers projéts ...* Paris: Hachette et Cie., 1886. (With appendixes of treaties, contracts, etc.)

OFFICIAL AND SEMIOFFICIAL PUBLICATIONS
UNITED STATES*

Designated in footnotes by (U.S.), following the citation.

BOARD OF CONSULTING ENGINEERS ON PANAMA CANAL. *Report (Jan. 10, 1906) . . . . for the Panama Canal* (prefatory letters of transmittal from the President and Secretary of War), 426 pp., 1906.

BOARD OF ENGINEERS Appointed to Accompany ex–Secretary of War . . . . Taft to the Isthmus. *See* Roosevelt, *Isthmian Canal.*

BRISTOW, JOSEPH L. *Report of Special Panama Railroad Commissioner to the Secretary of War, June 24, 1905.* Washington, D.C.: Office of Administration, Isthmian Canal Affairs, 1905.

BURNSIDE, AMBROSE E., GENERAL, U.S.A., SENATOR. "Joint Resolution (Sen. Res. No. 43) in Relation to the Construction of a Canal Across the Isthmus of Darien by European Powers," *Congressional Record,* Vol. IX, Pt. 2, p. 2312. (46th Cong., 1st sess., June 25, 1879.)

Canal Record. Various dates, 1907–1914. illus. tables, diagrs. (The complete set covers Volumes 1–34, Sept. 4, 1907—April 30, 1941. Issued weekly, 1907–June 1933; monthly, July 1933–1941. Published under the authority and supervision of the Isthmian Canal Commission, 1907–March 1914; by The Panama Canal, April 1914–1941. No more published. After August 16, 1916, title is *Panama Canal Record.* Available in The Panama Canal Library, Balboa Heights, Canal Zone, and in Library of Congress.)

COMMISSION OF FINE ARTS. *Panama Canal . . . . Report . . . . of Fine Arts in Relation to the Artistic Structure of the Panama Canal,* 1913. (Sen. Doc. 146, 63d Cong., 1st sess.)

* As each reference in this group was published by the Government Printing Office and by authority of Congress unless otherwise indicated, the phrase "Washington, D.C., Government Printing Office" is not used here. Likewise, the introductory letters, "U.S.," are omitted here and in footnotes.

CONGRESS
  Documents:
    Senate
      No. 102 (58th Cong., 2d sess.). *Interoceanic Canal Congress, Paris,* 1879. Instructions to .... Delegates .... of the United States .... and Reports of the Proceedings of the Congress (June 21, 1879). Ordered printed, Jan. 19, 1904.
      No. 286 (59th Cong., 1st sess.). *Quarantine Conditions in the Isthmian Canal Zone* .... Letter from Walter Wyman, Surgeon General of the Marine Hospital Service ...., March 22, 1906.
  Hearings: *

    House Committee on Appropriations
      No. 1 (60th Cong., 1st sess.). *Hearings Concerning Estimates for Construction of Isthmian Canal for Fiscal Year 1908,* conducted at Culebra, C.Z., Nov. 11–12, 1907. Printed 1908.
      No. 2 (61st Cong.). *Same,* for Fiscal Year 1911, conducted on the Canal Zone, Nov. 17–18, 1909. Printed 1910.
      No. 3 (62d Cong.). *Same,* for Fiscal Year 1913, conducted on the Canal Zone, Nov. 20–21, 1911. Printed 1912.
      No. 4 (62d Cong.). *The Panama Canal.* Hearings Concerning Estimates for Construction of (Conducted on Canal Zone, Nov. 18, 1912) and Fortification of (Conducted in Washington, D.C., by the Subcommittee in Charge of the Sundry Civil Appropriation Bill, Jan. 16, 20, 1913) .... for Fiscal Year 1914. Printed 1913.
      No. 5 (63d Cong., 2d sess.). *The Panama Canal 1915.* Hearings Concerning Estimates for Construction of (Conducted at Ancon ...., C.Z., Nov. 18–20, 1913) and Fortification of (Conducted in Washington, D.C., by the Subcommittee ...., Feb. 23–25, 1914) for Fiscal Year 1915. Printed 1914.
      No. 6. Supplement to Hearings before Subcommittee .... in Charge of Sundry Civil Appropriation Bill for 1907

* All hearings concerning the Isthmian Canal for the fiscal years 1904 to 1915 were consulted, but only those cited in footnotes are included in this list. Where titles of hearings are too lengthy to appear in footnotes, the serial designations are substituted there.

(April 10 to May 9, 1906), Isthmian Canal (May 25–28, 1906). Printed 1906.

No. 7. Hearings (Jan. 5 to Feb. 11, 1907) before Subcommittee . . . . in Charge of Sundry Civil Appropriation Bill for 1908. Printed 1907.

No. 8. Supplement to Hearings before Subcommittee . . . . in Charge of Sundry Civil Appropriation Bill for 1910 . . . . , Isthmian Canal (Feb. 15–16, 1909). Printed 1909.

No. 9. Hearings (Jan. 13–15, 1906) before Subcommittee . . . . in Charge of Deficiency Appropriations for 1906 and Prior Years on Urgent Deficiency Bill. Printed 1906.

House Committee on Interstate and Foreign Commerce

No. 10. Hearings (June 5, 1906) . . . . on the Isthmian Canal. Printed 1906.

No. 11. Hearings (Jan. 14, 1906) . . . . on Panama Canal. Printed 1908.

No. 12. Hearings (Jan. 6–7, 1909) . . . . on Panama Canal, Hotel Tivoli, Ancon, C.Z. Printed 1909.

No. 13. Hearings (Feb. 11, 1911) . . . . on the Bill H.R. 31436, Operation of Panama Canal, etc. Printed 1911.

No. 14 (62d Cong.). Hearings . . . . on Operation of Panama Canal, etc. . . . . , June 7, 1911. Printed 1911.

No. 15 (62d Cong., 2d sess.). *The Panama Canal.* Hearings . . . . (at Ancon, C.Z., Dec. 18–22, 1911; at Washington, D.C., Jan. 17 to March 13, 1912). 5 volumes in 2, paged continuously, 1–1127. Printed 1912. *Same* in one volume (House Doc. 680).

House Committee on Naval Affairs

No. 16. Hearings (Dec. 6, 1912–Feb. 19, 1913) . . . . on Estimates Submitted by the Secretary of the Navy, 1913. Printed 1913.

Senate Committee on Interoceanic Canals

No. 17 (57th Cong., 1st sess.). Report on the Proposed Ship Canals through the American Isthmus Connecting the Continents of North and South America, December 1901 (Sen. Report No. 1). (Appendix 22, pp. 493–507: "Maury's Estimate of the Resources of the Gulf of Mexico and of the Caribbean Sea, and of the Importance of Interoceanic Communication, July 2, 1849.") Printed 1901.

No. 18 (59th Cong., 2d sess.). *Investigation of Canal Mat-*

ters. Hearings (Jan. 11, 1906, to Feb. 12, 1907) . . . . in the Matter of the Senate Resolution Adopted January 9, 1906 . . . . 4 volumes paged continuously, 1–3310. Printed 1907. (Sen. Doc. 401.)

No. 19. *Panama Canal* . . . . (Hearings . . . . Jan. 16–23, 1908). Printed 1908.

No. 20 (62d Cong., 2d sess.). *Panama Canal.* Hearings . . . . held at Ancon, Canal Zone, Oct. 26–28, 1911. Printed 1912. (Sen. Doc. 191.)

No. 21 (62d Cong., 2d sess.). *Panama Canal.* Hearings . . . . (March 29 to June 14, 1912) on H.R. 21,969, a Bill to Provide for the Opening, Maintenance, Protection, and Operation of the Panama Canal, and the Sanitation and Government of the Canal Zone. Printed 1912.

COOPER, GEORGE H., REAR ADMIRAL. *Progress of Work on Panama Ship-Canal: Report, March 2, 1883.* Printed 1884. (Sen. Exec. Doc. 123, pp. 1–4, 48th Cong., 1st sess.)

EDMUNDS, GEORGE F., SENATOR. "Joint Resolution (Sen. Res. 122), Dec. 19, 1888," *Congressional Record,* Vol. 20, Pt. 1, p. 338. (50th Cong., 2d sess., Dec. 3, 1888, to Jan. 19, 1889.)

GOETHALS, GEORGE W., LIEUTENANT COLONEL, U.S.A. *The Isthmian Canal.* Printed 1909.

————. *Slides at the Panama Canal.* Printed 1916. (Covers history of slides from 1884 to 1916, with various theories about their causes.)

ISTHMIAN CANAL COMMISSION, 1899–1902. *Report* . . . . *1899–1901* . . . . Printed 1901–1902. 2 volumes. (Sen. Doc. 54, 57th Cong., 1st sess.) Incomplete report.

————. *Same.* Complete in one volume, printed 1904. (Sen. Doc. 222, 58th Cong., 2d sess.)

ISTHMIAN CANAL COMMISSION, 1904–1905. *Proceedings,* March 22, 1904, to March 29, 1905; meetings 1 to 90, with *Circulars* (Nos. 1 to 13, June 25, 1904, to April 3, 1905; *Index*) ; succeeded by *Minutes of Meetings.*

————. *Letter from the Secretary of War* [Jan. 12, 1905], *Transmitting the First Annual Report of the* . . . . *Commission, December 1, 1904* (covering the period March 22 to Nov. 10, 1904). Printed 1905. (House Doc. 226, 59th Cong., 3d sess.)

ISTHMIAN CANAL COMMISSION, 1905–1914. *Annual Report for the Year ending December 1, 1905* (with President Roosevelt's Letter of

Transmittal, Jan. 8, 1906). Printed 1906. (Sen. Doc. 127, Pts. 1–2, 59th Cong., 1st sess.)

    Pt. 1, as above; 440 pp. Illus.

    Pt. 2, *Isthmian Canal,* Message from the President (Jan. 10, 1906) Transmitting Certain Papers to Accompany His Message of January 8, 1906.

ISTHMIAN CANAL COMMISSION, 1905–1914. *Annual Report for the Year ending December 1, 1906.* Printed 1907.

————. *Minutes of Meetings of the Isthmian Canal Commisison and of the Executive and Engineering Committees, April 1905 to March 29, 1914.* Printed from 1905 to 1914. 15 volumes in 4.

    (Beginning with the 91st meeting, April 1905, this publication continues the *Proceedings* of March 22, 1904, to March 29, 1905; Meetings No. 1 to 90.)

————. *General Index, Minutes of Meetings . . . . March 1904 to March 1907* (covering meetings of I.C.C. No. 1 to 122; of its Executive Committee, No. 1 to 24; of its Engineering Committee, No. 1 to 49). Printed 1908.

    An Index (entitled "Panama Canal") to the technical reports of I.C.C. and its committees for the years 1899 to 1914 is embodied in Vol. 2 of *Index to the Reports of the Chief of Engineers, United States Army,* published in 1915–16 as *House Doc. 740* (63d Cong., 2d sess.).

————. *Population and Deaths from Various Diseases in the City of Panama . . . . from November 1883 to August 1906* (pp. 1–16); *Number of Employees and Deaths from Various Diseases among the Employees of the French Canal Companies . . . . from January 1881 to April 1904* (pp. 17–37), Isthmian Canal Commission, Government of the Canal Zone, Health Dept., W. C. Gorgas, Chief Sanitary Officer. Printed 1906.

————. *Report of the Department of Health for the Month of January, 1906,* W. C. Gorgas, Chief Sanitary Officer. Printed 1906.

————. *Sanitary Conditions on the Isthmus of Panama; Reply . . . . to the Report of Dr. C. A. L. Reed,* with letters of the President and Secretary of War in reference thereto. Printed 1905.

    (Contains Dr. Reed's Report to Taft, March 2, 1905, pp. 38–63.)

————. *Catalogue of Equipment, November 1, 1913, Purchased for Use on The Panama Canal and The Panama Railroad between July 1, 1904, and January 1, 1913,* available in Panama Canal Library, Balboa Heights, C.Z.

JOHNSON, EMORY R. *Panama Canal Traffic and Tolls* (Report to Secretary of War, Aug. 7, 1912). Printed 1912.

KIMBALL, WILLIAM W., LIEUTENANT, U.S.N., AND W. L. CAPPS, U.S.N., *Special Intelligence Report on the Progress of the Work on the Panama Canal during the Year 1885.* Printed 1886. (House Misc. Doc. 395, 49th Cong., 1st sess.)

KNOX, PHILANDER C., SENATOR. *Panama Canal,* Speech in the Senate of the United States . . . . June 18, 1906. Printed 1906; reprint from *Congressional Record,* Vol. XL, Pt. 9, pp. 8702–8 (59th Cong., 1st sess.).

NOURSE, JOSEPH E., U.S.N. *The Maritime Canal of Suez from Its Inauguration, November 17, 1869, to the Year 1884;* Prepared under Orders of the Bureau of Navigation, Navy Department. Printed 1884. (Sen. Exec. Doc. 198, 48th Cong., 1st sess.)

PRESIDENT. *A Compilation of the Messages and Papers of the Presidents* . . . . with additional encyclopedic index by private enterprise . . . . New York; Bureau of National Literature, Inc.; prefatory note signed by James D. Richardson. 20 volumes.

RICHARDSON, JAMES D. *Compilation of the Messages and Papers of the Presidents. See* President.

RODGERS, RAYMOND P., LIEUTENANT, U.S.N. *Progress of Work on Panama Ship-Canal:* First Report, Feb. 28, 1883; Second Report, Jan. 27, 1884. Printed 1884. (Sen. Doc. 123, pp. 4–15; 15–25, 48th Cong., 1st sess.)

ROGERS, CHARLES C., LIEUTENANT, U.S.N. *Intelligence Report of the Panama Canal, March 30, 1887.* Printed 1889. (House Misc. Doc. 599, 50th Cong., 1st sess.)

ROOSEVELT, THEODORE, PRESIDENT. *Executive Orders Relating to the Isthmian Canal Commission, March 1904, to June 12, 1911, inclusive.* Printed 1909.

———. *Isthmian Canal,* Message (Feb. 17, 1909) . . . . transmitting Report (Feb. 16, 1909) of the Board of Engineers Appointed to Accompany ex-Secretary of War Taft to the Isthmus . . . . and to Look into the Condition and Safety of the Gatun Dam, etc. Printed 1909. (House Doc. 1458, 60th Cong., 2d sess.)

———. *Special Message* . . . . *to Congress Concerning the Panama Canal* . . . . *December 17, 1906.* Printed 1906. (Sen. Doc. 144, 59th Cong., 2d sess.)

STATE DEPARTMENT, *Register* . . . . *1876–1878.* Printed 1876–1878.

SULLIVAN, JOHN T., LIEUTENANT, U.S.N. *Report of Historical and Technical Information Relating to the Problem of Interoceanic Com-*

munication by Way of the American Isthmus. By Order of the Bureau of Navigation, Navy Dept. Printed 1883.

SULLIVAN, JOHN T., LIEUTENANT, U.S.N. *Same.* Issued as *House Exec. Doc. 107* (47th Cong., 2d sess.).

TAFT, WILLIAM H., SECRETARY OF WAR. *The Panama Canal* (cover title); Speech . . . . at the St. Louis Commercial Club, St. Louis, Mo. . . . ., November 18, 1905, Washington, D.C., Office of Administration Isthmian Canal Affairs, 1905 (justifying action regarding Wallace).

———. "Secretary Taft's Statement Regarding Mr. John F. Wallace," as printed in the *Washington Post* on June 30, 1905; reprinted, together with Wallace's Letter to Shonts, June 26, 1905, in Congress: *Hearings No. 18*, II, 1362–69 (Sen. Doc. 401, 59th Cong., 2d sess.).

TRIPLER, CHARLES S., SURGEON, U.S.A. "Report of the Regimental Surgeon, Fourth Infantry, to Surgeon General, Sept. 14, 1852," *Sen. Doc. 96,* pp. 454–58 (34th Cong., 1st sess.). Printed 1856; available in Library of Congress and in War College Library.

———. *Same,* in Bullard, Arthur, *Panama, the Canal,* etc., pp. 400–407.

———. *Same,* under the title "Crossing the Isthmus in 1852," *Canal Record,* I, (July 1, 1908), 347–48.

MANUSCRIPTS

Designated in footnotes by (MS).

LIBRARY OF CONGRESS, *Division of Manuscripts,* Washington, D.C.
Taft Papers:
Taft-Roosevelt . . . . .Boxes II, III
John Barrett Papers.

NATIONAL ARCHIVES, *Legislative Division,* Washington, D.C.
Brown, Robert M. G., Lieutenant, U.S.N.
Report to the Secretary of the Navy, June 2, 1884, Regarding Progress of Work on the Panama Canal; Transmitted to the Senate January 19, 1885 (48th Cong., 2d sess., Exec.) and 77 Copies Ordered Printed in Confidence for Use of the Senate.

THE PANAMA CANAL, *Archives,* Balboa Heights, C.Z. (P.C. Rec. Bur.)

INDEX

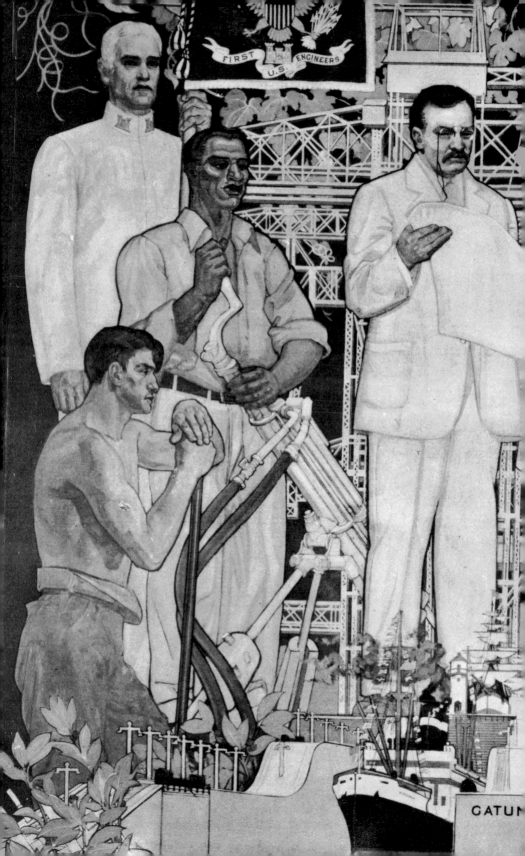

FIRST
U.S. ENGINEERS

GATUN